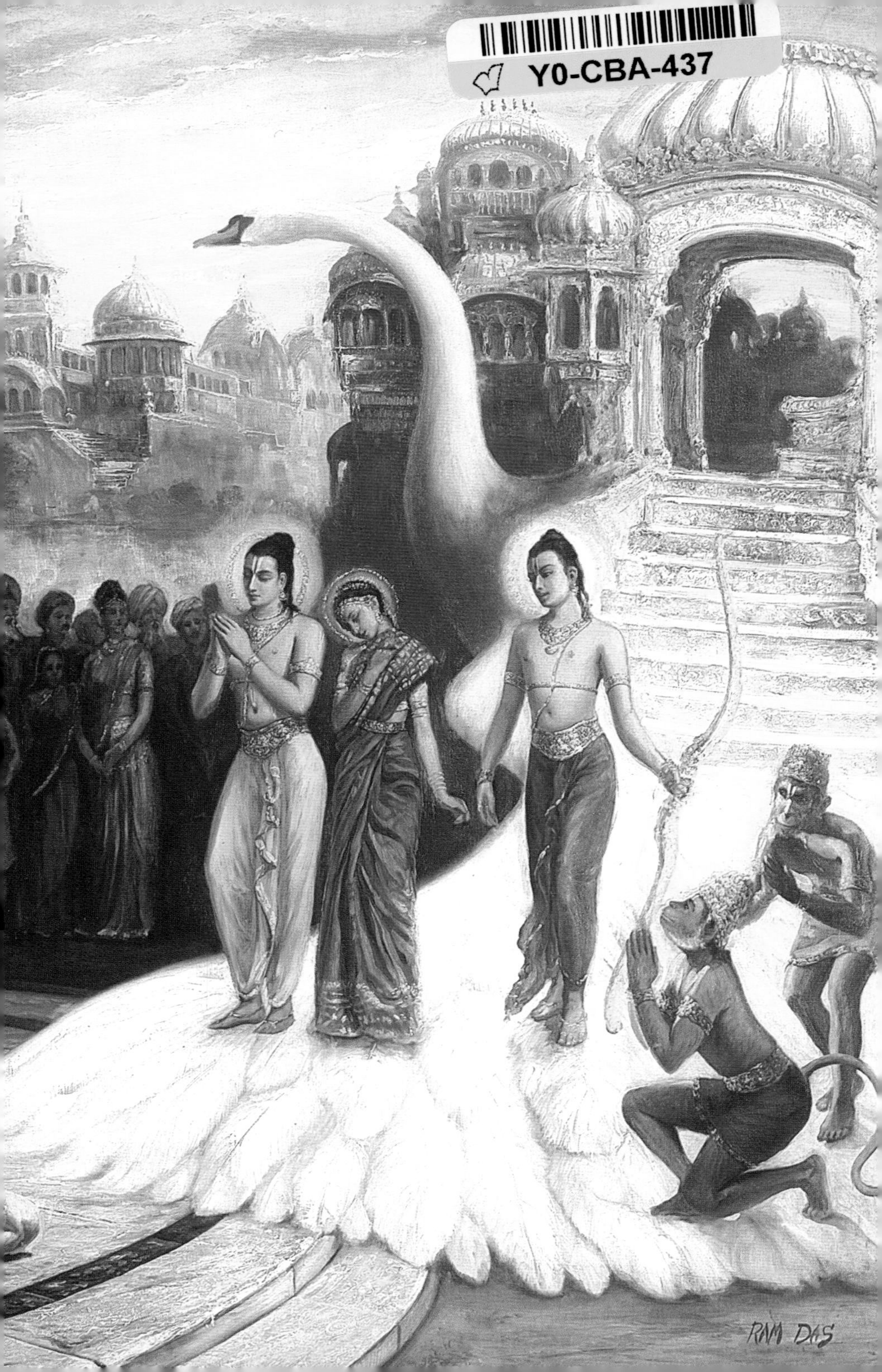
RNM DAS

Other Publications from Bhakti Vikas Trust

Books by His Holiness Bhakti Vikāsa Swami

A Beginner's Guide to Kṛṣṇa Consciousness
A Message to the Youth of India
Brahmacarya in Kṛṣṇa Consciousness
Glimpses of Traditional Indian Life
Jaya Śrīla Prabhupāda!
Lekha-mālā
Mothers and Masters
My Memories of Śrīla Prabhupāda
On Pilgrimage in Holy India
On Speaking Strongly in Śrīla Prabhupāda's Service
Patropadeśa (two volumes)
Rāmāyaṇa
Śrī Bhaktisiddhānta Vaibhava (three volumes)
Śrī Caitanya Mahāprabhu
Śrī Vaṁśīdāsa Bābājī
The Story of Rasikānanda
Gauḍīya Vaiṣṇava Padyāvalī (Bengali)
Vaiṣṇava Śikhā o Sādhana (Bengali)

Books by Other Authors

Śrī Cāṇakya-nīti (by Patita Pāvana Dāsa Adhikārī)
Rethinking Darwin (by Lalitānātha Dāsa)
Who is Supreme? (by Gokula Candra Dāsa)
Viveka-śatakam (by Prabodhānanda Sarasvatī)

Dedicated to

His Divine Grace A.C. Bhaktivedanta Swami Prabhupāda

Founder-*Ācārya* of the

International Society for Krishna Consciousness (ISKCON)

Rāmāyaṇa (The Story of Lord Rāma)
ISBN 978-81-902332-0-0

Previous printings : 43,000 copies
Fifth printing (2017) : 20,000 copies

www.bvks.com
books@bvks.com
WhatsApp # +(91)-7016811202

Published by Bhakti Vikas Trust, Surat, India.
Printed in India

Contents

Note: This edition of Rāmāyaṇa is based on the original text by Vālmīki. The well-known descriptions of Lakṣmaṇa-rekhā, of the ascetic woman Śabarī tasting fruit before offering it to Lord Rāma, and of Lord Rāma worshiping Lord Śiva, are not included because they do not appear in the Vālmīki Rāmāyaṇa.

Introduction

Lord Rāmacandra is not a mythical figure, an ordinary person, or even a very great human being. He is the Supreme Personality of Godhead—the source, maintainer and controller of uncountable universes, both spiritual and mundane. As the Supersoul, He is present in every atom and in the heart of every living being. He knows everything past, present and future.

Lord Rāma is fully replete with six opulences, namely strength, fame, wealth, knowledge, beauty and renunciation. He is the reservoir of all auspicious qualities, and is the ultimate goal of life for the yogis, renunciates, and especially the devotees, who ever delight in glorifying His inconceivable pastimes.

Being an expansion of Kṛṣṇa, the original form of the Personality of Godhead, Lord Rāmacandra eternally resides in His own planet in the spiritual world. He is accompanied there by His expansions and associates, headed by His consort Sītā, His brothers Lakṣmaṇa, Bharata, Śatrughna, and His celebrated servant Hanumān.

Out of extraordinary compassion for the suffering conditioned souls, the Lord occasionally descends into this material world, and is thus known as an *avatāra* (literally "one who descends"). The Lord explains this in the *Bhagavad-gītā* (4.7-8):

yadā yadā hi dharmasya
glānir bhavati bhārata

abhyutthānam adharmasya
tadātmānaṁ sṛjāmy aham

paritrāṇāya sādhūnāṁ
vināśāya ca duṣkṛtām
dharma-saṁsthāpanārthāya
sambhavāmi yuge yuge

"Whenever and wherever there is a decline in religious practice, and a predominant rise of irreligion—at that time I descend Myself. To deliver the pious and to annihilate the miscreants, as well as to reestablish the principles of religion, I Myself appear, millennium after millennium."

When the Supreme Lord comes to this world, He does so out of His own sweet will. Unlike the conditioned souls, He is not forced to take a body according to previous karma. Being far above the laws of karma, and never even slightly under their jurisdiction, the Supreme Lord descends in His eternal *sac-cid-ānanda* form.

"Although I am unborn and My transcendental body never deteriorates, and although I am the Lord of all living entities, I still appear in every millennium in My original transcendental form." (*Bhagavad-gītā* 4.6)

When the Supreme Lord descends, He shows His sublime nature by performing incomparable activities. When He came in His original form as Kṛṣṇa, He killed many apparently unconquerable demons; held the Govardhana Hill on the tip of His little finger for seven days (when He was apparently only a small child); made the sun rise again after it had set; and took His friend Arjuna on a journey Introduction beyond the edge of the universe. When He came as Vāmanadeva, He assumed the form of

a dwarf, yet with two footsteps crossed over the whole creation. Assuming a gigantic form as the transcendental boar, Varāha, He picked up the earth planet, which had fallen out of its orbit. As half-man half-lion Nṛsiṁha, He stopped the atrocities of the demon king Hiraṇyakaśipu by killing him. Although such extraordinary feats are doubted by men of puny intelligence, they are simply play for the Supreme Lord, who effortlessly creates, maintains and destroys millions of universes.

Similarly, when the Supreme Lord appeared as Rāmacandra, He performed the wonderful activity of slaying the tyrant Rāvaṇa, who was not to be killed by any other person. Ostensibly assuming the form and personality of a human being, Lord Rāma enjoyed many sweet pastimes with His dear devotees. These pastimes are inconceivable to the faithless, but are a source of transcendental joy for the theists.

The story of Lord Rāma has given pleasure and solace to theists for many thousands of years, and continues to do so. Not so long ago, when the people of India were accustomed to discuss the transcendental activities of the Lord, every Hindu knew the pastimes of Lord Rāma as well as the back of his hand. Among the three great epics famous in India (*Rāmāyaṇa, Mahābhārata* and *Śrīmad Bhāgavatam*), the Rāmāyaṇa was traditionally most popular, due to its relative simplicity and cohesiveness of plot. The action, drama and pathos of *Rāmāyaṇa* still place it among the world's most popular stories.

Recently, with the spread of the *bhakti*[1] movement throughout the world, there has been a revival of interest

1. Devotion to the Supreme Lord as inculcated in *Bhagavad-gītā* and other Vedic texts.

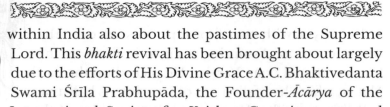

within India also about the pastimes of the Supreme Lord. This *bhakti* revival has been brought about largely due to the efforts of His Divine Grace A.C. Bhaktivedanta Swami Śrīla Prabhupāda, the Founder-*Ācārya* of the International Society for Krishna Consciousness, and the prime exponent of *bhakti* in the modern age. Śrīla Prabhupāda elaborately described the pastimes of Kṛṣṇa in his writings, and also wished that the pastimes of Lord Rāma be widely broadcast.

> Regarding seeing your book on Lord Rāmacandra partly translated into English, I am very much eager to see it. I have to translate all the *Purānas, Rāmāyaṇa, Mahābharata,* and many other theistic literatures left by the Gauḍīya Vaiṣṇavas. I have a great desire to translate the Vālmīki Rāmāyaṇa because that is authorized. It appears that in the Western countries there is a great demand for real knowledge of Vedic literature. So you are a learned scholar both in English and Hindi, and you can do this completely devoted to the service of Lord Rāmacandra. (Letter from Śrīla Prabhupāda to Dinanatha N. Mishra, 26 July, 1975)

Rāmāyaṇa was originally composed in Sanskrit by the great sage Vālmīki, and later many versions were composed in the vernacular languages of India. Unfortunately, many of the translators and commentators did not come in the pure devotional lineage of Vālmīki, and introduced many Introduction misconceptions and speculations about Lord Rāma in their works. As a result, the pristine position of Lord Rāma as the Supreme Absolute Truth Personality of Godhead remains hidden to the readers of such texts.

This present edition attempts to present the pastimes of Lord Rāma in their true glory. Although it is a summary study, nothing of the main body of the story has been left out. It is hoped that in the not too distant future, a devotional scholar will present a verse-by-verse translation of Vālmīki Rāmāyaṇa for the ever-increasing number of devotees throughout the world.

We pray that by the mercy of Śrīla Prabhupāda, this edition of Rāmāyaṇa will shower the highest fortune on its readers by awakening in their hearts loving feelings for the lotus feet of Lord Rāma. We beg the devotees to bless us with their mercy, so that we may also attain such a benediction.

Again, it must be emphasized that the reading of the Rāmāyaṇa will give greatest benefit if taken not simply as an exciting story, but with the understanding of the supramundane and eternally supreme position of Lord Rāma. Those who read with this awareness will ultimately attain the greatest benediction of life, that of going back to Godhead.

janma karma ca me divyam
evaṁ yo vetti tattvataḥ
tyaktvā dehaṁ punar janma
naiti mām eti so 'rjuna

"One who knows the transcendental nature of My appearance and activities does not, upon leaving the body, take his birth again in this material world, but attains My eternal abode." (*Bhagavad-gītā* 4.9)

"Lord Śrī Rāma, the Absolute Personality of Godhead, is attractive not only in His personal features, but also in His transcendental activities. It is so because the Absolute is absolute by His name, fame, form, pastimes, entourage, paraphernalia, etc. The Lord descends on this material world out of His causeless mercy and displays His various transcendental pastimes as a human being so that human beings attracted towards Him become able to go back to Godhead. Men are naturally apt to hear histories and narrations of various personalities performing mundane activities, without knowing that by such association one simply wastes valuable time and also becomes addicted to the three qualities of mundane nature. Instead of wasting time, one can get spiritual success by turning his attention to the transcendental pastimes of the Lord. By hearing the narration of the pastimes of the Lord, one contacts directly the Personality of Godhead, and by hearing about the Personality of Godhead, from within, all accumulated sins of the mundane creature are cleared. Thus being cleared of all sins, the hearer gradually becomes liberated from mundane association and becomes attracted to the features of the Lord. The whole idea is that simply by hearing about the Lord's pastimes one can become one of the associates of the Lord. One can attain to the highest perfection of life simply by attentive hearing of the transcendental pastimes of the Lord from the right sources. This process of hearing in the association of the devotees is especially recommended in this age of quarrel (Kali)." (Adapted from *Śrīmad- Bhāgavatam* 1.5.26 purport, by His Divine Grace A.C. Bhaktivedanta Swami Prabhupāda)

Bhakti Vikāsa Swami

Bāla-kāṇḍa

Once, in a time long ago, there lived a great sage named Vālmīki, who was never so happy as when he was discussing the pastimes of the Supreme Personality of Godhead.

One day, while Vālmīki was explaining the nectar of Kṛṣṇa consciousness to a group of disciples, the great sage Śrī Nārada Muni, who travels continuously throughout the spiritual and material worlds glorifying the pastimes of the Supreme Personality of Godhead, appeared at Vālmīki's hermitage. Upon seeing Śrī Nārada, Vālmīki and his disciples immediately offered their respectful obeisances. Then, according to custom, they offered Śrī Nārada an elevated sitting place and washed his feet, while sweetly inquiring about his welfare.

After this, Vālmīki inquired from Śrī Nārada, "O best of all knowers of truth, please tell me who, present now on earth, is a reservoir of all opulences in full? Who is the most accomplished, learned, powerful, noble-minded, truthful and grateful? Who possesses flawless character and remains engaged looking after the genuine welfare of all living entities? Who is there present that is without an equal, clever, the most beautiful, and is never subject to the influence of anger or malice, yet instills fear within the hearts of even the great demigods when enraged? Who has the prowess to give protection to everyone within the three worlds? To whom has the goddess of fortune bestowed all blessings? O great sage, please answer my inquiries fully."

The great sage Nārada, who is able to know everything that happens within the three worlds, replied, "O *ṛṣi*, there is an illustrious king by the name of Rāma who has appeared in the royal dynasty of Ikṣvāku, as the son of Mahārāja Daśaratha. He is the embodiment of all transcendental qualities and the possessor of all opulences. Rāma perfectly controls His senses and is the master of unlimited potencies.

"Rāma has mighty arms that extend down to his knees, and His throat is marked with three auspicious lines like those on a canticle. He has high and broad shoulders, a wide chest, a beautifully formed head, a graceful forehead, powerful jaws, and deeply embedded collarbones. His eyes are large. He is majestically medium-tall in stature, and all His limbs are well formed and symmetrical. His bodily complexion is dark greenish-blue and has a great luster. His intelligence is unfathomable, His manner is grave, and His speech is superb in tone and eloquence.

"Lord Rāma has a supremely pure character and is a follower of true religious principles. He is full in self-realization, and is the upholder of *varṇāśrama-dharma.* Truly, He is the support of the entire universe. He is simultaneously the destroyer of all foes and the only shelter for those who are fully surrendered. Lord Rāma is the absolute knower of the Vedas. Furthermore, He is fully conversant with the use of all weapons. He possesses unflinching determination and is a genius with unfailing memory. Indeed, His learning is without bounds. He is wise, compassionate and heroic in battle. He is loved by all creatures and is impartial toward friends and foes alike. He is grave like an ocean.

In fortitude He is like the Himālayan Mountains. In strength He is like Lord Viṣṇu. In beauty He is like the moon. In forbearance He is like the earth, and in anger He is like the fire that blazes forth at the time of universal destruction. In wealth He is like Kuvera, and in devotion He is like Dharma, the lord of righteousness."

Nārada then briefly described to Vālmīki the pastimes of Lord Rāmacandra. He concluded by telling him that this same Lord Rāma now rules over His subjects in a most righteous and exemplary manner.

He explained that during the reign of Lord Rāma no one would suffer from any disease or mental disturbance. Everyone within Lord Rāma's kingdom would be happy and prosperous, never fearing thieves, scarcity or hunger. All the cities and villages would be filled with abundant grains, fruits, vegetables and milk products. Indeed, the people would experience the same degree of piety and happiness that was exhibited during the Satya-yuga. There would be no natural disturbances, like floods, earthquakes or famine, and all the women would be chaste and never suffer widowhood. Lord Rāmacandra will rule over the earth in this way for 11,000 years before returning to His supreme abode in the spiritual sky, Vaikuṇṭha.

After satisfying the inquiry of Vālmīki Muni, which was for the benefit of the three worlds, Śrī Nārada again took up his travels, spreading the glories of the Supreme Lord. The sage Vālmīki then journeyed to the banks of the River Tamasa, accompanied by his disciple, Bharadvāja. At the riverbank, Vālmīki sat down to meditate upon the words of Śrī Nārada. Sitting within the forest, Vālmīki happened to see a pair of cranes, fully absorbed in sexual intercourse and singing in melodious jubilation. At that time a malicious hunter of the Niṣāda race appeared from his hiding place and released an arrow that pierced the body of the male bird, causing it to fall shrieking to the ground. Then, upon seeing her mate writhing upon the ground and smeared with blood, the she-bird cried out in terror, having suddenly been cast down from the heights of sensual pleasure to the depths of despair.

When Vālmīki witnessed this tragic scene, feelings of great compassion welled up within his breast. Considering the Niṣāda's violent act to be extremely sinful, Vālmīki became

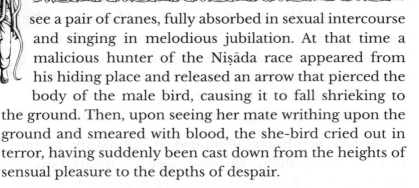

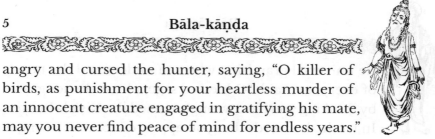

angry and cursed the hunter, saying, "O killer of birds, as punishment for your heartless murder of an innocent creature engaged in gratifying his mate, may you never find peace of mind for endless years."

However, no sooner was this curse uttered, than Vālmīki felt a pang of shame for becoming a victim of uncontrolled anger. Indeed, as an enlightened soul, he knew that all living beings are acting helplessly under the influence of material nature. Thus, he regretted retaliating against the hunter. At the same time, Vālmīki was astonished that the curse he uttered had come from his mouth in a wonderfully poetic meter. Indeed, his curse seemed to hint of the predominant emotional expression of the *Rāmāyaṇa*, which he had been contemplating since his meeting with Śrī Nārada.

This caused Vālmīki to remark to his disciple Bharadvāja, "From my sorrow came a verse of four lines, each containing eight syllables. From *śoka* (lamentation) has come a wonderful *śloka* (verse), for without compassion, there is no possibility of genuine poetic expression."

Thereafter, Vālmīki bathed in the River Tamasa and returned to his *āśrama* with Bharadvāja. While continuing to meditate upon his curse of the hunter, he suddenly saw Lord Brahmā descending from his abode, the topmost planet within the universe. Overwhelmed with wonder and jubilation, the speechless Vālmīki stood up to receive the first-born being of the universe.

When Lord Brahmā appeared before him, Vālmīki offered his respectful obeisances and worshipped Lord Brahmā with great awe and reverence. Then, Lord Brahmā, the universal grandsire, who can understand the hearts of everyone, said, "O blessed sage, please do not grieve by thinking you have wrongly cursed the Niṣāda hunter. In truth, the words that you appeared to utter in anger were my own. They were spoken through your mouth for the purpose of inspiring you to accomplish a great task. Indeed, the time has come for you to compose the history of Lord Rāmacandra's life—great transcendental pastimes meant for the ultimate welfare of the world.

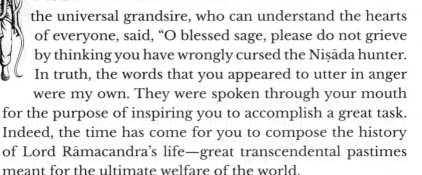

"My dear Vālmīki, there is no cause for you to be anxious, for by the strength of my benediction, everything that is unknown to you will become clearly revealed within your heart. Thus, by my grace, your narration of the *Rāmāyaṇa* will be faultless."

After bestowing this benediction upon Vālmīki, Lord Brahmā departed for his abode upon his celestial swan carrier, filling all who beheld him with wonder. Vālmīki then sat down in meditation to discover all the pastimes of Lord Rāmacandra, as indicated by Lord Brahmā.

Absorbed in a deep trance, Vālmīki clearly envisioned within his heart all the events of Lord Rāma's appearance. Vālmīki then composed the *Rāmāyaṇa* in 24,000 verses.

After completing the epic poem, he wondered whom he could teach it to so that it would remain preserved in

memory and propagated all over the world. While Vālmīki was thus contemplating, his disciples, Lava and Kuśa, who were dressed as *ṛṣis*, came before him and touched his feet, as was their daily custom. Sītā had given birth to the twin brothers while in exile, and they had remained under Vālmīki's care ever since.

Sītā's forced exile had come about when a citizen of Ayodhyā doubted her chastity after being touched by the ten-headed monster, Rāvaṇa. Thus, Lord Rāmacandra was forced to banish her. Their two sons, Lava and Kuśa, were gifted with fine memories and musical abilities. Moreover, they were well versed in the Vedas. Physically, the twins were exact replicas of their father, and musically they were as talented as the heavenly Gandharvas. Thus, as Vālmīki gazed fondly upon the twins, he realized that they were fully qualified to receive the *Rāmāyaṇa*.

Thereafter, Vālmīki proceeded to teach Lava and Kuśa the entire *Rāmāyaṇa* with great care. The twins committed the entire text to memory. Following Vālmīki's instructions, they chanted Lord Rāmacandra's wonderful pastimes before great sages, learned *brāhmaṇas*, and other pious men pure in heart. The learned *brāhmaṇas* experienced great transcendental pleasure in reciting the pastimes of Lord Rāmacandra. Thus, the *brāhmaṇas* praised Lava and Kuśa, rewarding them with many valuable gifts.

From that day Lava and Kuśa began traveling all over the world, reciting the epic *Rāmāyaṇa*. In the course of their wanderings, they eventually came to Ayodhyā. There Lord Rāmacandra saw the two boys wandering through the city streets dressed in the garb of *ṛṣis*. Upon hearing the wide

acclaim of their expert recitation of His transcendental pastimes, Lord Rāma took great pleasure in inviting them to His palace to recite the *Rāmāyaṇa*. Still, although they were His sons, He did not recognize them.

After respectfully receiving the twin sages, the Lord invited them into His royal assembly. Lord Rāma observed that the boys, although dressed as ascetic *brāhmaṇas*, had the features of *kṣatriyas*. Speaking to His brothers, Bharata, Lakṣmaṇa and Śatrughna, Rāma said, "O best of King Raghu's dynasty, please listen to this wonderful narration. Although these two singers appear like ascetics, they have the marks of great rulers. Listen to this story, because it is full of literary beauty and has universal appeal."

As Lava and Kuśa began the narration of the beautiful epic poem, Rāma and His brothers soon forgot everything else, becoming fully absorbed in hearing the *Rāmāyaṇa*. The bonds of material existence can be completely cut by simply chanting and hearing the Lord's glories.

The great tract of land known as Kosala extended along the banks of the Sarayū River. This land was verdant, prosperous and rich in grain. Within this vast territory was the renowned city of Ayodhyā, built by the desire of Vaivasvata Manu, the ruler of mankind. This glorious city was ninety-six miles long and twenty-four miles wide. It was well laid out, and its beautiful, straight roads were perfumed with scented water sprayed from the trunks of intoxicated elephants. Every day, the damsels of the celestial planets hovered above it in their beautiful airplanes and showered it with flowers.

The arched gateways of Ayodhyā were made of marble, and the gates were wrought with gold and silver and embedded with precious jewels. Cannons and catapults, capable of repulsing any enemy, protected the city walls. The marketplaces were well planned, and seven-story houses symmetrically lined the streets. Adorned with multi-storied palaces and surrounded with exquisite gardens, Ayodhyā resounded with the vibrations of musical instruments, rivaling Amarāvatī, the abode of the heavenly king, Indra. Throughout the city, bards and singers recited the glories of the Supreme Personality of Godhead, and dancers acted out the Lord's pastimes for everyone's benefit.

Within Ayodhyā were many beautiful gardens abounding with flowers and shaded by fruit trees. Blue, red, and golden lotuses filled the ponds, and fountains shot water high into the air. Gentle breezes carried the aromatic spray from the fountains, cooling the citizens by their touch, and making even a hot summer day seem like spring. The sounds of cranes and peacocks could be heard everywhere. The water flowing through Ayodhyā's streams and rivulets tasted as sweet as sugarcane sap, and it was used not only for drinking but for irrigating numerous mango orchards. Many houses and palaces, perfectly designed, were built of precious stones and decorated with flags and festoons. Their beauty rivaled the palaces of Vaikuṇṭha.

Thousands of warriors protected the great city: skilled archers, well versed in the use of weapons, and chariot fighters who were able to fight with thousands of men at a time.

The streets leading into Ayodhyā were always filled with travelers. Kings and princes from all parts of the world came to render their annual tribute and pay respects to the King of Ayodhyā. Traders from near and far flocked to the markets to barter.

Brāhmaṇa priests could often be seen pouring ghee into sacrificial fires and chanting Vedic hymns, proclaiming the glories of Lord Viṣṇu. Having mastered their senses and devoted themselves to truth, these *brāhmaṇas* were blessed with all good qualities.

Mahārāja Daśaratha was the emperor of the entire world and was a great *rājarṣi*, considered almost on the level of a *maharṣi*. He was a formidable warrior, capable of fighting alone with an unlimited number of opponents. Because he and the citizens were completely pious, Ayodhyā was the picture of perfect Vedic civilization. Every imaginable opulence was exhibited in perfection, and material miseries, coming from the results of sinful life, were practically nonexistent. In Ayodhyā, the four social orders, namely the *brāhmaṇas*, *kṣatriyas*, *vaiśyas* and *śūdras,* participated cooperatively for the peace and prosperity of the kingdom. No one cheated and no one was miserly. Arrogance, atheism, and harsh behavior and speech were conspicuous by their absence.

Even though Mahārāja Daśaratha possessed such fantastic opulence and prestige, he remained unhappy. Try as he may, the King was unable to beget a son to continue his dynasty. Finally, after much deliberation, King Daśaratha decided to perform a horse sacrifice[2] for the purpose of

---

2. Śrīla Prabhupāda explains: "A Vedic sacrifice is not an ordinary performance. The demigods used to participate in such sacrifices,

getting a son. With this in mind he sent his chief minister, Sumantra, to call for his family priests.

When the *brāhmaṇas*, headed by Vasiṣṭha and Vāmadeva, assembled, Mahārāja Daśaratha addressed them, saying, "O best among the twice born, for many years I have ardently desired to beget a son. However, all my efforts have been in vain. Because I am without an heir, I can no longer feign happiness. Indeed, my days seem wasted and are filled with grief. Thus, after much careful consideration, and with your kind permission, I have decided to perform a horse sacrifice. Because you are fully knowledgeable in scripture, I am confident that you will be able to lead me on the proper path."

The priests unanimously approved of Mahārāja Daśaratha's idea to perform the horse sacrifice, and thereafter, the king ordered his ministers to make all necessary arrangements without delay.

Sumantra then took Mahārāja Daśaratha aside to narrate the following story that he had formerly heard from Sanat-kumāra, who had spoken it in an assembly of great sages.

"You will be very interested to hear this story, my dear king," Sumantra said, "because it predicts that in the future you will become the father of four glorious sons.

---

and the animals sacrificed in such performances were reincarnated with new life. In this age of Kali there are no powerful *brāhmaṇas* who can invite the demigods or give renewed life to animals. Formerly, the *brāhmaṇas* well conversant in Vedic mantras could show the potency of the mantras, but in this age, because there are no such *brāhmaṇas,* all such sacrifices are forbidden."

"It so happened that Sanat-kumāra previously related this same story in the Satya-yuga of the previous millennium. Thus, none of the events which were described by him had yet occurred, but were destined to take place in the far distant future.

"Due to some offense on the part of King Romapāda, there once came to be an extremely severe drought within his kingdom, causing great fear among all the living beings. When the conditions became intolerable, Mahārāja Romapāda summoned his council of learned *brāhmaṇas* and inquired from them the cause of the drought: 'I know that it is because of some fault of mine that this terrible drought has now overcome my kingdom. O best of the twice-born, because your knowledge is boundless, please prescribe the proper atonement for my past sins.'

"The *brāhmaṇas* replied, 'O king, there is a great brāhmaṇa sage named Mṛgī Ṛṣi who is residing in the forest. Mṛgī Ṛṣi is the son of Kaśyapa, and his son is named Ṛṣyaśṛṅga.[3] If you can bring this *ṛṣi's* son to your kingdom and give him your daughter Śānta in marriage, the drought will immediately end.'

"Śānta was actually the daughter of Mahārāja Daśaratha, but had been given to the king's childless friend, Romapāda, at the latter's request. King Romapāda was very glad to learn the means for ending the drought, but when he requested his priests to summon Ṛṣyaśṛṅga, they refused. The *brāhmaṇas* explained, 'O king, we fear that Mṛgī Ṛṣi will curse us if we try to lure his son away from home. Ṛṣyaśṛṅga has been

3. The name Ṛṣyaśṛṅga indicates that the young sage was born with a deerlike horn growing out of his forehead.

brought up by his father in complete isolation. He has never even seen another human being. Because Ṛṣyaśṛṅga has never once beheld a member of the fair sex, he is completely unaware of the pleasure of their association.

"'My dear king, since we desire your welfare, we have devised a method for bringing Ṛṣyaśṛṅga to your kingdom. Have the most beautiful of courtesans go there and allure him with their feminine ways. We are certain that by this means your aim will easily be accomplished.'

"Mahārāja Romapāda agreed to their plan and then sent for the foremost of young and beautiful prostitutes. After being thus instructed by the king and promised sufficient rewards, the girls departed for the forest, determined to bring back the young *ṛṣi* at all costs.

"Thereafter, the prostitutes set up their camp at the *āśrama* of Mṛgī Ṛṣi and waited for the opportune time. It so happened that one day Ṛṣyaśṛṅga wandered away from home and came to the camp of the prostitutes.

"Seeing him, the girls jubilantly approached Ṛṣyaśṛṅga. When they asked about his identity the boy replied, 'I am the son of Mṛgī Ṛṣi, and I am engaged in performing austerities nearby at my father's *āśrama.* How wonderfully beautiful all of you are to look at! I wish that you would come to my home and accept my worship and hospitality.'

"The prostitutes then went with Ṛṣyaśṛṅga, where they were very nicely received at his *āśrama* with offerings of water to drink, water for washing their feet, and various kinds of fruits and roots. However, the girls were extremely afraid of the father's imminent return and did not wish to stay too long. As the prostitutes were leaving, they said, 'My dear friend, our customs for receiving guests are quite different from yours. Now, please accept our offerings of honor and respect in return.'

"Saying this, the girls embraced Ṛṣyaśṛṅga tightly with great affection, and then fed him sumptuous sweets. Never before had the *ṛṣi's* innocent son tasted anything so pleasing, for he had been accustomed to eating only fruits and roots. Indeed, he thought that the sweets were a type of wonderful fruit. Moreover, since he had previously seen only his father, he took the prostitutes to be enchantingly beautiful men.

"After the girls departed, Ṛṣyaśṛṅga began to experience feelings of unease and restlessness within his heart. The seed of lusty desire, which had remained dormant within his heart had sprouted. Ṛṣyaśṛṅga began to constantly think of the beautiful women. Ṛṣyaśṛṅga could hardly sleep that night. His mind and heart became overwhelmed by thoughts of their sweet speech and tender embraces.

"Unable to think of anything else, the following day Ṛṣyaśṛṅga went to the prostitutes' camp. The girls received Ṛṣyaśṛṅga with great delight and then explained, 'This is not our real home. Please come aboard our magnificent floating hermitage and accompany us to a place where we will be able to entertain you in a much better fashion. We have many nice varieties of fruit and roots, and we shall pass the time so enjoyably that you will hardly be able to perceive how time is passing.'

"Being captivated at heart, Ṛṣyaśṛṅga unhesitatingly accompanied the prostitutes. Thus, the women allured him

back to the capital of Romapāda within the kingdom of Aṅga. Indeed, even as Ṛṣyaśṛṅga was being carried down the Gaṅgā, Indra began to send forth showers of rain, giving joy to all the living creatures.

"As soon as he understood that Ṛṣyaśṛṅga had arrived, King Romapāda came out from his palace and bowed down before the young *ṛṣi*. Then, after worshipping Ṛṣyaśṛṅga with great attention, Romapāda escorted him into the inner apartments of his palace, where he presented his daughter to the *ṛṣi* in charity.

"When he could understand that Ṛṣyaśṛṅga was fully satisfied, Mahārāja Romapāda begged from him the benediction that neither he nor his father would show their wrath toward him because of the duplicitous manner in which he had allured Ṛṣyaśṛṅga away from home.

"Ṛṣyaśṛṅga gave the king his assurance, and thereafter, the marriage between him and Śānta was celebrated with great festivity. After the wedding, the newly married couple continued to live in Mahārāja Romapāda's palace, and thus, passed their days happily in royal comfort."

Sumantra concluded his narration to Mahārāja Daśaratha: "O king, Sanat-kumāra predicted that you would take help from your friend Romapāda by requesting him to allow Ṛṣyaśṛṅga to come to the kingdom of Kosala and perform a horse sacrifice. It was further indicated that after the performance of the horse sacrifice, you would gain the fulfillment of your desires by receiving four incomparable sons."

Mahārāja Daśaratha was very pleased to hear this story from Sumantra. Then, without delay, he went with his retinue to the kingdom of Aṅga. There, he was received by Mahārāja Romapāda with great respect, and at that time the king of Aṅga informed Ṛṣyaśṛṅga that Daśaratha was his real father-in-law. After enjoying Romapāda's hospitality for about one week, Mahārāja Daśaratha addressed his friend as follows: "For a long time I have been morose on account of not having a son to perpetuate my illustrious dynasty. Now, I beg you to allow Ṛṣyaśṛṅga to come to Ayodhyā to perform a horse sacrifice on my behalf."

Romapāda happily agreed, and Mahārāja Daśaratha soon returned to his capital with Ṛṣyaśṛṅga and Śānta. Then, when spring arrived, Mahārāja Daśaratha humbly approached Ṛṣyaśṛṅga, begging him for instructions regarding the performance of the horse sacrifice. Thus, preparations for the sacrifice commenced and a site was selected on the northern bank of the River Sarayū.

The system was for an emperor to send a challenge horse all over the world to establish his supremacy over subordinate kings. The horse would be accompanied by soldiers of the emperor, and upon its arrival in a kingdom, the local king would either have to offer tribute to the emperor's representatives, or fight to capture the horse. Any ruling prince or king was at liberty either to express his tacit willingness to obey the emperor, or to accept the challenge and thus disobey the supremacy of the particular emperor. One who accepted the challenge had to fight with the emperor's men and establish his own supremacy by victory. The defeated challenger would have to sacrifice his life, making place for another king or ruler. Only when the horse returned after touring the world, with no more challengers left, could a horse sacrifice begin.

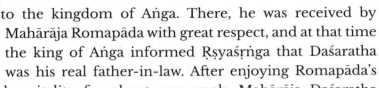

Understanding that King Janaka would be the future father-in-law of his sons, Mahārāja Daśaratha sent him the first invitation. Likewise, other subordinate kings were requested to attend the sacrifice. After one full year, the challenge horse returned to Ayodhyā, having wandered over the earth under the protection of 400 princes. Only then could the sacrifice begin.

After the preliminary rites had been performed, Mahārāja Daśaratha's eldest queen, Kauśalyā, circumambulated the challenge horse, which was tied to one of the sacrificial stakes. Then, with three strokes of a sword, she severed the horse's head, as prescribed by scriptural injunction.

Thereafter, Ṛṣyaśṛṅga offered the fat of the dead horse into the sacrificial fire. Mahārāja Daśaratha was directed to inhale the fumes, to free him from all sins. Then, the assisting priests offered the limbs of the horse into the sacrificial fire, bringing the three-day sacrifice to an end.

Mahārāja Daśaratha then gave away the four directions of the earth in charity to the four chief priests. The *brāhmaṇas* returned the gifts, however, saying, "O king, we are devoted to Vedic study and the performance of austerities, and have no interest in ruling over a kingdom. Therefore, please give us other gifts like cows and gold."

Ṛṣyaśṛṅga then approached Mahārāja Daśaratha, saying, "My dear king, you will surely receive four glorious sons. However, I propose that a separate sacrifice, known as Putreṣṭī, be performed for that purpose."

Mahārāja Daśaratha readily assented, and soon the sacrifice was begun. Meanwhile, in the higher planets,

the chief demigods approached Lord Brahmā and explained, "O grandsire, because of your benedictions, Rāvaṇa has become so powerful that he is harassing everyone at will. Even we cannot subdue the wicked Rākṣasa. Therefore, we request you to personally devise the means for his destruction."

Lord Brahmā considered the situation and then replied, "At the time of asking for benedictions, Rāvaṇa did not bother to ask for immunity from death at the hands of human beings, for he considered them to be too insignificant."

While Brahmā was thinking how Rāvaṇa could be killed, Lord Viṣṇu suddenly appeared, riding on His carrier, Garuḍa. As effulgent as many suns, Lord Viṣṇu appeared in His four-armed form, dressed in bright saffron garments and carrying His disc, conch, club and lotus flower.

The demigods worshipped the Supreme Lord with great reverence and then requested, "O master of the universe, please come to our rescue by dividing Yourself into four, becoming the sons of Mahārāja Daśaratha for the purpose of killing Rāvaṇa.

Lord Viṣṇu replied, "Rest assured, there is no longer any need to be afraid. I will soon incarnate to rule over the earth for 11,000 years after vanquishing your enemy, the king of the Rākṣasas." After saying this, Lord Viṣṇu disappeared as the demigods looked on with wonder.

Meanwhile, from the sacrificial fire of Mahārāja Daśaratha, there appeared an exceptional being of dark complexion with all auspicious bodily features. This personality appeared to be unlimitedly powerful. He was

decorated with transcendental ornaments, and in his hand he carried a large golden pot of sweet rice. That divine person then told Mahārāja Daśaratha, "I am a messenger of Lord Viṣṇu."

With folded hands, the king replied, "O Viṣṇudūta, please order me to perform whatever service I can render."

The servant of Lord Viṣṇu said, "This pot of sweet rice is the reward for your two sacrificial performances. Give portions to your three wives to eat. Through them you shall beget four sons who will forever perpetuate your fame."

Mahārāja Daśaratha happily accepted the sweet rice and circumambulated the Viṣṇudūta. After Lord Viṣṇu's messenger disappeared from view, Mahārāja Daśaratha quickly gave portions of the sweet rice to his wives for he was eager to have sons.

Mahārāja Daśaratha gave Kauśalyā one half of the sweet rice, Sumitrā one fourth, and Kaikeyi one eighth. Then, after some deliberation, he gave the remaining eighth to Sumitrā. All three wives were overjoyed, for they were confident that they would soon become mothers.

The three Queens eagerly ate their shares and soon thereafter, each felt the presence of divine offspring within their wombs. When Mahārāja Daśaratha understood that his wives were pregnant, he too became very satisfied.

Meanwhile, Lord Brahmā ordered the demigods as follows: "Beget partial manifestations of yourselves to assist Lord Viṣṇu in His forthcoming incarnation. The children which you produce in the form of monkeys (by uniting with Apsarās, she-monkeys, and female Yakṣas, Nāgas, Vidyādharas and other celestial beings), must be capable of assuming any form at will and must possess all other mystic powers. In addition, they must be very intelligent, highly skilled in the use of weapons, having prowess almost equal to Lord Viṣṇu, and possess ethereal bodies."

After receiving the order of Lord Brahmā, Indra begot Vāli, Sūrya begot Sugrīva, Bṛhaspati begot Tāra, Kuvera begot Gandhamāda, Viśvakarmā begot Nala, Varuṇa begot Suṣeṇa, and Vāyu begot Hanumān. Besides these principal monkeys, many thousands of others took birth to assist Lord Viṣṇu in His mission. All of them were gigantic like mountains and were very eager to fight with Rāvaṇa. Like the demigods who begot them, these monkeys were born just after conception. They were so powerful that they could agitate the ocean with their impetuous energy.

There were three classes of these created beings: bears, monkeys, and monkeys that had long tails like cows. Because there were more than ten million of these monkeys and bears, the earth soon became overrun with them as they wandered throughout the forests, eating wild fruits and various roots.

His Divine Grace A.C. Bhaktivedanta Swami Prabhupāda

Founder-*Ācārya* of the

International Society for Krishna Consciousness (ISKCON)

When Mahārāja Bhagīratha expressed his desire, Lord Śiva agreed to bear the force of the Gaṅgā's falling water upon his head. (p. 43)

When the Supreme Personality of Godhead in the form of Mohinī understood how the demon named Rāhu was cheating, He immediately cut off the demon's head. (p. 50)

The famous and terrible warrior Paraśurāma appeared before Lord Rāma in ferocious aspect, although previously, after annihilating the *kṣatriya* community twenty-one times, he had vowed to give up his anger. (p. 72)

Following the order of Mahārāja Daśaratha, Lord Rāma along with Sītā and Lakṣmaṇa mounted the chariot and departed for the forest. (p. 111)

When Bharata saw Rāma, He rushed forward with tears in His eyes. Coming forward to touch Rāma's feet, Bharata suddenly fainted. Rāma quickly lifted Him up, and was disturbed to see that He was also wearing tree bark. (p. 150)

The present-day shrine at the site of Rāma-Bharata Milāp, in Citrakūṭa, where Bharata met Lord Rāma. (See p.162)

Lord Rāma, Sītā and Lakṣmaṇa in Daṇḍakāraṇya forest. (p. 178)

Hanumān assumed his gigantic form and jumped onto the roof of the Prime Minister's palace, setting it afire. Then, jumping from rooftop to rooftop, he ignited a great fire that spread all over Laṅkā, including Rāvaṇa's palace. (p. 318)

As Lord Rāma drew His bow taut, darkness enveloped the sky. Celestial winds raged furiously, lightning streaked across the sky, while thunder reverberated in all directions. Suddenly the ocean god rose up from water and approached Rāma with folded hands. (p. 349)

Unable to find the required herbs in the mountain, Hanumān roared ferociously and challenged the mountain. Receiving no response, he broke off the top of the mountain and sprang into the air and quickly flew the 1,000 *yojanas* to Laṅkā. (p. 417)

As the population of Ayodhyā sighted the Puṣpaka chariot which appeared to be just like the full moon rising in the sky, a loud spontaneous cheer suddenly arose from them. Bharata began worshipping Rāma from a distance. (p. 470)

Lord Rāma and Sītā at last again dressed in royal style, and were decorated with garlands and ornaments. Being served by Bharata, Śatrughna, Lakṣmaṇa, Vibhīṣaṇa and others, they entered Ayodhyā. (p. 472)

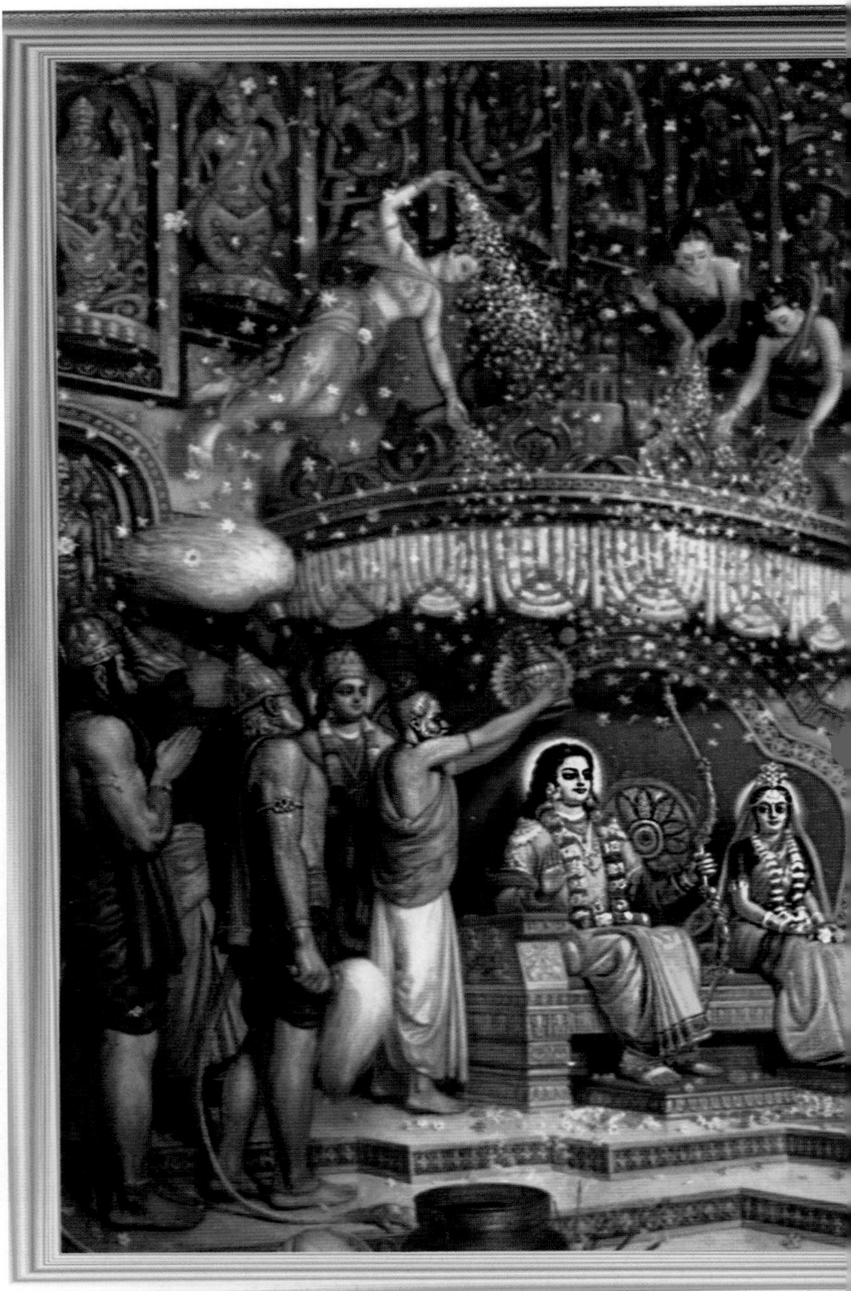

As the coronation was witnessed by chief demigods, Rama sat upon a golden throne bedecked with valuable gems, Vasiṣṭha placed the royal crown upon His head. Vāyu placed a garland made from

100 golden lotuses, as Sugrīva and Vibhīṣaṇa fanned Him from both sides. (p. 473)

As being requested by Sītā in order to prove her chastity, the earth opened up, and the goddess Bhūmi majestically rose up, seated upon a golden throne borne by divine serpents. The goddess welcomed Sītā, seated her at her side, and then the celestial throne slowly descended into the earth. (p. 563)

After the completion of the Putreṣṭī sacrifice, the demigods (who personally came to accept their offerings) and the priests, Ṛṣyaśṛṅga and Śānta, departed for their respective residences. Then, after a pregnancy of twelve months, on the ninth day of the waxing (bright) fortnight in the month of Caitra, Kauśalyā gave birth to a son. This divine child had reddish eyes and lips, long arms, and was decorated with all auspicious markings. The son of Kauśalyā represented one-half of the potency of Lord Viṣṇu.

Soon thereafter, a son representing one-fourth of the prowess of Lord Viṣṇu was born of Kaikeyī, Mahārāja Daśaratha's youngest queen. Then, two days after the appearance of Kauśalyā's son, Sumitrā gave birth to twins, each representing one-sixth of the potency of Lord Viṣṇu. All four of the newborn children highly resembled one another and were exceedingly effulgent and pleasing to behold. Indeed, upon the appearance of Mahārāja Daśaratha's four sons, the demigods showered flowers from heaven, while the Gandharvas sang and played musical instruments as the Apsarās danced. In Ayodhyā there was a great festival, as musicians, dancers and actors crowded the streets, with all the citizens participating in the merrymaking.[4]

---

4. Śrīla Prabhupāda explains: "Being prayed for by the demigods, the Supreme Personality of Godhead, the Absolute Truth Himself, directly appeared with His expansion and expansions of the expansion. Their holy names were Rāma, Lakṣmaṇa, Bharata and Śatrughna. These celebrated incarnations thus appeared in four forms as the sons of Mahārāja Daśaratha. Lord Rāmacandra and His brothers, Lakṣmaṇa, Bharata and Śatrughna, are all *viṣṇu-tattva.* The Supreme Personality of Godhead expands into

Thirteen days after the birth of Kauśalyā's child, Vasiṣṭha Muni, the family priest of Mahārāja Daśaratha, performed the name-giving ceremony. The fortunate *ṛṣi* named the son of Kauśalyā, Rāma, while the son of Kaikeyī was named Bharata. The twin sons of Sumitrā were named Lakṣmaṇa and Śatrughna.

Thereafter, Vasiṣṭha took charge of performing all the purificatory rituals for the sons of Mahārāja Daśaratha, culminating with the sacred thread ceremony. Under Vasiṣṭha's guidance, all four brothers became masters of the Vedas, great heroic warriors, and reservoirs of all godly qualities.

From birth, however, Rāma outshone His brothers in all respects. Quite naturally, He became the favorite son of Mahārāja Daśaratha. Likewise, from childhood, Lakṣmaṇa was very attached to Rāma. Similarly, Rāma was not willing to eat anything or even go to sleep without Lakṣmaṇa. Whenever Rāma went hunting, Lakṣmaṇa unfailingly accompanied Him. Śatrughna and Bharata were also very dear to each other, and thus inseparable.

After Rāma, Lakṣmaṇa, Bharata and Śatrughna completed their education, Mahārāja Daśaratha began to

---

many, many forms. Although they are one and the same, *viṣṇu-tattva* has many forms and incarnations. The Lord is situated in many forms, such as Rāma, Lakṣmaṇa, Bharata and Śatrughna, and these forms may exist in any part of His creation. All these forms exist permanently, eternally, as individual Personalities of Godhead, and they resemble many candles, all equally powerful. Lord Rāmacandra, Lakṣmaṇa, Bharata and Śatrughna, who, being *viṣṇu-tattva,* are all equally powerful, became the sons of Mahārāja Daśaratha in response to prayers by the demigods."

consult with his family priest, Vasiṣṭha, about their marriages. During one such discussion, the great and powerful *brahmarṣi,* Viśvāmitra, arrived in Ayodhyā. When he entered the palace, Mahārāja Daśaratha and Vasiṣṭha immediately got up from their seats to greet him.

After worshipping Viśvāmitra properly, Daśaratha brought him into the court and seated him on a throne. Mahārāja Daśaratha greeted Viśvāmitra, saying, "O foremost of saintly persons, may all your endeavors to conquer repeated birth and death meet with success. I consider your coming here as welcome a gift as nectar placed in one's own hands, as torrential rainfall after a long drought, as the birth of a son for one who was childless, as the recovery of a great treasure that was considered irrevocably lost, or as the joy one feels on a festive occasion."

When Viśvāmitra then asked about Mahārāja Daśaratha's welfare, the king humbly replied, "O great *ṛṣi,* your coming here is a great blessing for me. Indeed, you have bestowed a great honor upon me. Please inform me of your desire so that I may serve the purpose of your visit."

Pleased with Mahārāja Daśaratha's reception, Viśvāmitra replied, "I was engaged in the performance of a great sacrifice, and it had almost reached completion when two Rākṣasas named Mārīca and Subāhu interrupted the performance by dropping flesh and blood upon the sacrificial arena. These vicious Rākṣasas are determined to frustrate my attempt. Thus, they have repeatedly polluted my altar.

O king, so that I may successfully complete the sacrifice, I have come here to take your son, Rāma, to my *āśrama* to

kill these terrible Rākṣasas. Please do not hesitate to fulfill my request out of parental affection, for I assure you that Rāma will easily be able to accomplish this task. In return for your generosity, I shall certainly give you ample benedictions. Therefore, please allow me to take Rāma for just ten days. You may rest assured that He will return here safely."

Viśvāmitra's words pierced the very core of Mahārāja Daśaratha's heart. The king's entire body began to tremble. Then, after the *ṛṣi* fell silent, he fainted upon his throne. Moments later when Mahārāja Daśaratha regained consciousness, he again considered the prospect of losing Rāma, and fainted for a second time, falling down onto the floor.

After an hour the king regained consciousness. Then, upon seeing Viśvāmitra before him, he pleaded, "O foremost of sages and well-wisher of everyone, my dear son Rāma is only sixteen years old. He has not even finished His military training, and has never entered the battlefield. Please, do not ask for my inexperienced son. Instead, let me accompany you along with an *akṣauhiṇī* of soldiers to kill the Rākṣasas. However, if you insist that Rāma must go, then let me and my army come to fight alongside Him. My dear Viśvāmitra, I am an old man. Without Rāma, I could not bear to continue living. Please tell me, who are these two Rākṣasas and what is the extent of their prowess?"

Viśvāmitra replied, "The king of the Rākṣasas is named Rāvaṇa and he is now oppressing the entire world. When he does not personally obstruct a sacrifice he deputes these two powerful Rākṣasas, Mārīca and Subāhu, to do the mischief."

Upon hearing the name of Rāvaṇa, Mahārāja Daśaratha became increasingly despondent. He said, "No one is capable of fighting with Rāvaṇa. Just these two Rākṣasas are too formidable, either for my son or for me. Therefore, O *ṛṣi*, I cannot fulfill your request. Indeed, I cannot bear to think of allowing my son to accompany you."

Becoming nearly mad with grief, Mahārāja Daśaratha began to speak incoherently, refusing Viśvāmitra's request. Thus, the *ṛṣi* became highly insulted and angrily declared, "O foolish king, your impudence will cause the ruin of your dynasty. You have promised to serve me and have now gone back on your word! Such behavior toward a *brāhmaṇa* has never before been heard of in the Raghu dynasty. Therefore, I shall quickly leave this condemned place!"

Because of Viśvāmitra's sudden anger, the earth began to shake, and even the demigods in heaven became afraid. Appraising the situation, Vasiṣṭha hurriedly approached Mahārāja Daśaratha, saying, "O king, do not destroy all your previously acquired merit by abandoning righteousness. You have made a solemn promise, and must now fulfill Viśvāmitra's request by giving him your son, Rāma.

"I do not think you have anything to fear. Formerly, when Viśvāmitra was a king, he received celestial weapons from Lord Śiva which had been born of Dakṣa's daughters, Jayā and Suprabhā. Viśvāmitra will surely give these weapons to Rāma, as well as the necessary prowess to kill the Rākṣasas. Indeed, Viśvāmitra could easily kill Mārīca and Subāhu himself, but he is seeking Rāma's help just to enhance the glory of your son."

After hearing his preceptor's words, Mahārāja Daśaratha's fear subsided, allowing his mind to again become balanced. Thus pacified, the king agreed to Viśvāmitra's proposal.

Mahārāja Daśaratha then summoned Rāma to the royal court. Because the two were inseparable, Lakṣmaṇa also presented Himself before His father. Mahārāja Daśaratha affectionately smelled his sons' heads, and the brothers then departed, with Viśvāmitra walking in front and Rāma and Lakṣmaṇa following, their bows in hand. As they left the palace, flowers showered on them from the sky.

After walking along the banks of the River Sarayū for twelve miles, Viśvāmitra stopped and said, "My dear Rāma, please sip some water for purification. I shall now teach You two mantras known as Bala and Atibala. After learning them You will become freed from the influence of fatigue and old age, and also gain incomparable wisdom and strength. Although I know that these qualities already exist in You, I still want to impart these mantras unto You for Your benefit."

After receiving the mantras, Lord Rāma shone with the brilliance of a thousand suns. The three then spent the night happily on the banks of the Sarayū and the Gaṅgā. Upon seeing an *āśrama* of *ṛṣis* situated there, Rāma inquired about its history. Viśvāmitra then replied, "This is the very place where Lord Śiva burnt Cupid to ashes after the god of love tried to disturb his deep meditation."

The next morning, Viśvāmitra and the two brothers crossed the Gaṅgā. While in midstream Rāma could hear the loud sound of cascading water, although there seemed no apparent reason for the sound. Asked why this was so,

Viśvāmitra explained, "Once, Lord Brahmā created a lake from his mind. That reservoir of water became known as the Mānasa-sarovara. The River Sarayū flows from that lake and the sound You hear is the water coming down from the Mānasa-sarovara and joining with the Gaṅgā. O Rāma, You should offer Your prayers and obeisances at this sacred place."

After arriving at the southern bank of the Gaṅgā, Rāma saw a dense, uninhabited forest, and thus He inquired, "This desolate forest invokes fear in the heart of whoever beholds it. Please tell Me why."

Viśvāmitra replied, "After King Indra killed the apparent demon Vṛtrāsura, he became overwhelmed by sinful reactions and lost his splendor. To restore Indra to his normal condition, the demigods bathed him in Gaṅgā water empowered with Vedic mantras. Then, taking the water containing Indra's impurities, the demigods deposited it in this place.

"Because this land accepted his sinful reactions, Indra gave it the benediction that it would become a very prosperous country. In this way two flourishing kingdoms named Malada and Karūṣa were established here. Later on, however, a wicked Rākṣasī named Tāṭaka came here and began to terrorize the citizens. This Rākṣasa woman was the wife of Sunda, and their son is Mārīca, whom I have brought You here to kill.

"Gradually, all of the inhabitants of this place became so greatly harassed by Tāṭaka that now it remains deserted. My dear Rāma, I want You to destroy this she-demon today, freeing this country from its oppression. As long as

this Rākṣasī lives, no one will even dare to enter this forest."

Lord Rāma then asked, "O great *ṛṣi*, if it is appropriate, please explain how this Rākṣasī became so powerful."

Viśvāmitra replied, "There was once a powerful Yakṣa named Suketu who pleased Lord Brahmā by his performance of severe austerities. Being childless, Suketu desired a son, but instead Lord Brahmā awarded him a powerful daughter. This very beautiful girl was named Tāṭaka, and when she grew up she was given in marriage to Sunda, the son of Jambha. Later, the sage Agastya cursed Sunda to die. In their attempt to retaliate, Tāṭaka and her son Mārīca rushed at the *ṛṣi*, hoping to devour him. However, Agastya immediately cursed both mother and son to become man-eating Rākṣasas. Thus, the beautiful Tāṭaka became transformed into a horrible looking ogress. Because Agastya Ṛṣi used to meditate in this area, Tāṭaka is obsessed with creating disturbances here."

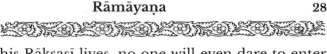

Viśvāmitra continued, "My dear Rāma, please understand that Tāṭaka is thoroughly wicked. Therefore, cast aside all hesitation in killing a woman.

Remember how Indra formerly killed Virocana's daughter when she desired to ravage the earth. Likewise, Lord Viṣṇu killed the wife of Bhṛgu Muni when she had desired to slay Indra. Please then, shake off all uneasiness and prepare Yourself to fulfill my command."

Receiving this order, Rāma twanged His bow. Its awesome sound reverberated throughout the four directions, terrifying all creatures that heard it. When Tāṭaka heard the sound of Lord Rāma's bow, she became simultaneously struck with wonder and inflamed with rage. She rushed madly toward the place from where the sound had emanated.

When Rāma saw her approaching, He exclaimed, "O Lakṣmaṇa, just see this hideous and gigantic creature! She is so horrible that pious hearts break at the very sight of her. Still, since this Rākṣasī is a woman, I shall not kill her. Instead I will render her harmless by cutting off her hands, feet, nose and ears. Thus mutilated, she will not be able to commit further crimes."

Rushing forward, Tāṭaka created a dust storm that temporarily blinded Rāma and Lakṣmaṇa. Then, using her powers of illusion, Tāṭaka created a shower of stones. Regaining His composure, Rāma smashed all the rocks to pieces and then quickly cut off Tāṭaka's arms. Simultaneously, Lakṣmaṇa cut off Tāṭaka's ears and, at Rāma's urging, the tip of her nose. However, by utilizing her mystic powers, Tāṭaka immediately disappeared. While remaining invisible, she again began showering stones. With an impassioned voice, Viśvāmitra then urged, "O Rāma, twilight is rapidly approaching, and at that time the Rākṣasa's prowess greatly increases. Therefore, give up Your merciful attitude and kill Tāṭaka at once."

As Rāma released a shower of arrows, Tāṭaka suddenly became visible and rushed toward Him. Undisturbed, Rāma selected an especially powerful golden arrow from His quiver and shot it at the demoness. Although Tāṭaka rushed forward at the speed of Indra's thunderbolt, Rāma's single blazing arrow pierced Tāṭaka's chest, causing her to fall to the ground dead, making a tumultuous sound.

From the heavens, the demigods applauded and threw down showers of flowers. The Gandharvas and Apsarās began to sing and dance in ecstasy, and great *ṛṣis* praised the prowess of Lord Rāma.

The demigods headed by Indra then approached Viśvāmitra in private and said, "O *ṛṣi*, because Rāma has a very important mission to accomplish on our behalf, you should now impart to Him all your knowledge of celestial weapons."

After saying this, the demigods disappeared, and Viśvāmitra, Rāma and Lakṣmaṇa happily spent the night there. The next morning, Viśvāmitra imparted unto Rāma his complete knowledge of celestial weapons. When Rāma received the mantras for these celestial weapons, the weapons appeared before Him in their personified forms, saying, "O Rāma, please give us Your order. What service can we do for You?"

Rāma replied, "My request is that all of you appear before Me when I think of you."

After receiving this command, the personified weapons disappeared. Viśvāmitra, Rāma and Lakṣmaṇa continued on their journey.

Later in the day, as the party approached Viśvāmitra's *āśrama,* known as Siddhāśrama, Rāma inquired from the *ṛṣi* about the history of that holy place. Viśvāmitra then explained, "Siddhāśrama was formerly the abode of Lord Vāmana, who dwelt there for many hundreds of millenniums. Once the demigods came to see Lord Vāmana, requesting Him to approach Bali Mahārāja, who was engaged in performing sacrifices. Since the king of the demons had conquered the entire three worlds, the demigods petitioned Lord Vāmana to take away his kingdom by begging.

"Just at this time, Kaśyapa also happened to arrive at Siddhāśrama, and after worshipping Vāmana with great devotion, he prayed for the Lord to appear as his son. The Lord agreed to do so, and thus He later took birth as the dwarf *brāhmaṇa* son of Kaśyapa and Aditi. He thus fulfilled the purpose of the demigods by taking away the kingdom of Bali Mahārāja, on the plea of begging for three steps of land."

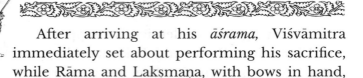

After arriving at his *āśrama,* Viśvāmitra immediately set about performing his sacrifice, while Rāma and Lakṣmaṇa, with bows in hand, awaited the arrival of Mārīca and Subāhu. Six days and nights passed as the two brothers guarded the sacrificial arena, completely foregoing sleep. Then, on the critical sixth night, when the *soma-rasa* was about to be extracted, the sacrificial fire suddenly blazed brightly, indicating the imminent arrival of the Rākṣasas.

Soon thereafter, a fearful clamor was heard in the sky. Mārīca, Subāhu and their followers swooped down without warning, causing torrents of blood, pus, stool, flesh and other contaminated substances to rain down upon the sacrificial altar. Lord Rāma then told Lakṣmaṇa, "I will subdue these evil Rākṣasas with My weapons, but I shall not kill them, for they are destined to live some years more."

Rāma discharged a mighty weapon that struck Mārīca in the chest and flung him 100 *yojanas* into the middle of the ocean, but didn't kill him. Then, taking up another powerful arrow, Rāma pierced Subāhu's chest, causing him to fall down dead upon the ground. By invoking a third weapon, Rāma drove away all the other Rākṣasas. Thereafter, the area again became calm.

All the *ṛṣis* who had previously resided at Siddhāśrama joyfully came home and congratulated Lord Rāma for His wonderful accomplishment. That evening the sacrifice was successfully concluded.

After passing the night, Rāma came before the *ṛṣis* and inquired, "O worshipable *brāhmaṇas*, now that this area has been freed from the disturbances caused by the Rākṣasas,

is there anything more that we can do to be of service?"

At the behest of Viśvāmitra, the *ṛṣis* replied, "We are about to depart for the kingdom of Mithilā to take part in a grand sacrifice arranged by King Janaka. We request you two brothers to accompany us. There is a wonderful bow being kept in the sacrificial arena that was formerly presented to the demigods by Lord Śiva. Later, the demigods gave the bow to Devarāta, who was the king of Mithilā long ago. This celestial bow is immeasurably strong, and even great demigods cannot bend it, what to speak of human beings. The bow has remained at Mithilā for a long time and is worshipped on an altar with flowers, sandalwood paste and other auspicious articles."

Rāma agreed to accompany the *ṛṣis*, and thereafter a great caravan set out with one hundred cars loaded with the paraphernalia required for Janaka Mahārāja's sacrifice.

After traveling all day, the party reached the banks of the Śoṇa River, where they stopped for the night. Then, while He was seated at leisure, Rāma asked Viśvāmitra if there was any history he could narrate concerning that place. Thus, the *ṛṣi* related to Rāma the following story:

"Once there was a great *ṛṣi* named Kuśa, a direct son of Lord Brahmā. Kuśa had four *kṣatriya* sons who founded four cities, one of which was on the banks of the River Śoṇa. Kuśa's son Kuśanābha begot one hundred daughters through the Apsarā, Ghṛtacī. When these girls grew up they were very beautiful, and would happily play together on the banks of the river.

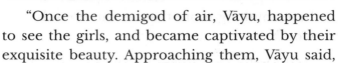

"Once the demigod of air, Vāyu, happened to see the girls, and became captivated by their exquisite beauty. Approaching them, Vāyu said, 'My dear beautiful girls, if you all become my wives, I shall transform your fleeting human beauty into ever fresh celestial youthfulness.'

"The girls had no attraction for Vāyu, however, and instead felt insulted. They replied, 'We would never think of choosing our own husbands. We will only marry according to the choice of our father. Being the daughters of a great *rājarṣi*, we certainly have the power to curse you for your vulgar behavior. However, we shall not do so, for we do not wish to diminish the accumulated merit of our austerities.'

"Vāyu, who is easily angered, became highly offended. Taking revenge, he subtly entered the bodies of the one hundred girls, and by his mystic power, distorted their bodily features. When the girls returned to the palace crying, their father was shocked to see that they had all been transformed into hunchbacks. In reply to Kuśanābha's inquiries, the girls related all that had happened. Mahārāja Kuśanābha congratulated his daughters for refraining from cursing Vāyu, and began considering how he could get them married.

"Previously, a great *brahmacārī* named Chuli had been performing severe austerities. An unmarried Gandharva girl attended to him like a menial maidservant. Eventually Chuli became pleased by her selfless service and offered her a benediction. The girl requested the *ṛṣi* to give her an exceptional son while allowing her to remain a virgin. Chuli agreed, and thus appeared a mind-born son of great ascetic prowess, named Brahmadatta. Later Brahmadatta ruled as

a king, and it was he whom Kuśanābha decided would be a suitable match for his daughters.

"Thus, after being invited to Kuśanābha's palace, Brahmadatta accepted the one hundred girls. Upon touching their hands at the marriage ceremony, one after another, their bodily deformities vanished, and each girl became beautiful again."

Viśvāmitra then concluded his narration by explaining, "Kuśanābha had no son, however, so he performed a sacrifice for that purpose. As a result, Gādhi was later born to Kuśanābha, and I am the son of King Gādhi."

The next morning, the party continued their journey, and by evening they reached the bank of the Gaṅgā. As they passed the night there, Rāma requested Viśvāmitra to narrate the history of the river Gaṅgā. Thus Viśvāmitra related the following story:

"The presiding deity of the Himālayas, Himavān, begot two daughters by Menā, the daughter of Mount Meru, named Gaṅgā and Umā. Once upon a time, Lord Brahmā approached Himavān and requested him to allow the demigods to adopt Gaṅgā for the future welfare of the universe. Himavān readily agreed, and later gave his daughter, Umā, to Lord Śiva, for she had always meditated upon him while performing severe austerities.

"After receiving Umā, Lord Śiva began enjoying with her in an uninterrupted conjugal relationship. However, even after passing one hundred celestial years in conjugal embrace, no offspring came from their combination.

"At this time the demigods approached Lord Śiva and begged, 'Please desist from your sexual activities, O lord, for we fear that the offspring produced will be too powerful for the universe to bear. Instead, we humbly request you to restrain yourself and practice austerities and meditation.'

"Lord Śiva replied, 'I accept your proposal, for my heart is actually inclined toward self-realization. However, since my semen has already become unseated from my heart, it will have to be received somewhere.'

"The demigods then suggested, 'Let the earth, which can bear any amount of burden, receive your seed.'

"Thereafter, Lord Śiva released his powerful semen and it proceeded to cover the entire surface of the earth. Upon seeing this, the demigods feared the earth might crack. Thus, they began praying to Agni and Vāyu, requesting them to devour the all-encompassing semen of Lord Śiva.

"In answer to the demigod's prayers, Agni took the help of Vāyu and went to consume the semen. As soon as the fire god touched it, some of the Lord's semen turned into a white mountain, and a part of that further transformed into a thicket of effulgent, white reeds. The rest of the semen remained unchanged and was conserved within Agni.

"The demigods were elated to see that the earth had been saved from the impending calamity. With grateful hearts, they went to worship Lord Śiva and his wife. However, Umā was very angry with the demigods for interrupting her while she was absorbed in sexual enjoyment. Seeing the demigods before her, Umā cursed them, saying, 'May all your wives become barren. Likewise, let the earth not only remain

childless, but also come to have an uneven surface and be ruled over by numerous kings.' Thereafter Lord Śiva and Pārvatī retired to the northern Himālayas to perform austerities.

"Some time later, when the demigods were being harassed by the demons, they approached Lord Brahmā, hoping to acquire a formidable military commander. In reply to the demigod's plea, Lord Brahmā advised them, 'Because of Pārvatī's curse, you are unable to produce a child to serve your purpose. Therefore, I suggest that Agni place the semen of Lord Śiva into the womb of Gaṅgā. In this way a heroic son will be begotten.'

"Thereafter, the demigods approached Agni and related Lord Brahmā's instructions. Hearing this, Agni approached the heavenly river, Mandākinī Gaṅgā. He then requested her to accept the semen of Lord Śiva, which he had been holding for a long time.

"Gaṅgā agreed to the proposal. Then, after assuming a most beautiful form, she allowed herself to be impregnated by Agni. However, soon after receiving the fiery semen of Lord Śiva, Gaṅgādevī felt an intense, agonizing pain. With great agitation, she told Agni, 'I cannot continue to bear the semen of Lord Śiva in my womb. Its burning is intolerable.'

"Agni then instructed Gaṅgā to cast off the semen at a certain place in the Himālayas, and she hurriedly went there. In this way, the semen of Lord Śiva, which had acquired a shiny golden luster because of its contacting Gaṅgādevī, fell to the thicket of white reeds on the white mountain. In this way, a wonderful child was born. Other portions of the semen that fell upon the earth transformed into gold and

silver mines. Indeed, because of the fierce energy of Lord Śiva's semen, mines of copper and iron were created in distant places.

"After the birth of the child, the demigods brought six goddesses, called the Kṛttikās, to nurse him. They assured the women that the baby would come to be known as their son. For this reason the child became known as Kārttikeya. The boy was also called Skanda ("to flow"), because he had fallen from the womb of Gaṅgā.

"Because he saw six mothers before him, the baby assumed six faces to suck breast milk from all of them. Skanda was so strong that when he was only one day old, he killed many fierce demons, as the commander-in-chief of the demigods."

Viśvāmitra then related to Lord Rāma the story of King Sagara, who long ago ruled the world from his capital, Ayodhyā. Because Mahārāja Sagara was unable to beget a son, he, along with his two wives, went to the Himālayas to perform austerities. After some time the king was benedicted by the great *ṛṣi*, Bhṛgu, with the boon that he would receive a son by one wife who would become the perpetuator of his dynasty, while his other wife would give birth to 60,000 more sons. Hearing this, the two queens questioned Bhṛgu Muni who would receive the one son and who would receive the 60,000 sons. Bhṛgu replied that the decision would be left to them.

Thus, Keśinī, the elder queen, chose to have a single son who would perpetuate the Ikṣvāku line. Sumatī, the sister of Garuḍa, chose to have 60,000 sons.

Mahārāja Sagara returned home, and in due course, a son was born to Keśinī, and given the name Asamañjasa. Sumatī, however, gave birth to a lump of flesh shaped like a bitter melon. Shortly thereafter, when the lump was opened up, 60,000 embryonic sons emerged. They were immediately placed in jars of ghee by their nurses until they could complete their development. Later, when these 60,000 sons began growing up, their cruel elder step-brother, Asamañjasa, began to throw them into the river Sarayū, laughing with great pleasure to see them drown.

Being very aggrieved due to the vicious behavior of his son, Mahārāja Sagara finally decided to exile Asamañjasa from his kingdom, although he kept the son of Asamañjasa, Aṁśumān, who was loved by all the subjects.

After some time, Mahārāja Sagara inaugurated the performance of a horse sacrifice, with Aṁśumān protecting the challenge horse as it wandered over the earth. However, during the performance of the sacrifice, King Indra appeared in the guise of a Rākṣasa and stole the horse from the sacrificial arena. The priest fervently urged Mahārāja Sagara to recover the horse at all costs. He warned that if the sacrifice remained incomplete, it would be most inauspicious.

Mahārāja Sagara then ordered his 60,000 sons to search the entire earth for the horse, allotting each of them one square *yojana*. He further instructed his sons that if the horse could not be found elsewhere, they should look below the earth.

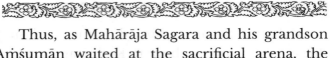

Thus, as Mahārāja Sagara and his grandson Aṁśumān waited at the sacrificial arena, the 60,000 princes searched the entire earth. When they were unable to find the horse anywhere, the sons of Sagara began digging into the earth. This, however, upset the inhabitants of the lower worlds, such as the Nāgas. Indeed, even the Earth herself became extremely disturbed. Seeing this, the demigods approached Lord Brahmā and petitioned him to set right the situation.

Lord Brahmā pacified the demigods, explaining that since the Earth was a consort of Lord Viṣṇu, the Lord, in His form of Kapila, would soon annihilate all 60,000 sons of Sagara.

Even after digging up the earth and killing many living beings in the process, the sons of Sagara could not find the sacrificial horse, and thus returned to their father disappointed. When the 60,000 princes inquired from their father what they should do next, the king ordered them to continue digging further down, until the horse was found.

The sons of Sagara resumed their excavation of all four quarters of the earth's surface, and soon came to see the four colossal elephants that protect the four directions and support the earth. (These gigantic elephants support the entire weight of the earth upon their backs, and when, due to exhaustion, they sometimes shake their heads for relief, it creates earthquakes.)

Finally, after penetrating the earth all the way down to Rasātala, the sons of Sagara came upon Lord Kapila sitting in meditation, while nearby, the sacrificial horse stood grazing peacefully. Sagara's sons assumed Kapila to be the

thief. Thus they angrily took up their digging implements and rushed to kill Him. Seeing this act of aggression, Kapila became angry. Then, simply by uttering the mantra "hum," He reduced the 60,000 sons of Sagara to ashes.

After a long time, when his sons had not returned, Mahārāja Sagara sent his grandson, Aṁśumān, to search for his 60,000 sons and the sacrificial horse. By following the path his uncles had taken, Aṁśumān came to the passage excavated by them. After entering the earth, Aṁśumān came upon the great elephants and inquired from them about the whereabouts of his uncles. In reply, the elephants assured him that by continuing down the passage he would soon come to know everything.

At last, Aṁśumān reached the place where the ashes of the sons of Sagara lay. Seeing this, he became overwhelmed with grief. Aṁśumān found the sacrificial horse nearby, and decided to first offer water for the departed souls of his uncles before returning to his grandfather. Unfortunately, there was no water to be found in that place. While Aṁśumān was thinking what to do, Garuḍa suddenly appeared, and said "My dear Aṁśumān, do not grieve for your uncles. Their deaths are ultimately meant for achieving a glorious purpose. The sons of King Sagara will be instrumental in bringing the sacred river Gaṅgā down to earth for the welfare of all people. Your uncles were burnt to ashes by the great sage Kapila.

When their remains are washed over by the waters of the Gaṅgā, they will attain a heavenly destination. Now, take the sacrificial horse and return to your grandfather so that the sacrifice can be completed."

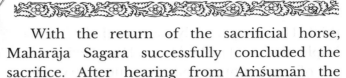

With the return of the sacrificial horse, Mahārāja Sagara successfully concluded the sacrifice. After hearing from Aṁśumān the prophetic words of Garuḍa, the king became absorbed in trying to formulate the means to make the Gaṅgā descend to the earth. However, Mahārāja Sagara passed away before achieving that goal.

After the death of his grandfather, Aṁśumān ruled the kingdom for some time. He later gave the throne to his son Dilīpa, and retired to the forest to perform austerities, hoping to induce Gaṅgā to descend to earth. After his death, Aṁśumān went to the heavenly planets, but his desire to cause the descent of the Gaṅgā remained unfulfilled.

Dilīpa also sought to bring Gaṅgā to earth, but he too died before his desire was fulfilled. Dilīpa's son, Bhagīratha, then inherited the kingdom, and likewise, desired to perform austerities to cause Gaṅgā to descend. Since he had no son, Bhagīratha entrusted the rule of the kingdom to his ministers and retired to the forest.

After Mahārāja Bhagīratha had performed austerities for a thousand years, Lord Brahmā became pleased with him. Accompanied by the demigods, Lord Brahmā appeared before the king to award him a benediction. Mahārāja Bhagīratha worshipped Lord Brahmā and then begged, "Please allow my ancestors, the sons of King Sagara, to receive the water of the Gaṅgā. In addition, kindly benedict me to have a son."

Lord Brahmā replied, "I agree to award you these benedictions. However, the earth is incapable of bearing the weight of the Gaṅgā's descent. You should request Lord Śiva

to absorb the impact of the falling water, for only he is powerful enough to do so."

Determined to gain Lord Śiva's favor, Mahārāja Bhagīratha began performing severe austerities. He stood motionless on the tip of a single toe for one year. At that time, Lord Śiva was pleased to appear before the king. When Mahārāja Bhagīratha expressed his desire, Lord Mahādeva agreed to bear the force of the Gaṅgā's falling water upon his head.

Soon afterward, the Gaṅgā began to descend toward earth from her course in the heavenly planets. All the demigods

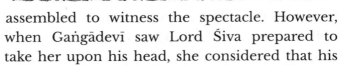

assembled to witness the spectacle. However, when Gaṅgādevī saw Lord Śiva prepared to take her upon his head, she considered that his contact would contaminate her. Thus, upon seeing the expression of disgust displayed by Gaṅgādevī, Lord Śiva became insulted. In retaliation, he angrily captured her and concealed her waters within his matted hair, thwarting her descent to earth.

When Mahārāja Bhagīratha saw how Gaṅgā had become entangled, he resumed his austerities. Finally, Lord Śiva gave up his anger and released Gaṅgādevī, allowing her to fall into the Bindusarovara in the Himālayas. Afterwards, the Gaṅgā split into seven streams. Six of these formed other rivers, while the seventh followed Mahārāja Bhagīratha as he rode upon his royal chariot.

While wending her way through various lands, it so happened that the Gaṅgā inundated the sacrificial arena of the great sage Jahnu. Becoming excited with rage, the *ṛṣi* swallowed up the entire river. Upon seeing this, the demigods were struck with wonder. They then approached Jahnu and requested him to release Gaṅgādevī on the condition that she would become known as his daughter. The *ṛṣi* agreed, and thus the Gaṅgā was able to continue her journey.

Finally, the Gaṅgā reached the site that had been excavated by the sons of Sagara. By entering that great crevasse, the Gaṅgā went down to Rasātala. In doing so, she submerged the ashes of Sagara's 60,000 sons, enabling them to reach their heavenly destination.

Lord Brahmā appeared once more before Mahārāja Bhagīratha and declared, "O king, your mission has now

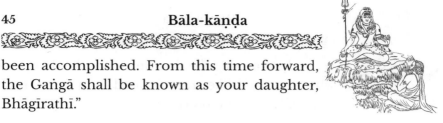

been accomplished. From this time forward, the Gaṅgā shall be known as your daughter, Bhāgīrathī."

After thus delivering his forefathers, Mahārāja Bhagīratha returned to his capital and resumed ruling over his kingdom.

Thus, the entire night passed away as Viśvāmitra narrated to Rāma the fascinating history of the River Gaṅgā and her descent to earth.

When morning arrived, Rāma expressed His eagerness to cross the Gaṅgā and continue the journey. The caravan was soon made ready to depart. After reaching the far bank of the Gaṅgā, the caravan traveled on and eventually came to the city of Viśāla. When Lord Rāma requested Viśvāmitra to speak about the dynasty of kings that ruled this city, the *ṛṣi* narrated the following history:

"The demigods and demons are by nature inimical toward one another. Once, following the advice of the Supreme Personality of Godhead, the demigods executed a truce with the demons for the purpose of churning nectar from the sea. This was done with the understanding that when the nectar was churned, both sides would share it equally. Thus, both the demons and the demigods, desiring to become immortal, started for the ocean of milk, taking with them Mandara Mountain and Vāsuki.

"By the expert arrangement of the Supreme Personality of Godhead, the demons held the snake near the mouth, and the demigods held his tail. Vāsuki, with his thousands of eyes and mouths, breathed smoke and blazing fire, which

severely wounded the demons. Thus the demons, who appeared like trees burned by a forest fire, gradually became powerless.

"Because the demigods were also affected by the blazing breath of Vāsuki, their bodily luster diminished, and their garments, garlands, weapons and faces were blackened by smoke. However, by the grace of the Supreme Personality of Godhead, clouds appeared on the sea, pouring torrents of rain, and strong breezes carried particles of water from the sea waves, thus giving relief to the demigods.

"Because of the mountain's great weight, the demigods and demons became fatigued, and some were dying. Thus, because Mandara Mountain was very heavy and was not held by any support, it sank into the ocean. In this way the prowess of both the demons and the demigods was vanquished.

"The Supreme Personality of Godhead, Viṣṇu, then appeared on the back of His carrier, Garuḍa. The Lord appeared like a blackish cloud. Wearing a garland of flowers, He was dressed with yellow garments, and earrings that shone on His ears like lightning. His eyes were pinkish and His hair was spread over His shoulders. By His mercy He brought the demigods and demons back to life.

"The Lord then lifted the mountain with one hand and placed it on the back of Garuḍa. Then He sat on the mountain, and Garuḍa carried Him to the spot of the churning, and placed the mountain in the middle of the sea. The Lord then asked Garuḍa to leave, because as long as Garuḍa was present, Vāsuki could not come there.

"The Supreme Personality of Godhead, appearing in His incarnation as Kūrmāvatāra, a gigantic tortoise, supported

the mountain upon His back as He lay at the bottom of the ocean. Then Lord Viṣṇu used His strong, glorious arms, which award fearlessness throughout the universe, and took hold of Vāsuki like a rope and began churning the ocean, using Mandara Mountain as a churning rod. Engaged in this way, the Lord appeared like the beautifully situated mountain named Indranīla.

"The mountain moved back and forth, scratching the back of Lord Tortoise, who, while partially sleeping, was experiencing an itching sensation. Lord Viṣṇu then further expanded Himself in a gigantic form and supported the top of Mount Mandara with one hand to keep it steady.

"As the churning resumed with great force, the fish, sharks, tortoises and snakes became agitated. The entire ocean became turbulent, and even the large aquatic animals like whales, water elephants, crocodiles and *timiṅgila* fish (large whales that can swallow small whales) came to the surface. While the ocean was being churned in this way, it first produced a huge amount of a dangerous poison called *hālahala*.

"The demigods, seeing no one else to save them, approached

Lord Śiva and offered him prayers. Lord Śiva is called Āśutoṣa because he is very pleased if one becomes his devotee. Therefore, he readily agreed to drink all the poison generated by the churning. The goddess Durgā, Lord Śiva's wife, was not at all disturbed when Lord Śiva agreed to drink the poison, for she knew Lord Śiva's prowess. Indeed, she was pleased with this agreement.

"Lord Śiva gathered the devastating poison, which had spread everywhere. He took it in his hand and drank it, which made his neck become bluish. However, a small quantity of the poison spilled from his hands to the ground. It is because of this poison that there are poisonous snakes, scorpions, toxic plants and other poisonous things in the world.

"Thereafter, in the course of churning the Milk Ocean, 600 million Apsarās were produced, and because neither the demigods or demons accepted them, they became prostitutes. When Vāruṇī, the goddess of liquor (*sura*), next emerged from the Milk Ocean, the demons would not accept her. The demigods did, however, and for this reason the sons of Aditi became known as Suras, whereas the sons of Diti became known as Asuras.

"Finally, after many years, Lord Viṣṇu, in the form of Dhanvantari (the inaugurator of the medical science), appeared from the ocean of milk, holding a waterpot filled with nectar in one hand and a staff in the other.

"A great fight ensued between the demigods and the demons over the nectar. When both sides neared destruction, the demons took possession of the nectar. Lord Viṣṇu then assumed the form of Mohinī-mūrti. When this extraordinarily beautiful form of the Lord as a young woman appeared before them, the demons immediately became captivated by Her. Because the demons were then fighting among themselves to possess the nectar, they selected this beautiful woman to settle their quarrel. Taking advantage of their weakness, Mohinī, the incarnation of the Supreme Personality of Godhead, enticed the demons to promise that whatever decision She gave, they would agree to.

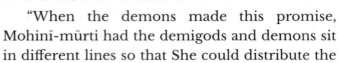

"When the demons made this promise, Mohinī-mūrti had the demigods and demons sit in different lines so that She could distribute the nectar. Mohinī-mūrti approached the demons and spoke graciously to them. The demons thought themselves most fortunate to talk with Her. Since the demigods were seated at a distant place, the demons thought they would get only a small portion of the nectar. Indeed, the demons concluded that because Mohinī-mūrti appeared so pleased with them, She would give the demons all the nectar. Enchanted by the exquisite, transcendental beauty of the Mohinī form, the demons agreed to hand over the nectar to Mohinīdevī, who then artfully delivered it to the demigods.

"The demons were so captivated by the tricks and friendly words of Mohinī-mūrti, that although the demigods were served first, the demons were pacified merely by Her sweet words. The Lord said to the demons, 'The demigods are very miserly and are excessively anxious to take the nectar first. So let them have it first. Since you are not like them, you can wait a little longer. You are all heroes and are therefore pleased with Me. It is better for you to wait until after the demigods drink.'

"The Lord intended to distribute the nectar only to the demigods. She knew that the demons were quite unfit to drink the nectar. When the demons saw that Mohinī-mūrti was cheating them, however, they remained silent. Nevertheless, one demon named Rāhu dressed himself like a demigod and sat down in the line of the demigods, sitting beside the sun and the moon. When the Supreme Personality of Godhead understood how Rāhu was cheating, He immediately cut off the demon's head. Rāhu, however, had already tasted the

nectar, and therefore although his head was severed, he remained alive.

"After the demigods finished drinking the nectar, the Supreme Personality of Godhead assumed His own form and quickly carried off the nectar by an act of deception. When the demons opposed Her, Mohinī-mūrti easily vanquished them, and thus enabled Indra to become the undisputed ruler of the three worlds.

"Upon seeing the defeat of her sons, Diti became very unhappy and began performing austerities with the aim of obtaining a son capable of killing Indra in revenge. Knowing that Diti was intent upon performing austerities for a thousand years to attain his destruction, Indra came to her and began rendering menial service to her with great care and attention. When only ten years of her vow remained, Diti, being pleased with Indra, assured him that she would pacify her son once he was born, so that Indra could continue ruling over the three worlds without fear. Indra, however, remained wary.

Some time later, Diti became very tired and carelessly laid down, placing her head where her feet normally would rest. In this way, Diti neglectfully allowed her hair to become contaminated. Taking advantage of this fault, Indra utilized his mystic power to enter her womb. Indra then cut Diti's embryo into seven parts. When the fetus cried out in a shrill voice, he again cut each part into seven, making a total of 49 pieces. Diti, however, could understand what was happening, and begged Indra to stop killing her child. Having been discovered, the repentant Indra came out from her womb and begged forgiveness from his stepmother. Thus, Diti requested that her 49 children be allowed to become

wind-gods. Indra agreed, and thus he and Diti were reconciled, while the 49 children became recognized as demigods known as the Maruts."

Viśvāmitra concluded, "This city, Viśāla, is situated at the place where Diti formerly performed her austerities. Later, the son of Ikṣvāku, named Viśāla, built the city, and the present king in his dynasty is Sumati."

Mahārāja Sumati then came out of the city to receive and worship Viśvāmitra. At his invitation, the party rested there for the night. The next morning the caravan again proceeded on its journey toward the kingdom of Videha. Upon reaching the outskirts of Mithilā, the capital city of Mahārāja Janaka, Lord Rāma saw an old desolate hermitage. After Rāma inquired about it from Viśvāmitra, the *ṛṣi* explained, "This *āśrama* formerly belonged to Gautama Ṛṣi, who practiced austerities here along with his wife, Ahalyā.

"Once upon a time, knowing that Gautama was away from his *āśrama,* King Indra assumed a form that closely resembled the *ṛṣi*. He went to the *āśrama* in that disguise and approached Gautama's wife, saying, 'My dear beautiful one, I desire union with you immediately. Please do not disappoint me.'

"Although Ahalyā recognized that it was Indra disguised as Gautama, she did not refuse him, for she too, eagerly desired his embraces. Thus, the union took place, and after their lusty urges had been gratified, Ahalyā begged, 'O Indra, please protect us from the wrath of my husband, Gautama.'

"Indra assured Ahalyā that he would depart immediately, unnoticed by anyone. However, while Indra was sneaking

away from Gautama's *āśrama,* the *ṛṣi* suddenly returned. When Gautama saw Indra disguised as himself, his head hanging down in shame, he could well understand the nature of his misconduct. Thus, with great anger, the *ṛṣi* cursed Indra, 'O lusty fool, may your testicles immediately fall off as punishment for this abominable act!'

"No sooner had the curse been pronounced when Indra's testicles fell from his body and dropped to the ground. Then, after entering his *āśrama,* Gautama cursed his wife, 'O wretched woman! From now on you shall be incapable of eating or drinking, and you will have to lie down on a bed of ashes.'

"Thus, Ahalyā was turned into a pillar of stone. Gautama then said, 'Only when Lord Rāma visits this spot in the distant future will you be absolved of your sin, freed from all lusty desires, and reunited with me as your husband.'

"Saying this, Gautama departed for the Himālayas. Meanwhile, Indra informed the demigods, 'I have successfully thwarted Gautama Ṛṣi's attempt to attain my position as king of heaven by making him angry. However, in the process I have lost my testicles. Now, somehow or other, please arrange for my manhood to be restored.'

"Responding to Indra's plea, the demigods arranged for the Pitās to castrate a ram, and grafted its testicles onto Indra's body."

After narrating this story, Viśvāmitra invited Lord Rāma to enter the *āśrama* of Gautama. As soon as Rāma entered the hermitage, Ahalyā regained her original form, dazzling

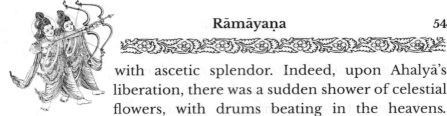

with ascetic splendor. Indeed, upon Ahalyā's liberation, there was a sudden shower of celestial flowers, with drums beating in the heavens. Rāma and Lakṣmaṇa respectfully touched Ahalyā's feet, and she reciprocally welcomed the two brothers and Viśvāmitra. Gautama Ṛṣi then came to be reunited with his wife, and worshipped Lord Rāma and Lakṣmaṇa with great reverence.

Thereafter, the caravan entered Mithilā. Upon arriving at the sacrificial arena of King Janaka, Lord Rāma was pleased to see that thousands of *brāhmaṇas* had assembled from all parts of the world. Hearing of Viśvāmitra's arrival, Mahārāja Janaka hurriedly went to greet him, and addressed him, saying, "O best of saintly persons, this sacrifice will take twelve days to complete, with the demigods appearing personally to accept their shares of the offerings. My dear sir, please tell me who these two exalted personalities are that have accompanied you. Indeed, They appear to be like gods in human form."

Viśvāmitra replied, "These two young men are Rāma and Lakṣmaṇa, the sons of King Daśaratha. They have come here to examine the great bow that you have been worshipping. I brought Them from Ayodhyā to my *āśrama* to kill the Rākṣasas that were disturbing my sacrifice. On the way, They killed the she-demon, Tāṭaka, and then at Siddhāśrama, Rāma hurled Mārīca 100 *yojanas* into the sea and killed Subāhu. Before arriving at Mithilā, Rāma freed Ahalyā from her husband's curse and received the worship of Gautama Ṛṣi."

Later, when everyone was comfortably seated, Śatānanda, the chief priest of Mahārāja Janaka and eldest son of Gautama Ṛṣi, requested Viśvāmitra to recount in detail the story of how

his mother had regained her original form at the sight of Lord Rāma. The *ṛṣi* then happily related the entire incident. Thereafter, Śatānanda reciprocated by narrating the glorious history of Viśvāmitra.

"Viśvāmitra was born as the son of Gādhi and formerly ruled his kingdom as a righteous *kṣatriya*. Once, taking an *akṣauhiṇī* of soldiers with him, Viśvāmitra began to travel over the earth. In due course he came upon the hermitage of the great *brahmarṣi*, Vasiṣṭha.

"Entering the beautiful hermitage, which was inhabited by many sages, he bowed respectfully before Vasiṣṭha. The *ṛṣi* received Viśvāmitra cordially, and the two became engaged in friendly conversation. Vasiṣṭha said, 'My dear king, please remain here for a few days as my guest so that I may entertain you in a manner befitting your position.'

"Viśvāmitra humbly replied, 'I am already fully satisfied with your kind reception. I ask only for your permission to leave.'

"Vasiṣṭha , however, repeatedly insisted that Viśvāmitra and his men remain. Finally, Viśvāmitra relented. This being settled, Vasiṣṭha brought his *kāmadhenu* cow named Sabala before Viśvāmitra, and ordered her to produce a sumptuous royal feast. Being so commanded, the celestial cow immediately brought forth a huge quantity of seemingly unlimited varieties of food and drink, all arranged on sparkling silver platters. Viśvāmitra and his men then feasted to their full satisfaction.

"However, before long, Viśvāmitra began to feel envious of Vasiṣṭha, wishing he had the celestial cow for himself.

As the pangs of greed surfaced, Viśvāmitra told Vasiṣṭha, 'I must have this wonderful cow of yours at all costs. Please give her to me and I will reward you appropriately.'

"Viśvāmitra offered the sage hundreds of thousands of cows, gold, unlimited jewels and more. Regardless, Vasiṣṭha refused to give up his celestial cow, saying, 'I am very sorry, but I shall never be able to part with this *kāmadhenu*, even in exchange for one billion cows. This wish-fulfilling cow is inseparable from me, for I need her to supply all the ingredients for my sacrificial performances.'

"Viśvāmitra then replied, 'This cow should rightfully belong to me, for the king is meant to possess the very best of everything.'

"Because Vasiṣṭha's refusal only fanned the flames of Viśvāmitra's desire, the king proceeded to offer the sage more and more. Regardless, Vasiṣṭha refused to part with his cow. Finally, out of frustration and anger, Viśvāmitra grabbed the cow and began dragging her out of the āśrama.

"At this, the *kāmadhenu* cried out pitifully, imploring Vasiṣṭha, 'O *ṛṣi*, why are you allowing me to be taken away like this? Although I have served you faithfully, are you now going to desert me?'

"Sabala freed herself from the hundreds of men assisting Viśvāmitra in dragging her away. As she fled back to the *āśrama,* Vasiṣṭha replied, 'My dear Sabala, I am certainly not abandoning you. However, my power is not equal to the king's. I am helpless to rescue you."

"Sabala replied, 'Dear *ṛṣi*, the king's material strength is insignificant in comparison to your spiritual strength. If you

allow me to do so, I will utilize your superior energy to vanquish Viśvāmitra's army myself.'

"When Vasiṣṭha gave his consent, Sabala proceeded to create innumerable fierce warriors from her body that began to consume Viśvāmitra's army. However, the powerful king destroyed them all. Moreover, his *kṣatriya* spirit bristling, he challenged Sabala to create more soldiers, if she desired to continue fighting.

"Sabala then proceeded to produce more, fiercer warriors, that sprang from her udders, genitals, anus and other body parts. These superior soldiers completely vanquished Viśvāmitra's army. Seeing this, Viśvāmitra's 100 sons angrily rushed at Vasiṣṭha, but the *brahmarṣi* reduced them to a mere pile of ashes simply by uttering a mighty roar.

"Having thus lost not only his entire army, but his sons as well, Viśvāmitra departed, pale and dejected. , Viśvāmitra ordered his only remaining son to rule the kingdom and retired to the forest to perform austerities, hoping to please Lord Śiva.

"After some time Lord Śiva became satisfied with Viśvāmitra's austerities and appeared before the king to reward him. The delighted Viśvāmitra expressed his desire to possess the knowledge of all celestial weapons. Lord Śiva, known as Āśutoṣa, because he is easily pleased, awarded Viśvāmitra his desired benediction. Thus, Viśvāmitra, who was already too proud, became exceedingly puffed up after receiving the celestial weapons, thinking his prowess to be invincible.

"Viśvāmitra went directly to the *āśrama* of Vasiṣṭha, and began showering down his weapons so fiercely that

it appeared the *āśrama* was on the verge of annihilation. All the sages residing there began to flee in terror, despite Vasiṣṭha's assurances. Indeed, in a short time, the area appeared desolate.

"Picking up his brahminical rod, Vasiṣṭha addressed Viśvāmitra as follows, 'Because of your rash act of aggression, I shall now cut down your false pride and show you the futility of your so-called prowess.'

"Vasiṣṭha held out his brahminical rod and neutralized all of Viśvāmitra's weapons. Viśvāmitra then resorted to hurling his remaining celestial weapons. When this, too, failed, he prepared to release the ultimate weapon, the *brahmāstra*.

"From above, the demigods witnessed the spectacular duel. When Viśvāmitra invoked the terrible *brahmāstra*, they became wonder-struck and fearful. However, after Viśvāmitra released the *brahmāstra*, Vasiṣṭha countered it by assuming an awesome form of gigantic proportions, with flames blazing forth from every pore of his body, neutralizing the energy of the *brahmāstra*.

"The tremendous form exhibited by Vasiṣṭha stunned everyone who witnessed it. Indeed, after seeing the *ṛṣi's* great prowess, the sages began to offer Vasiṣṭha prayers. With the *brahmāstra* weapon countered, Vasiṣṭha again assumed his normal form. In the meantime, Viśvāmitra desisted from battle and departed, condemning the meager powers of the *kṣatriyas*.

"Understanding brahminical power to be superior, Viśvāmitra became determined to become a *brahmarṣi* like Vasiṣṭha. He then went into seclusion with his wife and began to execute severe penances. After 1,000 years, Lord Brahmā

appeared before Viśvāmitra and formally conferred upon him the status of *rājarṣi* as a reward. However, as Lord Brahmā departed, Viśvāmitra hung his head in shame over the meagerness of his achievement. Remaining determined to achieve the status of *brahmarṣi* and nothing less, Viśvāmitra again resumed his severe austerities.

"During this same time there was a king in the line of Ikṣvāku named Triśaṅku who ruled from his capital, Ayodhyā. Desiring to perform a sacrifice that would enable him to ascend to heaven in his human body (without changing bodies), he requested Vasiṣṭha to become his priest. Vasiṣṭha, however, refused, claiming it would be impossible to perform such a sacrifice. Afterward, Triśaṅku approached Vasiṣṭha's 100 sons, who were engaged in performing sacrifices, and asked them to assist him in the performance of his sacrifice. However, when they learned of their father's refusal, they angrily chastised him for attempting to solicit their help after being turned down by his guru. Hearing their criticism, Triśaṅku replied, "If you are not willing to help me, I will seek the assistance of others more magnanimous."

"Upon hearing Triśaṅku's impudent statement, the *ṛṣis* became furious and cursed Triśaṅku to become a *caṇḍāla*. Soon thereafter, Triśaṅku's golden complexion turned black, his garments became old and soiled, his long lustrous hair began to fall out, his cosmetics turned to ashes, his gold ornaments turned to iron, and his garland transformed into flowers from a crematorium.

"When Triśaṅku's ministers witnessed this transformation they immediately abandoned him as untouchable. Having become a *caṇḍāla*, bereft of his former position, Triśaṅku went to see Viśvāmitra, who was engaged in performing austerities.

"Viśvāmitra welcomed Triśaṅku with compassion, hearing from him how he had been cursed by the sons of Vasiṣṭha. When Triśaṅku begged Viśvāmitra for help, the *ṛṣi* assured him of shelter and promised to provide him with priests that would assist him in the performance of his sacrifice.

"Thereafter, Viśvāmitra ordered his sons to petition all the priests and qualified *brāhmaṇas* to assist him, asking also for the names of those who refused. Thus, many *brāhmaṇas* from kingdoms across the earth came to his *āśrama*. Only Vasiṣṭha and his sons and the *ṛṣi* Mahādaya refused to participate, saying, ”What *brāhmaṇa* or demigod would be willing to accept an offering from the hands of a *kṣatriya*, what to speak of a *caṇḍāla*?"

"When Viśvāmitra heard these harsh and insulting words, he immediately uttered the following curse, ”May the wretched sons of Vasiṣṭha be reduced to ashes and sent to the abode of Yamarāja this very day. Thereafter, let them take 700 births as *caṇḍālas*, and may that fool Mahādaya become a Niṣāda!"

"The curses quickly took effect, and Viśvāmitra was able to perceive the results by dint of his mystic vision. Viśvāmitra then requested the *brāhmaṇas* present to perform Triśaṅku's sacrifice. Simply out of fear of being cursed, they complied, and started the sacrifice.

"When Viśvāmitra invited the demigods to attend and accept their share of the offerings, they desisted. This made Viśvāmitra very angry, and he declared to Triśaṅku that

he would elevate him to heaven by his own prowess. Indeed, as soon as Viśvāmitra made this vow, Triśaṅku began rising to heaven in his self-same body.

"When King Indra saw Triśaṅku approaching heaven without having earned sufficient pious merit, and after having disobeyed his guru, Vasiṣṭha, Indra forced Triśaṅku to fall headfirst back toward earth. While thus falling, Triśaṅku called out helplessly to Viśvāmitra to rescue him. Viśvāmitra not only stopped Triśaṅku's fall, but also created a replica planetary system, complete with imitation demigods, for Triśaṅku to reside in.

"The demigods, however, were outraged by this wonderful feat. Approaching Viśvāmitra they said, 'Give up your efforts to help Triśaṅku. He lacks the necessary qualifications for residing in the heavenly planets.'

"Viśvāmitra, however, insisted on keeping his promise. He declared, 'I will never go back on my promise to send Triśaṅku to the heavenly planets without a change of body. Therefore, let it be ordained that my newly created heaven be accepted by you and remain for the duration of the universe.'

"In the end the demigods relented, and thus Triśaṅku remained head-downwards in space. By the mercy of Viśvāmitra he enjoys heavenly bliss while shining brightly among the stars.

"Viśvāmitra then returned to executing austerities, determined to become a *brahmarṣi* like Vasiṣṭha. Then, after a long time had passed, a beautiful Apsarā named Menakā came to bathe at the Puṣkara Lake, where Viśvāmitra was

conducting his austerities. Seeing her, Viśvāmitra became overwhelmed by lust. Eager to enjoy sex, Viśvāmitra implored her to remain with him at his *āśrama.* Menakā happily consented, and thus they passed ten years together, enjoying each other while lost to the pleasures of sensual enjoyment.

"Finally, Viśvāmitra came to his senses and felt great disgust. He thought to himself, 'I have foolishly wasted ten years, merged in the so-called enjoyment of sense gratification. Now I can understand that Menakā was sent here by the demigods simply to steal my accumulated ascetic merit. By becoming a slave to lust I have neglected my austerities. Thus, I have fallen down from my exalted position.'"

"Viśvāmitra dismissed the fearful Menakā and then went to the northern side of the Himālayas, determined to remain celibate from then on.

"When Viśvāmitra again resumed his austerities, the demigods grew increasingly fearful and approached Lord Brahmā, begging him to award Viśvāmitra the status of *maharṣi.* Lord Brahmā agreed, but when he appeared before Viśvāmitra, Viśvāmitra replied that he would not be satisfied with anything less than the status of *brahmarṣi.* Thus, Lord Brahmā explained, 'You have not yet fully controlled your senses. Therefore you will have to practice more austerities before achieving your desired goal.'

"After Lord Brahmā departed, Viśvāmitra resumed his austerities, standing with arms upraised and subsisting on air alone for one thousand years. Thus, Indra and the other demigods again became fearful, and devised yet another plan to thwart Viśvāmitra.

"Indra requested the lovely Apsarā named Rambhā to allure Viśvāmitra away from his practice of austerities. Rambhā, trembling with fear, declined, saying that she feared Viśvāmitra's curse. Indra, however, assured her by saying, 'Dear girl, please do not be afraid, for you shall surely succeed. It is springtime, and Cupid shall accompany you. I shall also go, disguised as a sweet-singing cuckoo. Do not worry. Your beauty is irresistible. Viśvāmitra will become a toy in your hands.'

"Rambhā finally agreed, and thereafter she appeared before Viśvāmitra in a most pleasing manner, displaying her various feminine allurements. At first, Viśvāmitra was pleased to see her, thinking she had come of her own accord. However, after a moment's consideration, Viśvāmitra realized that her appearance was simply another trick to thwart him from his practice. Flaring with anger, Viśvāmitra roared, 'You foolish woman! You knew I was performing austerities for the purpose of controlling my senses. Still, you dare to persist, trying to seduce me. For this you will have to stand as a stone statue for 10,000 years, or until the *ṛṣi* Vasiṣṭha delivers you.'

"Rambhā immediately turned into stone, while Indra and Cupid fearfully fled from the scene. However, after cursing the Apsarā, Viśvāmitra became morose, realizing that he had fallen victim to uncontrolled anger, thus diminishing his accumulated stock of ascetic merit. Viśvāmitra then vowed to never again become angry. 'I will not breathe, utter a word, or eat a morsel of food or drink until I achieve the status of *brahmarṣi*.'

"Viśvāmitra then resumed his austerities. However, after fasting for 1,000 years he decided to eat something. Just as Viśvāmitra was about to take his first bite, King Indra appeared before him in the dress of a *brāhmaṇa* and begged for all his food. Without remorse or anger, Viśvāmitra humbly gave all he had planned to eat to the *brāhmaṇa*, and went back to performing his austerities for another 1,000 years.

"Viśvāmitra's powerful austerities began to heat up the entire universe, and smoke began to emanate from his head. Feeling great distress, the demigods again approached Lord Brahmā to appease Viśvāmitra. At that time Lord Brahmā, along with the demigods, went to Viśvāmitra and awarded him the status of *brahmarṣi*, just to persuade him to desist in his austerities.

"Viśvāmitra became very satisfied at heart. However, he further insisted, 'It is not enough for you to award me the status of *brahmarṣi*. I must also be accepted as such by the other *brahmarṣis*, especially Vasiṣṭha.'

"Thus, at the request of the demigods, Vasiṣṭha went to Viśvāmitra and agreed to recognize him as a *brahmarṣi*. In turn, Viśvāmitra also offered great respect to Vasiṣṭha. Their long standing enmity was soon forgotten and they became friends."

The next morning, Mahārāja Janaka called for Viśvāmitra, Rāma and Lakṣmaṇa. After respectfully greeting them, he said, "I know that such great personalities would not come here without some grave purpose. Therefore, please inform me what service I may offer you."

Viśvāmitra smilingly replied, "Rāma and Lakṣmaṇa have come here because They are eager to see the wonderful bow you keep and have worshipped for so long."

Mahārāja Janaka then explained, "This bow was used by Lord Śiva in a bygone age to disrupt the sacrifice of his father-in-law, Dakṣa. Being denied his sacrificial share, Lord Śiva angrily picked up this bow and threatened to annihilate the demigods. Coming to their senses, the demigods were able to pacify Lord Śiva. In turn, he handed over his bow to them. The demigods later entrusted the bow to Devavrata, the descendant of Mahārāja Nimi, my forefather."

After describing the history of Lord Śiva's bow, Mahārāja Janaka then related another interesting story. "Once upon a time, as I was leveling the sacrificial arena with a golden plow, much to my astonishment, I happened to uncover a baby girl. I named her Sītā (furrow), and raised her as my own daughter.

"Sītā quickly grew up, and when she attained maturity, many eligible princes came calling, hoping to win her hand in marriage. Since my daughter was not an ordinary being, I explained to the

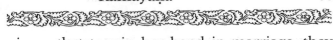

princes that to win her hand in marriage, they must possess great valor. Then I brought forth the bow of Lord Śiva and asked them to string it. However, none could even lift or hold it, what to speak of bending or stringing it. Most of the princes left, feeling insulted, and then banded together to attack Mithilā. A fierce battle raged for twelve months. Finally, as my army weakened, I prayed to the demigods for assistance. In answer to my plea, the celestials mercifully sent an army, and simply by seeing them, my enemies fled in fear.

"Since Rāma is eager to see the bow of Lord Śiva, I will bring it before Him to examine. If Rāma is able to string this wonderful bow, then I will gladly give Him my beautiful daughter, Sītā."

Soon 500 strong men pulled the immense bow, which was encased in a chest and mounted on a cart with eight wheels. Viśvāmitra invited Rāma to open the chest, while thousands of people gathered to watch. As Rāma gazed with admiration at the bow, Mahārāja Janaka warned, "Even great demigods, demons, Rākṣasas, Yakṣas, Gandharvas and Nāgas have failed to even bend this mighty bow. How then, will a mere mortal succeed in stringing it?"

Nevertheless, Rāma sportingly placed His left hand upon the middle of the bow. Then, in the presence of the huge crowd, He effortlessly lifted the bow out of its case. Holding the bow aloft, Rāma strung the bow in an instant, and bending it with great force, snapped it in the middle, just as a baby elephant breaks a stick of sugarcane. The thunderous cracking sound produced was like a mountain bursting apart, and caused all but Viśvāmitra, Janaka, Rāma and Lakṣmaṇa to fall to the ground.

Thus, with great pleasure, Mahārāja Janaka requested Viśvāmitra to send messengers to Ayodhyā, inviting King Daśaratha to attend the marriage of Rāma and Sītā. When the messengers arrived three days later at the court of Mahārāja Daśaratha, they related the glorious events of Rāma's breaking the bow and winning Sītā's hand in marriage. Hearing this, Mahārāja Daśaratha became overjoyed. Then, after consulting with Vasiṣṭha and Vāmadeva, Mahārāja Daśaratha decided that they should all depart for Mithilā the following day.

The next morning, Mahārāja Daśaratha started out, keeping his family priest in front and taking his army and a great quantity of wealth. After traveling for four days, the party reached the outskirts of Mithilā. Seeing his approach, King Janaka came out to meet Mahārāja Daśaratha, giving him a royal reception. Afterward, when Mahārāja Daśaratha had met with his sons, it was fixed that the preliminary marriage rituals would begin at an auspicious moment the next day.

The next morning everyone assembled, and before the wedding ceremonies commenced, Mahārāja Daśaratha requested King Janaka to hear of his royal lineage from Vasiṣṭha. Being so requested, the great sage Vasiṣṭha narrated the history of the Raghu dynasty.

"Marīci was the direct son of Lord Brahmā, and Marīci's son was Kaśyapa. From Kaśyapa was born Vivasvān, the sun god, and Vivasvān's son was Manu. The son of Vaivasvata Manu was Ikṣvāku, who was the first ruler of Ayodhyā. Many generations later in the Ikṣvāku line came Bharata, whose son, Asita, was conquered by his enemies, the Haihayas,

Tālajaṅghas and Śaśabindus. Being defeated, Asita decided to retire to the Himālayas along with his two wives.

When Asita passed away, one of the widows, named Kālindī, was pregnant. The other widow became envious of her and mixed poison in with Kālindī's food, desiring to kill the child within her womb. When Kālindī began to suffer the effects of the poison, the great *ṛṣi* Cyavana happened to arrive at that spot. Kālindī tearfully sought his blessings so that her child might live. The *ṛṣi* assured her that a son would be born, along with the excreted poison. Because of these unusual circumstances, Kālindī's son was named Sagara, or one who is born along with poison.

Later on, in the line of Ikṣvāku, the great grandson of Mahārāja Bhagīratha named Pravṛddha was cursed by Vasiṣṭha to become a Rākṣasa, and thus he came to be known as Kalmāṣapāda. There were many great kings who descended from Ikṣvāku, such as Ambarīṣa, Nahuṣa, Yayāti, Nabhāga, and Aja, the father of Mahārāja Daśaratha.

After describing their histories, as well as many others, Vasiṣṭha formally requested King Janaka to give away his two daughters, Sītā and Ūrmilā, in charity to Rāma and Lakṣmaṇa. Janaka Mahārāja then described his own genealogy, beginning with King Nimi, and concluding with his own father, Hrasvaromā. The king then happily concluded the solemn agreement, giving away his daughters to the sons of Mahārāja Daśaratha.

First, Janaka requested Daśaratha to have the Samāvartana ceremony performed for Rāma and Lakṣmaṇa. This entails shaving the head and underarms when a student returns

home from the *gurukula*. Then, the fire sacrifice was fixed for three days later, at an auspicious time.

Vasiṣṭha requested that the two daughters of King Janaka's younger brother, Kuśadhvaja, be given in charity to Bharata and Śatrughna. Janaka agreed, and when the Samāvartana ceremony was performed, Mahārāja Daśaratha gave away 100,000 cows in charity to the *brāhmaṇas* for each of his four sons.

Thereafter, at the auspicious hour known as Vijaya, on the day chosen for the marriage, Vasiṣṭha approached Mahārāja Janaka and said, "O king, the ruler of Kosala and his four sons wait outside for he who shall give away his daughters. Let the auspicious wedding sacrifice now begin without delay!"

Thereafter, Mahārāja Daśaratha escorted his four sons into the sacrificial arena while Vasiṣṭha Muni prepared the sacred altar, decorating it with sandalwood paste, flowers, potted plants, bowls filled with scented water, grains, incense, and pots of turmeric, along with other auspicious articles. Then, when all was ready, Vasiṣṭha lit the sacrificial fire and began offering oblations while other *brāhmaṇas* chanted Vedic mantras.

King Janaka then escorted Sītā into the sacrificial arena and seated her next to Rāma. With a voice trembling with emotion, Janaka said, "O noble Prince, this is my daughter Sītā. Please take her hand and accept her as Your life-long partner. She is a reservoir of all auspicious qualities, and she will forever be devoted to You as faithfully as Your own shadow."

Then, as Gandharvas sang and Apsarās danced with joy, amid showers of flowers from heaven and the vibration of celestial drums, King Janaka joined the hand of the goddess of fortune, Sītā, with the hand of the Supreme Lord Rāma. Then King Janaka placed the hand of Ūrmilā into Lakṣmaṇa's hand, then Maṇḍavī's hand in Bharata's, and finally, Śrutakīrti's hand into Śatrughna's. The four brothers then circumambulated the sacrificial fire three times while clasping the hands of their newly wedded wives. Afterwards, they circumambulated King Janaka and the great *ṛṣis*.

Upon gaining Sītā, the embodiment of all loveliness and virtue, Rāma felt unlimited satisfaction and happiness. Similarly, Sītā felt unprecedented bliss upon achieving her beloved Rāma, the Lord of her heart, and the emblem of goodness, chivalry, intelligence and handsomeness. Sītā and Rāma were equally endowed with transcendental qualities of form, beauty, behavior, age and nature. Dedicating their hearts to each other, Sītā and Rāma shone resplendently, just as Lord Viṣṇu shines in the company of His divine consort, Lakṣmī.

Even today, opulent marriage festivals are enjoyed universally. The Supreme Lord Rāma Himself has kindly shown us that a man and woman can enjoy a successful marriage by combining to follow religious principles. Human beings should not mate simply out of sex impulse like cats and dogs, for the way of the beasts is characterized by fear, suffering and rebirth. Therefore, every civilized society has some systematic arrangement for married life according to religious codes, aimed at bringing peace and, in the best of societies, Kṛṣṇa conscious living.

Eternally related as husband and wife, Rāma and Sītā are inseparable. Materialists sometimes want to worship and possess the goddess of fortune without Lord Rāma, but this is never possible. Without Rāma, Sītā turns into Durgā, the material energy personified, and to embrace her is to embrace death. However, if we concentrate on pleasing Lord Rāma or Lord Kṛṣṇa, the goddess of fortune will automatically bestow all her blessings upon us. The secret of successful living, including family affairs, is to put the Lord in the center of our life and make His service the goal of our endeavors.

After the day's festivities were concluded, the marriage party retired for the night. The next morning, Viśvāmitra left Mithilā for the Himālayas, and later that day, Mahārāja Daśaratha departed with his four sons and their wives, after receiving a large dowry from King Janaka.

On the way back to Ayodhyā, Mahārāja Daśaratha observed the inauspicious sign of numerous fearful birds screeching overhead. At the same time he saw the auspicious sign of deer crossing his path from left to right. Fearing some impending danger, the king inquired from Vasiṣṭha for an explanation. The *ṛṣi* replied, "The screaming birds indicate some imminent danger. However, the deer crossing from left to right indicate there is no need to worry on that account."

While Mahārāja Daśaratha and his priest were thus discussing the matter, a fierce wind began blowing, shaking the very earth and knocking down many tall trees. Dust rose up and began to cover everything from all directions. It became so dark that nearly everyone except Mahārāja

Daśaratha, his sons, and Vasiṣṭha and the other *ṛṣis*, became bewildered and panic-stricken.

Suddenly, the famous and terrible warrior Paraśurāma appeared, with matted hair, an ax on his right shoulder, a bow on his left, and a powerful arrow in his hands. The *ṛṣis* were surprised to see Paraśurāma in this ferocious aspect, since previously, after annihilating the *kṣatriya* community twenty-one times, he had vowed to give up his anger and remain fixed in the execution of austerities.

As the *ṛṣis* were wondering why he had again become moved to anger, the son of Jamadagni addressed Lord Rāma as follows, "You have certainly performed a heroic feat by breaking the bow of Lord Śiva. However, I am carrying an even greater bow, that of Lord Viṣṇu. If You consider Yourself a great hero, then take this bow and string it. If You are able to draw the arrow back to its full length, then I shall consider You a fit person to fight with."

Hearing Paraśurāma's challenge, Mahārāja Daśaratha became overwhelmed with grief, afraid to lose his beloved son. With a trembling voice, the king pleaded, "O best of the *ṛṣis*, Paraśurāma! Please desist from your aggressive spirit. I beg to remind you of your vow to give up fighting. After handing over the earth to Kaśyapa, you retired to Mount Mahendra to perform austerities."

Paraśurāma, however, ignored Daśaratha, and continued to address Rāma, saying, "Both Lord Śiva's bow and this bow of Lord Viṣṇu were constructed by Viśvakarmā. Lord Śiva was given one of the bows to kill Tripurāsura.

"One day, after Lord Śiva killed the demon, the demigods went to Lord Brahmā and curiously inquired, 'Who is more

powerful, Lord Śiva or Lord Viṣṇu?' To resolve their doubt, Lord Brahmā arranged to create some conflict between the two. As a result, a fierce battle ensued. During the fight, Lord Viṣṇu cut off Lord Śiva's bowstring and then, simply by releasing a tumultuous roar, He stunned Lord Śiva's senses. At the behest of the demigods, the fighting was then stopped. Everyone who witnessed the duel concluded that Lord Viṣṇu is superior to Lord Śiva in all respects.

"Lord Śiva, however, felt bitter because of his defeat, and was insulted by the verdict of the demigods. Thus, in gloom and disgust, he gave away his bow to Devarāta, a king in the line of Ikṣvāku. Lord Viṣṇu gave away His bow to the great sage Ṛcīka, who later gave it to his son Jamadagni. However, my father never used that bow, for he had vowed not to retaliate against any wrong done to him.

"Thereafter I received the bow from him, and after killing the *kṣatriyas* twenty-one times as revenge for Kārtavīryārjuna slaying my father, I became the sole ruler of the earth. When Kaśyapa performed a great sacrifice so that I could make atonement for killing the *kṣatriyas*, I gave him the earth as his priestly reward and then retired to Mount Mahendra. While there I acquired great prowess by performing severe austerities. However, when I heard that You had broken the bow of Lord Śiva, I felt compelled to come and challenge You. If You consider Yourself a great hero, then take this bow and see if You are worthy of fighting with me."

Without speaking, Rāma accepted Paraśurāma's challenge by quickly snatching his bow and arrow from his hands, and took with it his long acquired ascetic prowess. Then, after effortlessly stringing the bow before the awe-

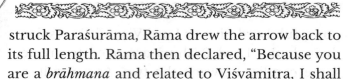

struck Paraśurāma, Rāma drew the arrow back to its full length. Rāma then declared, "Because you are a *brāhmaṇa* and related to Viśvāmitra, I shall not slay you. However, so that My taking up this arrow may not go in vain, and your challenge may be properly answered, I will use it to destroy the attainment of heaven which you earned as a result of your penances."

The demigods and celestial *ṛṣis* assembled in the sky to witness Rāma's shooting of the arrow. Paraśurāma had already been rendered impotent by Rāma, and all he could do was gaze at the Lord with wide open eyes. Finally, as Rāma continued to keep the arrow pulled back to His ear, Paraśurāma said in a subdued voice, "After I gave away the earth to Kaśyapa, he ordered me not to reside here again. For this reason, I must leave before night falls. Although my access to heaven has been taken away, I beg You to at least allow me to return to Mount Mahendra so that I may continue my austerities. O Rāma, I can now understand that You are Lord Viṣṇu Himself. Thus, I am not ashamed at having met defeat at Your hands."

Rāma silently accepted Paraśurāma's request and then released the mighty arrow, thus destroying the son of Jamadagni's eligibility for heavenly elevation. Thereafter, Paraśurāma returned to Mount Mahendra. As soon as he departed, the darkness previously created completely dissipated. From their position in the sky, the demigods glorified Lord Rāma with great enthusiasm and showered Him with fragrant flowers. Lord Rāma then presented the bow of Lord Viṣṇu to Varuṇa, and the party thus continued on its way.

Upon returning home, the four sons of Mahārāja Daśaratha began living very happily with their wives. After some time, King Yudhājit, the son of Kekaya and maternal uncle of Bharata and Śatrughna, came to Ayodhyā and invited his nephews to come and stay with him.

After His two brothers departed for the Kekaya kingdom, Rāma began serving His father and three mothers with great care. Rāma also carried out the state administrative functions so honestly and conscientiously that all the citizens came to love Him dearly.

Sītā and Rāma's natural attachment for each other grew day by day. They became completely dedicated to one another, being bound by each other's beauty and good qualities. In truth, Sītā was beauty incarnate, being the goddess of fortune, Lakṣmī herself. Within her mind, Sītā could vividly read everything in the innermost core of Rāma's heart. Being always determined to please her husband, and acting as the emblem of womanly gentleness and chastity, Sītā was soon able to bring the heart of Lord Rāma under her control.

Ayodhyā-kāṇḍa

Bharata and Śatrughna remained with their maternal uncle, Yudhājit, for some time, being well entertained by him. Meanwhile, at Ayodhyā, Rāma became the pet son of Mahārāja Daśaratha, and the beloved of all the citizens.

Rāma was Lord Viṣṇu Himself, incarnated within human society for the purpose of killing the wicked Rāvaṇa. As the Supreme Personality of Godhead, Lord Rāma exhibited Himself as the reservoir of all good qualities. Rāma's beautiful bodily features provided all who viewed Him with the full satisfaction of their eyes. Rāma played the part of a courageous and heroic *kṣatriya*, yet He was self-controlled, self-satisfied, without malice, and gentle in word and deed.

Rāma did not take offense when criticized by others, and was pleased by even the smallest show of kindness. He was forgiving and always humble about His own position. Rāma only embraced the association of persons who were pious and of superior wisdom. He was considerate and always the first to welcome guests. Rāma firmly adhered to truth and honored the *brāhmaṇas.* He loved the citizens, and they loved Him.

Rāma always acted according to religious principles and was learned in all the scriptures. He epitomized youthful vigor and was a mature judge of character. Rāma was always diligent in punishing wrongdoers and rewarding the virtuous. As a horseman and wielder of the bow, Rāma excelled all others, and He was the greatest of the chariot warriors. Indeed, Rāma was the Lord of the three worlds and the controller of

eternal time. He was unconquerable even by the greatest demigods and demons.

Mahārāja Daśaratha had ruled his kingdom for 60,000 years. Now, having grown old and fatigued, he finally desired to retire from his royal duties to prepare himself for an exalted destination after quitting his body. However, Mahārāja Daśaratha began to see various omens foreboding evil. Thus, he anxiously desired to install Rāma as the heir apparent as quickly as possible.

For this purpose, Mahārāja Daśaratha called a meeting of his ministers, prominent citizens and subordinate kings. However, in his haste, Mahārāja Daśaratha did not formally invite King Janaka or Kekaya, feeling confident of their support.

Thereafter, when all were assembled, Mahārāja Daśaratha announced, "I have grown old, and now desire to hand the royal throne over to my eldest son, Rāma, Who has reached the age of 27. It is now the sacred month of Caitra, and tomorrow the auspicious constellation Puṣyā will be ascending. Therefore, with your permission, I will direct that the ceremonies for installing Rāma as the heir apparent begin tomorrow."

The assembled ministers, kings and citizens, all applauded Daśaratha's proposal. They then glorified Rāma's incomparable virtues, equating Him with Lord Viṣṇu Himself. Thus, Mahārāja Daśaratha was both pleased and relieved.

After everyone departed, he requested Vasiṣṭha Muni to immediately begin preparations for the installation ceremony. Vasiṣṭha then ordered the chief minister, Sumantra, to arrange for the city to be gorgeously decorated

and make all other preparations so that the ceremonies could start early the next day. Mahārāja Daśaratha then summoned Rāma to the royal assembly.

Soon thereafter, Rāma entered the royal assembly and came before his father. Approaching His father with folded hands, Rāma fell flat at his feet, offering His respects. Mahārāja Daśaratha then picked up his son, and after tightly embracing Him, said, "My dear Rāma, I have grown old and weary, and feel it is now time for me to retire. I have sufficiently enjoyed all manner of royal opulences, I have performed innumerable sacrifices, and I have distributed huge amounts of wealth to the *brāhmaṇas*. You, Rāma, are my eldest and favorite son. Likewise, all the ministers and citizens love You dearly. Therefore, I have arranged that tomorrow You will be installed as the heir apparent to the royal throne."

Hearing this, some of Rāma's friends ran to Mother Kauśalyā, hoping to be the first to deliver the wonderful news to her. Upon hearing the news, she became overjoyed, and gave the bearers of the good tidings gold, jewels and cows in charity. Thereafter, when Rāma returned to His own palace, crowds of cheering citizens greeted him along the way.

Meanwhile, Mahārāja Daśaratha entered his inner apartments to lie down for some rest. Just as the king was drifting off to sleep, however, he experienced a recurring, ominous dream. Waking with a start, he immediately sent Sumantra to summon Rāma. The king felt apprehensive that there might be some obstruction to his son's planned installation.

Hearing that His father had again called Him, Rāma also felt a degree of apprehension. Making toward His father's

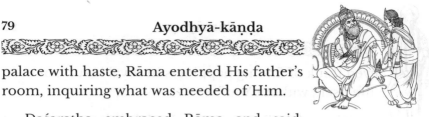

palace with haste, Rāma entered His father's room, inquiring what was needed of Him.

Daśaratha embraced Rāma and said, "My dear Rāma, all of my desires in life have been fulfilled, except to see You installed on the throne. Unfortunately, due to the influence of the Sun, Mars and Rāhu, this is a very bad astrological period for me. Moreover, I have been experiencing disturbing dreams, prompting me to think that a great calamity awaits me. Therefore, I am eager to expedite matters. I want the installation ceremonies to begin immediately, even without the presence of Your brothers, Bharata and Śatrughna. You and Sītā should fast tonight for purification. Then tomorrow, in the early morning, prepare Yourself for the installation."

Rāma returned to His palace to inform Sītā of the arrangements for the following day. Not finding her there, however, Rāma went to the residence of His mother. When Rāma entered Kauśalyā's room, He saw her sitting with half-closed eyes and suspended breath, silently praying to her household Deity, Lord Nārāyaṇa, for Rāma's good fortune. Kauśalyā, who was being attended by Lakṣmaṇa and Sumitrā, got up to greet her son, and Rāma addressed her, saying, "O mother, father wishes to install Me as the heir apparent to the royal throne!"

With tears in her eyes, Kauśalyā replied, "My austerities have surely not been in vain. May You and Sītā live long and happily together."

Smiling, Rāma turned to His brother Lakṣmaṇa and said, "My dear brother, you must rule the kingdom along with Me, for You are just like My second self. Indeed, I could not

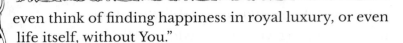

even think of finding happiness in royal luxury, or even life itself, without You."

Thereafter, Rāma returned to His palace in a jubilant mood. Sītā and Rāma worshipped Lord Nārāyaṇa together and then lay down to take rest for the night.

Meanwhile, within the city, all the citizens were merrily engaged in preparing for the coming festivities. All the streets in Ayodhyā were washed with perfumed water and scattered with fragrant flowers. Brilliant colorful lights burned in every house and meeting place, turning night into day. The noisy crowds swelled like waves of the sea, and the numerous elephants, horses and camels appeared to be like large aquatic animals within the ocean.

At the time of Kaikeyī's marriage to Mahārāja Daśaratha, her father, Aśvapati, the king of Kekaya, had given her a hunchbacked maidservant named Mantharā. Mantharā was actually an Apsarā, deputed by the demigods to appear on the earth to assist in the killing of Rāvaṇa.

The evening before Rāma's planned installation, Mantharā went onto the palace roof. From there she could see how the entire city of Ayodhyā was splendidly decorated, the streets crowded with citizens in a jubilant mood. Surprised at seeing this, Mantharā approached Rāma's former nurse and inquired, "What great occasion warrants such a celebration? Why do I see Kauśalyā in such a joyful mood and giving lavish charity to the *brāhmaṇas*?"

The nurse happily replied, "Tomorrow, the constellation Puṣyā will be in the ascendant. Taking advantage of the auspicious time, Mahārāja Daśaratha will install Rāma as his heir apparent to the royal throne."

This unexpected news pierced the envious heart of Mantharā. Suspecting foul play by the king, she suddenly became enraged, and thus sought Kaikeyī. Surprised at finding her mistress peacefully lounging on the couch in her apartment, Mantharā exclaimed, "Get up! Get up, you fool! Can't you see the disaster that is about to engulf you? Are you so deluded by your husband's sweet words that you do not realize what is happening before your eyes?"

Kaikeyī innocently replied that she could find no fault in her husband's plans. This, however, only further enraged Mantharā. Having mastered the art of persuasive speech, Mantharā then spoke to Kaikeyī in a way that eventually caused her to doubt her husband.

Posing as her well-wisher, Mantharā continued, "Surely you are aware of your husband's plans to install Rāma as his successor to the throne. Can't you see how deceitfully your husband has acted? He has merely sent Bharata away so that he can secretly install his pet son, Rāma, on the throne. Once Rāma becomes emperor, your son will meet His ruin, and you will be plunged into an ocean of despair. Moreover, because I am dependent on you, your fortune is also mine. Please let me help you before it is too late. Please act quickly to save your *own* son, Bharata, and yourself."

Kaikeyī was surprised to hear her maidservant speaking so boldly. She replied, "I am happy to know that Rāma will be installed on the throne. As a reward for delivering this wonderful news, please take this jewel. Indeed, you may ask for anything you desire."

Kaikeyī placed a priceless jewel in Mantharā's hand, but

the maidservant threw it aside. Mantharā indignantly replied, "I am shocked to see that you can express joy on the eve of disaster. Passing over Bharata to choose Rāma should be a great insult to you. You may imagine that you are Daśaratha's favorite. However, in truth, it is Kauśalyā whom he adores. Don't you feel humiliated? You imagine that you are happy, but it will be Kauśalyā who prospers. Once Rāma becomes king you will be compelled to act as Kauśalyā's maidservant, and Bharata will be forced to become Rāma's slave."

In this way, Kaikeyī's heart gradually became poisoned by Mantharā's hateful words. Indeed, when her enviousness of Kauśalyā was fully aroused, her face became flushed with anger. Thus, Kaikeyī relented, saying, "Mantharā, perhaps you are right. Somehow, Rāma must be banished to the forest so that my own son can be installed on the throne. Please tell me how I might accomplish this."

Mantharā then related how Daśaratha had formerly fought on the side of Indra against the demons, headed by Śambara. Because Śambara knew so many illusory tricks, the demigods were afraid to fight with him. Once, after the demons had severely routed the demigods, Daśaratha led an attack on their capital city, Vaijayanta. Although he fought heroically, Daśaratha was critically wounded during the battle and fell unconscious. Kaikeyī then removed him from the battlefield and saved his life. Out of deep gratitude, Mahārāja Daśaratha offered Kaikeyī two boons. However, she replied that she would ask for them when needed.

Mantharā then said, "Now is the time to ask for those promised boons. With one you will ask that Bharata be

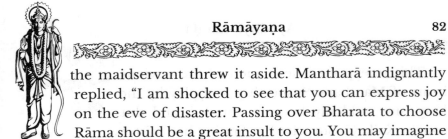

installed to the throne. With the other, demand that Rāma be banished to the forest for fourteen years. Rāma's absence will give Bharata the opportunity to establish His popularity among the citizens. Then His position as rightful ruler will be secure."

Then Mantharā further instructed Kaikeyī, saying, "Go to the sulking chamber and, after throwing off your costly ornaments and royal dress, put on old dirty clothes and lie on the cold floor. When Mahārāja Daśaratha comes to see you, remain silent at first. However, do not worry. His attachment to you is so great, he will not be able to bear

seeing you unhappy. He will do anything to pacify you. Regardless, keep your ambition firmly fixed in your mind. You will not settle for anything less than having your son installed on the throne. Do not allow him to pacify you with gold, jewels or anything else. Simply remind him of the two boons he promised. When he consents to this, then you shall demand that Bharata be installed immediately and Rāma banished to the forest."

Because her fickle heart had come completely under the sway of malice and greed, Kaikeyī was delighted with Mantharā's plan. She assured the maidservant that she would follow her advice to the letter. Indeed, through her twisted association, Kaikeyī had become obsessed with the idea of making Bharata the emperor of the world.

Like a madwoman, Kaikeyī glorified Mantharā, considering her to be the cause of all good fortune. She said, "My dear Mantharā, although hunchbacks are generally sinful, you are wise and honorable. I think your so-called deformed body is quite beautiful. Indeed, you stoop over like a lotus flower bending in the breeze. Thus, your appearance is very charming. Moreover, your breasts are large and lovely, concealing your delicate navel as they bend low. Your hips are graceful and your thighs are smooth and shapely. Dressed in bright silk, you appear to shimmer, while the ankle bells that circle your soft feet tinkle melodiously. The entire science of diplomacy must be residing within your hump, which is as large as the hub of a chariot wheel. My dear Mantharā, when Bharata is installed as heir apparent, I shall garland your hump with a chain of pure gold. When Rāma is exiled to the forest, I shall smear your hump with sandalwood paste. O Mantharā, I will reward you with

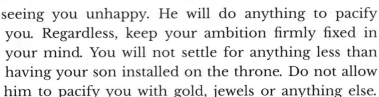

exquisite dresses and ornaments, and make all the other hunchback women become your maidservants and massage your feet."

Meanwhile, having completed all necessary arrangements for Rāma's installation, Mahārāja Daśaratha returned to his palace, desiring to see Kaikeyī. Filled with longing for his youngest queen, Daśaratha was surprised to find her absent when he entered her room. Thinking her to be nearby, the king called out her name. However, when there was no response he became apprehensive, for she had never before left her apartment without notice. Finally, after inquiring from a servant, Mahārāja Daśaratha learned that Kaikeyī had entered the sulking chamber. He hastened there with an anxious heart.

When the king entered the room, he was shocked to see Kaikeyī lying on the bare floor. With her ornaments and garlands scattered about, she looked like an Apsarā fallen from heaven. In the king's mind, the beautiful young Kaikeyī was dearer than life itself. Thus, seeing her in such a state caused him great pain and alarm.

Falling to his knees, the king lovingly stroked her face, and asked his beloved Queen, "What is troubling you, my dear Kaikeyī? What is the cause of your despondency? Whatever it may be, please know I am prepared to remedy it. Have I not been paying enough attention to you? Did you have an argument with one of your co-wives? Has someone done something to anger you? My dearest one, please know I am under your control. I could never avoid trying to please you. Please speak freely and tell me what troubles you. Let me dispel your sorrow, as the rising sun evaporates the morning mist."

Pierced by Cupid's shaft of love, Mahārāja Daśaratha was a slave to the urges of passion. Upon hearing the king's words, Kaikeyī felt confident that her goal would be achieved.

After a brief silence, Kaikeyī replied, "No one has insulted me or shown me any disrespect. My lord, I will tell you what is on my mind. However, you must first assure me that you will unhesitatingly accomplish whatever I desire."

While resting her head upon his lap, Mahārāja Daśaratha tenderly smoothed Kaikeyī's disheveled hair and replied, "You know that I love no one more, except Rāma. I swear that I will execute whatever you order. Feel free to tell me what you want and I will accomplish it without fail. Please know that I will always do whatever you want. Now, tell me what is troubling you."

After hearing his triple assurance, Kaikeyī was certain that her husband was completely under her thumb. Urged on by an inflamed desire born of partiality toward her son, the Queen proclaimed the following terrible words: "May the twelve Ādityas, the eleven Rudras, the eight Vasus and the twin Aśvinis bear witness! May the sun and moon, night and day, and the four directions also bear witness. May the Gandharvas, Rākṣasas, Pitās, Bhūtas, Piśācas and all other living creatures bear witness now. My illustrious lord, the follower of dharma and adherent to truth, has promised to fulfill my desire.

"Remember, my dear husband, the battle between the demigods and the demons when you were critically wounded and left for dead. Remember how I nursed you back to life.

Because of this you promised to award me two benedictions. O noble king, you must grant me these two boons today without fail. Otherwise, I shall give up my life from grief. Therefore, my request is this: let Bharata be installed as heir apparent to the royal throne, utilizing the very preparations you have made for Rāma. That is my first wish. Second, I desire for Rāma to depart for the Daṇḍakāraṇya forest this very day, to live in exile for the next fourteen years, wearing only tree bark and deerskin."

Hearing Kaikeyī's ultimatum, Mahārāja Daśaratha became stunned with bewilderment. Burning with distress, he wondered, "What is happening to me? Am I perceiving a vision from a previous life? Perhaps I have gone completely mad."

Thinking in this way, the king immediately became overwhelmed with grief. He lost consciousness and fainted onto the floor. Then, when he had recovered after a brief spell, the agonized Daśaratha found the situation too painful to cope with, and again fell into a swoon.

It was only after a long time that King Daśaratha regained full consciousness. Summoning his courage, he felt a burning rage swelling within his heart. With great agitation, Mahārāja Daśaratha rebuked Kaikeyī, "You vicious woman! Are you so perverse that you are determined to destroy my entire dynasty? What have I done to deserve this? What offense has Rāma ever committed against you? Rāma loves you as much as His own mother. Why are you so bent upon harming Him? Everyone loves Rāma more than life itself, and I also could not live without Him. I could abandon my other two wives if need be, but I could never forsake Rāma!"

His rage being vented, Mahārāja Daśaratha's mood suddenly changed. The king then humbly touched his head to Kaikeyī's feet and pleaded, "My dear beautiful Queen, please give up your terrible determination. Rāma is the embodiment of all virtues; He is kind, forgiving, truthful, gentle, fixed in His duty, and the well-wisher of everyone. Rāma has always served you as lovingly as your son Bharata, if not more. If you insist, I will install Bharata as heir

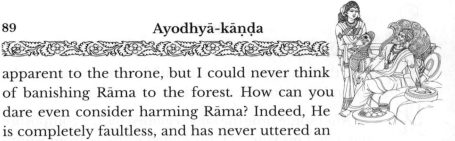

apparent to the throne, but I could never think of banishing Rāma to the forest. How can you dare even consider harming Rāma? Indeed, He is completely faultless, and has never uttered an unkind word to you.

"My dear beloved one, have pity on me. Ask for any other benediction. I am ready to give you the entire earth, but not this. If I banish Rāma, I will surely die. Please spare me from executing this most cruel and irreligious act."

As Mahārāja Daśaratha spoke, he writhed in agony, wailing piteously. Although the king prayed for her mercy, Kaikeyī remained unmoved. Standing fast in her determination, she responded, "How can you dare speak about dharma while you are trying to rescind your promise of granting me these benedictions? You solemnly promised and I shall not forget! Remember King Śibi who gave his own flesh to the hawk, just to fulfill his promise of protection to the pigeon. If you fail to keep your word, it will stain the reputation of your entire dynasty. Therefore, whatever the circumstance, you must fulfill your promise."

As Kaikeyī spoke, her determination increased. Overwhelmed by anger and greed, and giving up all sense of shame and decency, Kaikeyī said, "O king, I know your true motive! Once Rāma is installed as the heir apparent it will be easier for you to push my son and me away. With this impediment removed you will be free to enjoy your life fully with Kauśalyā. However, I vow that if you do not keep your promise, I shall drink poison and die this very day!"

Then Kaikeyī remained silent, as Mahārāja Daśaratha agonized over her words. Staring into space with unblinking eyes, the king again lost all equilibrium and fell to the ground, uttering, "Rāma, Rāma."

After some time the king regained partial composure and asked his wife, "O misguided woman, from whom did you learn such shameful wickedness? Do you not know that even if Bharata were to be installed, he would not accept the kingdom without Rāma? What will people think of me for performing such an ignoble act? Everyone will ridicule me, saying, 'There goes the lusty king, who was so attached to his wife that he sent his beloved son into exile.' How do you think there will be happiness under such conditions?"

Pausing in his speech, Mahārāja Daśaratha began wondering how Rāma, who had always enjoyed the comforts of royal opulence, would be able to live a harsh life in the forest. As his pain and anger increased with these thoughts, the king suddenly mocked, "O righteous Queen, I wish you all success in ruling the kingdom after having rid yourself of all your relatives! Do not expect me to play a part in your sinister plans. I shall never grant your demands! Never!"

Regardless, the king's bluster soon faded, as helplessness welled up within him. He again implored his Queen to retract her statements, saying, "Please take back all you have said!" Saying this, he again fainted.

After Daśaratha regained consciousness, he again rebuked Kaikeyī, "O how condemned women are. They are cruel, perverse and selfish by nature—if not all women, then surely you, O mother of Bharata. Your demands are evil and malicious. I will never grant them. You can scream as you like, take poison, or threaten me, but I shall never banish Rāma to the forest!"

Daśaratha's eyes were red from weeping and his voice pitiful to hear, yet Kaikeyī callously turned her head away. Again and again he begged her, but to no avail. The king prayed that the night would never pass so that he would not have to face the ordeal of banishing Rāma to the forest the following day. However, King Daśaratha finally realized that Kaikeyī was unwavering in her determination, and again fainted from hopelessness.

While King Daśaratha was arguing with Kaikeyī, Vasiṣṭha Muni completed the preparations for the coronation ceremony. The moon, lord of the stars, had entered the lunar mansion of Puṣyā, and the sacred hour of installation had arrived.

As Vasiṣṭha Muni made his way through the streets to the king's palace, he saw that flags, festoons, and garlands decorated all the houses. Likewise, the streets, which had been sprinkled with scented water, were filled with throngs of people anxiously awaiting Lord Rāma's appearance.

Passing through the joyous crowds, Vasiṣṭha Muni, followed by other great sages, entered the palace grounds, that were beautifully decorated with gardens and reservoirs of water, replete with lotus flowers, swans, and shade-giving flower trees.

As Vasiṣṭha Muni was about to enter the palace he saw Sumantra, King Daśaratha's chief minister, who had also just returned. "Please tell his majesty that I have returned," Vasiṣṭha told him. "I have brought golden water pots filled with water from the sacred rivers, and a special seat of sacred wood has been made for Rāma's use during the sacrifice.

I have also brought various seeds, aromatic perfumes, and precious jewels for the coronation. I have collected honey, curd, roots, ghee, milk, spices, flowers, parched paddy grains, and blades of sacred grass, all to be used in the sacrifice.

"I have also brought eight virgin girls and many excellent elephants, a splendid chariot drawn by four horses, a special sword, a bow, a palanquin with bearers, an umbrella resembling the moon, a pair of *cāmara* fans, a sacred bull, and a throne decorated with carved lions. Everything necessary for the sacrifice has been collected. Therefore, please ask the king to bring Rāma, so that the ceremony may begin as soon as the moon has fully entered the constellation Puṣyā."

Entering the king's chambers, Sumantra soon reached the room where Daśaratha and Kaikeyī were sitting. Not knowing what had taken place between the king and his wife, Sumantra was joyful. He was therefore quite surprised when the king, whose happiness had forever terminated, cried out, "O Sumantra, you are cutting my heart to pieces," and fell unconscious to the floor.

"The king has not slept all night because of his joy over Rāma's installation," Kaikeyī told him. Then the king regained consciousness and ordered Sumantra to summon Rāma. At Rāma's palace, Sumantra was quickly ushered into the presence of Sītā and Rāma. The Lord was garlanded with white lotus flowers, with golden necklaces covering His transcendental body. Being attended by servants who were fanning Him with *cāmaras* and offering Him various gifts with great devotion, Rāma appeared just like the Supreme Lord Viṣṇu—who, in fact, He was.

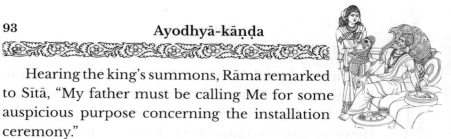

Hearing the king's summons, Rāma remarked to Sītā, "My father must be calling Me for some auspicious purpose concerning the installation ceremony."

As Rāma departed, Lakṣmaṇa was standing at the gate, waiting for Rāma with folded hands. Rāma took His brother with Him and then mounted His chariot, traveling through the streets of Ayodhyā.

Along the way, the citizens cheered, praising Rāma to the accompaniment of musicians. Wherever He went, the people could not take their eyes away from Him. Indeed, the natural characteristic of Lord Rāma is that whoever looks upon Him cannot bear to look away.

Reaching the inner gates of His father's palace, Rāma descended from His chariot and dismissed the citizens that had accompanied Him. As He entered His father's room, Rāma saw Mahārāja Daśaratha seated on a couch with Kaikeyī. The king's face was a withered mask of dejection and anxiety.

As Rāma approached, the king could only mutter, "Rāma, Rāma," as his eyes filled with tears, unable to look directly at his son. Seeing His father's distressed state, Rāma's heart became filled with grief and apprehension. He wondered, "What has happened to make My father so dispirited? Why is he not happy to see Me?"

Rāma then inquired from Kaikeyī, "What is the cause of My father's distress? Have I done something to offend him?"

"The king," Kaikeyī began, "is neither angry nor offended. He does, however, have something to tell You. He fears that by doing so, he will hurt You. Therefore, let me explain. Formerly, Your father offered me two boons after I had saved him in a precarious situation on the battlefield. However, due to unmanly weakness, he now hesitates to fulfill his promise. Therefore, Rāma, You should protect Your father's virtue by convincing him not to fall prey to dishonesty. O Rāma, if You promise me that You are fully prepared to carry out the king's order, then I shall disclose to You the nature of the two boons I desire."

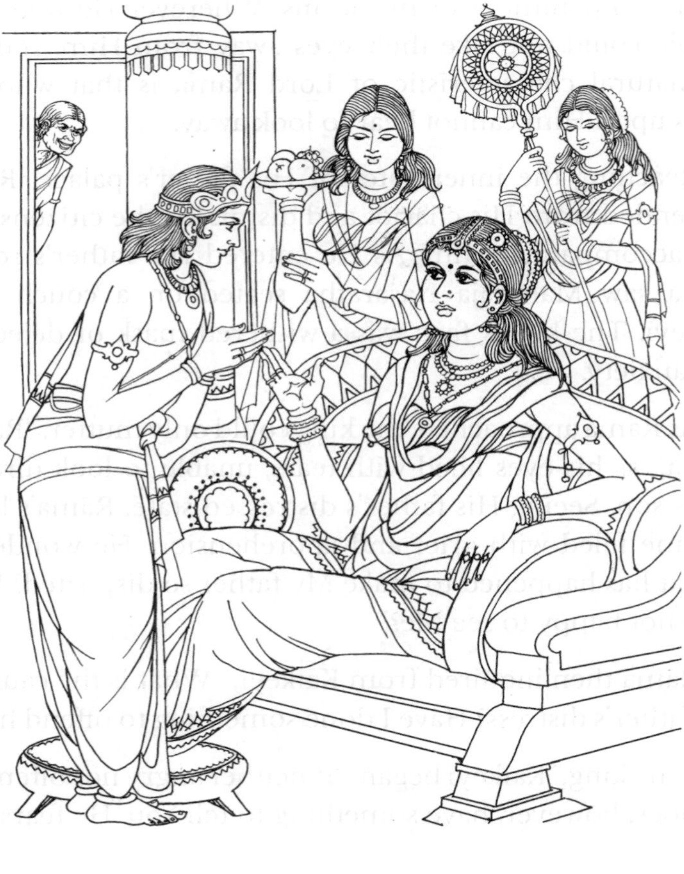

Feeling deeply hurt, Rāma replied, "My dear mother, I am surprised that there is any doubt in your mind that I would unflinchingly carry out My father's wishes, even if it meant entering into fire. Please tell Me what My father wants. Do not doubt that I will act accordingly. That is My solemn promise."

Gaining Rāma's assurance, the cruel Kaikeyī said, "Formerly, when Your father was severely wounded in fighting the demon Śambara, at the behest of the demigods, I carefully nursed him back to life. Feeling a deep sense of gratitude, the king begged me to accept two boons. I said that I would accept them later in a time of need. Now I wish to utilize those boons. First, I have requested Your father to install Bharata as the heir apparent to the throne. Secondly, I have asked the king to banish You to the forest for fourteen years, where You will live as an ascetic with matted hair, and dress with tree bark and deerskin. It is Your duty to ensure that Your father does not go back on his word and thus tread the path of unrighteousness."

Hearing her words, Rāma did not become even slightly distressed or agitated. Without any indication of displeasure, He cheerfully replied, "My dear mother, I shall immediately retire to the forest as you desire. Let messengers be sent at once to summon Bharata. I have no regrets. My only wish is that you and My father may always look upon Me favorably. My dear mother, please do not harbor any ill feeling toward Me."

At this, Kaikeyī exclaimed with delight, "It is settled! Send messengers to my brother's house so that my son may come here at once. As for You, Rāma, I urge You to depart for the forest without delay. Do not worry about Your father. For

the moment he is bewildered, but after Your departure, he will come around."

Rāma then said, "My dear mother, it grieves Me that My father has not ordered Me himself, but I am ready to depart for the forest with your command alone."

Hearing this conversation, Mahārāja Daśaratha could only mutter, "How painful! How terrible!"

When Kaikeyī finished speaking, the king again fainted onto the floor. Then, as Rāma gently lifted up His father, He told Kaikeyī, "I do not want to live in this world as a slave to greed and passion. Like the *ṛṣis*, I am devoted to righteousness. I would never give up the path of virtue for the sake of ruling a mere kingdom. Dear mother, there was no need in bothering My father. If you would simply have asked Me directly, I would have unhesitatingly given you the kingdom and retired to the forest."

Rāma bowed to King Daśaratha and Kaikeyī and departed to tell His mother the news. Lakṣmaṇa, who had heard everything at the door, followed His elder brother. It was only with great effort that He managed to control His rage.

As the two brothers left the palace, a pitiful wailing was heard from all who had found out about Rāma's impending exile. When Mahārāja Daśaratha heard those cries of lamentation, he hid himself under his bedsheets in shame.

When Rāma entered Kauśalyā's apartment, He was joyfully greeted and ushered into His mother's room. When he came in, she immediately embraced Him, saying, "I am so happy, Rāma. Today You will be installed as successor to the throne."

With great gentleness and humility, Rāma replied, "My dear mother, please do not allow yourself to be overcome by grief at what I must tell you. Because of two benedictions that My father formerly promised Kaikeyī, Bharata will be installed as the heir apparent to the throne, and this very day I shall leave Ayodhyā, to dwell in the forest for fourteen years."

Hearing this, Kauśalyā immediately fainted to the floor. Then, after Rāma tenderly lifted Kauśalyā to her feet, she bitterly lamented, "What greater misery could befall me than this? It would be better for me to have remained childless. Why has death not come to me instantly upon hearing of

this calamity? My younger co-wives will surely despise me now. By hearing their taunts my life will be made doubly miserable."

Until then, Lakṣmaṇa had controlled His rage. However, no longer able to remain silent, He suddenly burst out, "O Rāma, our father has become senile and perverse, being overpowered by lust. He has become a plaything in the hands of the wicked Kaikeyī. Why should we passively stand by and accept this? A father, a king or a spiritual master who cannot distinguish between what should and should not be done, must be rejected. Rāma, You should take over the government immediately—before everyone hears of the king's decision to install Bharata. Besides, even if all the ministers and citizens have found out, if they are against Your installation, I am prepared to annihilate the whole of Ayodhyā if necessary. My dear mother, you should know that I, at least, am loyal to Rāma. Indeed, I am ready to kill the foolish Daśaratha if it is necessary, to install Rāma upon the throne."

Kauśalyā, however, did not care for the kingdom. She only feared separation from her beloved son. She said, "O Rāma, please do not go into exile. It will be more virtuous for You to stay here and please Your poor mother than to go to the forest at the command of Your father. Rāma, if You leave Ayodhyā, then I shall fast to death, for life will become unbearable for me."

Rāma replied, "Mother, it is not possible for Me to disobey My father. Therefore, you must give Me your permission so I may depart for the forest at once. The order of one's father can never be avoided. Just consider how

Paraśurāma beheaded his own mother, Reṇukā, on the order of his father, Jamadagni. Likewise, the sage Kaṇḍu killed a cow at his father's command. Therefore I too must obey my father."

Turning to Lakṣmaṇa, Rāma said, "My dear brother, do not allow Yourself to come under the sway of all-devouring wrath. Give up the idea of seizing the throne by force and accept the order of our father."

Rāma again addressed Kauśalyā, "My dear mother, please do not torture yourself or talk of ending your life. After the term of My exile is over, I shall return to you. Therefore, please give Me your blessing so I may depart without unnecessary remorse."

Kauśalyā, however, could only cry in desperation. Then Rāma became stern and said to Lakṣmaṇa, "You are both causing Me more grief by opposing My desire to honor My father's command. I will not be swayed from My duty."

Then to pacify Lakṣmaṇa, Rāma said, "My dear brother, as soon as Bharata is installed, all of this will be forgotten. Then You will be able to easily give up Your grief. Do not blame Kaikeyī, for she is only an instrument in the hands of Providence, the real shaper of our destinies."

Lakṣmaṇa refused to be pacified. He angrily retorted, "O Rāma, it appears that You have become impotent, for You have given up Your *kṣatriya* reliance on personal prowess, and are just surrendering to destiny. I am not such a eunuch, however, and shall subdue fate by My own power. I will install You on the royal throne this very day."

Hearing this, Kauśalyā could understand that nothing could deter Rāma. She then pleaded, "O my son, if You are determined to execute Your father's command, then please allow me to accompany You to the forest.

Rāma replied, "Dear mother, after being deceived by Kaikeyī and then deserted by you, My father would certainly give up his life. The foremost duty of a chaste and virtuous wife is to never leave her husband under any circumstance. He is her lord for as long as she lives. Regardless of how noble or religious a woman may be, she commits sin if she fails to serve her husband. A wife's duty is to please and obey her husband, and no one else. This is the verdict of all the scriptures. Please, then, remain with My father and wait for Me, for I shall return after fourteen years without fail."

Kauśalyā gave up all hope of accompanying Rāma, and finally agreed to give Him her blessings. After giving Rāma permission to depart for the forest, Kauśalyā induced the *brāhmaṇas* to perform sacrifices for her son's well-being. Kauśalyā declared, "May You soon return so that my happiness will be restored. May righteousness be Your protector. May the demigods protect You, and may the celestial weapons defend You. May heaven and earth, the air, the wind, the land and water, and all animate and inanimate beings protect You. May day time and night, the sun and moon protect You. May You be happy, O Rāma, for my blessings shall go with You!"

Sītā had heard nothing of Rāma's exile. She had been waiting for Him in happy expectation for many hours. When Rāma finally entered her room, Sītā could immediately see that He was pale, perspiring and greatly troubled. Rāma

was also not accompanied by His usual royal entourage. Sītā inquired, "My Lord, what is the matter?"

Without hesitation, Rāma replied, "My father has ordered Me to leave the kingdom and to reside in the forest. Bharata is to be installed as the heir apparent to the royal throne. Utilizing two boons given her long ago by My father, Kaikeyī has asked that her son be installed, while I am to be banished to the forest.

"My dear Sītā, I have no other choice than to abide by My father's order. However, I want you to stay here. Go daily and offer your respects at the feet of My father and follow Bharata's commands implicitly. My dearest, I have come here just to see you before departing for the forest."

Hearing Rāma's words, Sītā grew increasingly agitated. With anger born of love, she replied, "O Rāma, my husband, most excellent of men, what advice are You giving me? It is the duty of the wife to share the husband's destiny. I *must* accompany You to the forest.

"A father, mother, brother, son and daughter-in-law all have their separate existence. A wife, however, has no choice but to follow her husband. I cannot take refuge in anyone else, not even myself. My husband is my only refuge. Therefore, I am determined to follow You. I shall walk behind You and eat only after You have eaten. I will never do anything to displease You, and I shall remain happy to gaze at the hills, lakes and rivers. I will never become tired, for I will feel secure in Your care. I would not want to live even in heaven if You were not there. O Rāma, it is You alone that I love. Without You, I would surely die."

Because of her frailty, Rāma was not inclined to take Sītā with Him. Thus, in an attempt to discourage her, Rāma said, "O delicate lady, one has to endure great discomfort while living in the forest. There are no soft beds to lie upon, and one has to bear the onslaught of excessive heat, cold and torrential rain. In the forest, one can only hope to eat fruits and roots. There is always danger from ferocious animals that stalk in search of prey. Considering these conditions, I could never allow you to accompany Me to the forest."

Rāma's words of refusal made Sītā tremble with fear at the prospect of separation from her Lord. As pearl-like tears rolled down her cheeks like drops of water falling from a lotus leaf, Sītā replied, "As long as I remain with You, any inconvenience or danger will be of no consequence. O Rāma, without her husband, a wife cannot live. If You do not allow me to go with You, I shall give up my life by taking poison, entering fire, or drowning myself.

"Before my marriage, an astrologer predicted that I would have to spend part of my life in the forest. Therefore, my dear husband, I know that it is my destiny to accompany You. To be with You is heaven and to live without You is hell. Therefore, You must take me with You."

Rāma remained reluctant to allow Sītā to accompany Him into exile. Sītā felt as though she were falling into a great abyss of calamity. Thus, she became almost mad, fearing separation from her husband. Unable to tolerate Rāma's stubbornness any longer, Sītā began to chastise Him, "My father made a big mistake in choosing *You* for a son-in-law! How can You think of deserting Your wife who

married You before puberty? Are You going to leave her unprotected and exposed to the stares of others? The citizens of Ayodhyā are fools for declaring, 'Rāma is as splendid as the sun—His glories are without equal.' I refuse to remain here alone while You go off to the forest. Either You take me with You, or I will take poison and die!"

Crying bitterly, her heart tormented with grief, Sītā was on the verge of fainting. Seeing her pitiful condition was more than Rāma could bear. His heart softened, and He took His chaste wife Sītā in His arms. Rāma then assured her that she could indeed accompany Him.[5]

"Dear Sītā," Rāma began, "I only tried to dissuade you because I did not understand the true situation of your mind. O Sītā, I could no more abandon you than a wise man could give up his sense of compassion. How could I ever rest peacefully, knowing that you were unhappy? Go then, and give away in charity all your valuables, clothes, jewels and whatever you possess to the *brāhmaṇas*."

---

5. Śrīla Prabhupāda comments: "In Vedic civilization there are hundreds of similar examples of such renunciation on the part of queens and dedication to the husband. The goddess of fortune mother Sītā followed her husband, Rāmacandra, when He went to the forest. Lord Rāmacandra went to the forest in compliance with the order of His father, Mahārāja Daśaratha, but mother Sītā was not so ordered. Nonetheless, she voluntarily accepted the path of her husband. Such queens also instructed the general people by showing them how to become a chaste wife and follow the husband in every stage of life. When the husband is king, she sits beside him as the queen, and when he goes to the forest, she also follows, despite having to tolerate all kinds of difficulties in living in the forest."

As Sītā joyfully departed, Lakṣmaṇa, who was standing nearby, came forward and caught hold of Rāma's lotus feet. With tear-filled eyes, Lakṣmaṇa pleaded, "O Rāma, please allow Me also to accompany You into the forest."

Hoping to discourage Lakṣmaṇa, Rāma replied, "My dear brother, You must remain here at Ayodhyā to serve Our two mothers, Kauśalyā and Sumitrā. Without Your protection, they will surely be mistreated by Kaikeyī."

To this, Lakṣmaṇa replied, "Surely Our brother Bharata will take care of everything. There is no need to be anxious for our mothers. O Rāma, as You traverse the forest, I shall walk in front with my bow in hand, allowing You and the daughter of the King of Videha [Sītā] to enjoy the scenic delights. I will also gather fruits and roots as You sleep, and stand nearby to guard You."

At last, Rāma agreed. He then instructed Lakṣmaṇa, "You may certainly come, but first take leave of Your mother. Afterward, bring the two mighty bows given by Varuṇa to Mahārāja Janaka, the impenetrable armor, two inexhaustible quivers, and a pair of powerful swords. After paying Your respects to Vasiṣṭha, return here with the weapons, and We shall depart."

Having fulfilled Rāma's orders, Lakṣmaṇa returned. Rāma then asked Him to summon the foremost of *brāhmaṇas* so He could distribute all His possessions in charity. Soon thereafter, Suyajña, the son of Vasiṣṭha, and the sons of Agastya and Viśvāmitra arrived at the royal palace.

After duly welcoming them, Rāma instructed His dependents to look after Their palaces in their absence.

Rāma then ordered His treasurer to bring forth all His wealth. Thereafter, a huge hill of gold and jewels was stacked high, along with other valuables, such as clothing, chariots and animals. In this way Rāma began to distribute His possessions.

It happened that a *brāhmaṇa* named Trijaṭa resided in the forest near Ayodhyā. Because of his extreme poverty, the *brāhmaṇa* was very weak and frail. His wife pleaded with him to go to Ayodhyā to ask some charity from Rāma. Thereafter, the *brāhmaṇa* set out, and happened to arrive just when Rāma was distributing His wealth. When the *brāhmaṇa* approached Him and described his impoverished condition, Rāma jokingly replied, "Take your staff and throw it as far as you can. As many cows as that stick passes over, I shall give you."

Trijaṭa tightened his belt and then excitedly threw his staff into the air. To everyone's surprise, his staff soared all the way across the Sarayū and landed amongst a herd of thousands of cows that were grazing from the river's edge up to the point where his stick had landed. Rāma then embraced the *brāhmaṇa*, saying, "Please do not be offended by My jest. I merely wished to see your exhibition of brahminical prowess."

After that, Rāma gave away everything in His possession. He made sure that no *brāhmaṇa*, relative, dependent or beggar failed to receive charity on that day.

Rāma, Sītā and Lakṣmaṇa then proceeded on foot through the streets of Ayodhyā toward the palace of Mahārāja Daśaratha. The citizens observing Rāma traveling about in this fashion, some from their seven-story mansions, and others in crowds on the street, all became greatly pained.

They cried, "O, how unfortunate that even common people are now able to see Sītā, who formerly never appeared in public. We shall take our families to accompany Rāma so that Ayodhyā will become like an uninhabited forest, and the forest will become like a populous city."

As Rāma entered Kaikeyī's quarters He saw Sumantra, and asked the charioteer to announce His presence to the king. Upon hearing of Rāma's arrival, Mahārāja Daśaratha ordered Sumantra to assemble his consorts so he could meet with his son in their presence. Shortly thereafter, 350 young maidservants came and surrounded Kauśalyā. Then, when Rāma, accompanied by Sītā and Lakṣmaṇa, entered His father's room, King Daśaratha ran to embrace Him. Overwhelmed by grief, the king fell unconscious before reaching his beloved son. At that, Rāma rushed forward, picking up His father in His arms, while all around the people cried in anguish.

After being brought to his couch, Daśaratha regained consciousness. Rāma then said, "My dear father, I have come to bid you farewell. Please give Me permission to depart for the forest with Sītā and Lakṣmaṇa."

Mahārāja Daśaratha urged, "Rāma, please accept my advice. Take me captive at once and then occupy the royal throne by force. No one can stop You."

Rāma replied, "Dear father, I have no desire to achieve sovereignty over the earth or royal opulence."

Mahārāja Daśaratha then said, "You may leave with my blessings, but please stay here for just one day so I may have the opportunity to see You."

However, Rāma replied, "I must leave immediately. It is my duty to fulfill your promise and do as Kaikeyī has ordered Me. I must leave for the forest at once."

Mahārāja Daśaratha then embraced Rāma, and afterward he again fell unconscious. Sumantra, who was weeping profusely, also fell to the floor. Everyone, except Kaikeyī, cried aloud with grief.

Sumantra had been the most intimate associate of the royal family. Thus, he, more than all others, suffered because of the calamity before them. Suddenly, Sumantra approached Kaikeyī and began chastising her harshly, saying, "O wicked woman! By sending away Rāma you will become the murderer of your own husband. Your selfish demands violate the religious principle that a kingdom be handed over to the eldest son. Indeed, you shall reap the bitter fruits of your evil deeds, for when Rāma goes away, all the *brāhmaṇas* will follow Him. Thus, your kingdom will become devoid of all auspiciousness. I will tell you something for your benefit:

"Once upon a time, your father, Kekaya, received a benediction from a *ṛṣi* that enabled him to understand all languages—even those of the animals. However, in giving the boon, the *ṛṣi* made one condition—if Kekaya ever disclosed the meaning of any speech that he heard from an animal, he would die.

"Later, the king once happened to hear the shrill cry of a bird. Because he understood its meaning, he began to laugh heartily. However, the queen, your mother, imagined that the king was laughing at her. Therefore, she demanded to know what he found to be so amusing. The king then

informed his queen of the *ṛṣi's* benediction, warning her that he would die if he disclosed what the bird had said. The foolish queen was so stubborn and jealous, however, that she replied, 'You can live or die, I do not care. I only insist that you tell me why you are laughing.'

"The mortified king then went to the *ṛṣi* who had given him the benediction, explaining his predicament. The *ṛṣi* advised that he not disclose the bird's speech, and that he should rebuke the queen for her impudence. Taking the *ṛṣi's* words seriously, Mahārāja Kekaya gathered his courage, and chastised his wife severely. After that, he lived happily thereafter.

"In the same way, Kaikeyī, you are acting impudently toward your husband. Admit your fault and give up your wicked plan." Kaikeyī, however, remained unmoved.

Thus, considering Rāma's exile to be inevitable, Mahārāja Daśaratha ordered Sumantra, "Make ready one *akṣauhiṇī* of soldiers and organize many merchants, hunters and the royal treasurer so that they may accompany Rāma into exile. Though He may reside in the forest, my beloved son does not have to go without the objects of comfort and enjoyment."

Hearing this, Kaikeyī was seized with fear. "Bharata will not accept the kingdom if you strip it of all its resources before His installation."

Growing progressively weaker, Daśaratha said, "If you will not let Rāma go to the forest in comfort, then I shall take all the citizens with me myself and accompany Him."

Kaikeyī snapped, "In our dynasty there is the example of how King Sagara exiled his eldest son, Asamañjasa. Therefore, you should cast off Rāma in the same way."

Hearing this, the elder minister Siddhārtha retorted, "Asamañjasa used to take delight in drowning other children in the River Sarayū. When the citizens complained of this to King Sagara, he rejected his cruel son. How is your comparison valid? Where is the fault of Rāma?"

Rāma interjected, "My dear father, please do not be upset. I have no use for the royal comforts you desire for Me. Let Kaikeyī's maidservants bring Me tree bark at once so that I can wear suitable clothing for My forest life."

Hearing His request, the shameless Kaikeyī personally went and brought clothes made from tree bark and asked Rāma to put it on. Without hesitation Rāma and Lakṣmaṇa obediently took off Their royal garments, and put on the clothes presented by Kaikeyī.

Sītā, however, felt very unhappy when she accepted her dress made from *kuśa* grass and tree bark, and her eyes filled with tears. When she tried to put the dress on, it kept slipping, for she was not at all accustomed to such clothing. Rāma then took the dress of tree bark and draped it over Sītā's silk sari. This was unbearable to Vasiṣṭha. With tears in his eyes he restrained Rāma and chastised Kaikeyī with strong words, "You wretched woman. Don't you see that everyone is prepared to follow Rāma? Indeed, you will find that even Bharata and Śatrughna will follow Him, leaving you alone to rule an empty kingdom. At least allow Sītā to

go into the forest with a comfortable dress and be carried on some conveyance."

Sītā, however, was determined to follow her husband's example, and kept the forest clothes on. Seeing Sītā dressed in this way, the palace residents began to condemn Daśaratha with strong words. Hearing their talk, the king lost all interest in continuing his life.

Nearly one hour passed as Mahārāja Daśaratha remained delirious, incoherently mumbling words of reproach to himself. Later, when the king became a little more composed, he ordered Sumantra to bring a chariot to carry Rāma to the forest.

At this time Kauśalyā embraced Sītā and gave her the following womanly advice: "It is well known that during times of misfortune, women will desert even righteous and loving husbands. Such wicked women forget all past favors, and nothing can bind them. Because of ingratitude, such selfish women cannot be controlled by wisdom, gifts or even marriage. However, there are also women who are gentle, truthful, and obedient by nature. Thus, they honor their husbands above all. O Sītā, please do not despise my son on account of His exile. Let Him always remain your worshipable Lord in all circumstances."

Sītā accepted her words with folded hands and replied, "I know well my duty toward my husband. Please do not speak to me about faithless women. My attachment to Rāma is like that of the moonlight to the moon. There is no *viṇā* without strings, or chariot without wheels. Similarly, there is no future for a wife without a husband, even though she may possess a thousand sons. Rāma is my Lord and He shall always be so. How could I despise Him?"

Kauśalyā began weeping, thinking of the impending separation from her son. Trying to comfort her, Rāma assured her that the time would pass quickly. Then He took leave of His stepmothers, as they wept loudly. Rāma then went and clasped the feet of His father.

Circumambulating the king with Sītā and Lakṣmaṇa, Rāma bowed low before His mother and father. Then, without further delay, Rāma, Sītā and Lakṣmaṇa mounted the chariot and departed for the forest. Thus Lord Rāmacandra left behind His kingdom, opulence, friends, well-wishers,

residence and everything else, just as a liberated soul gives up his life, and went to the forest with Sītā and Lakṣmaṇa.

Mahārāja Daśaratha kept his gaze fixed upon the dust raised by the chariot as it gradually disappeared over the horizon. Finally, after losing sight of Rāma's departing chariot, the king fainted and fell to the ground. When Kauśalyā and Kaikeyī ran to lift him up, Daśaratha forbade the younger queen, saying, "Do not touch me. I have disowned you. I no longer want to see you."

Kauśalyā lifted her husband, and while bringing him back, saw that all the stores and shops were closed, and a gloom pervaded the citizens. After entering his palace, the king asked to be taken to Kauśalyā's apartment. "From now on," the king declared in a faltering voice "I will stay here only."

Mahārāja Daśaratha passed the night with great difficulty. He felt that losing Rāma was like the dissolution of the universe. Seeing the king and Kauśalyā in such a miserable state, Sumitrā tried to pacify them. "Please do not lament for

your son, for Sītā and Lakṣmaṇa are with Him. Rāma will not experience the least difficulty. Indeed, Rāma is not an ordinary human being, but the God of gods Himself, the illuminator of the sun and controller of eternal time. While Rāma resides in the forest, the Earth herself and all natural phenomena will engage in His devotional service. Have faith that you will one day see the return of your beloved son. Your lamenting serves no purpose. Already the citizens of Ayodhyā have practically stopped all activity out of grief. You must pacify the subjects and not let them fall prey to anguish."

Meanwhile, some of the citizens had followed Rāma's chariot to the forest, begging Him to turn back. Rāma told them, "I cannot break My vow. I desire that you repose in Bharata the same love you have for Me."

As they traveled, Rāma saw how some of the elderly *brāhmaṇas* were having difficulty keeping up with His chariot. Hearing their anxious pleas, Rāma felt great compassion and descended from the chariot. Then, along with Sītā and Lakṣmaṇa, He proceeded on foot, allowing the *brāhmaṇas* to catch up with Him. Still, Rāma would not turn His face backward, for He was determined to keep His vow perfectly. Thus, as the *brāhmaṇas* constantly beseeched Rāma to turn back, they reached the banks of the River Tamasa.

As the sun slipped over the horizon, Sumantra and Lakṣmaṇa selected a site to rest for the evening. Then, after smoothing the ground, they made a bed of leaves for Rāma. When He lay down with Sītā, Rāma quickly fell asleep. Nearby, Lakṣmaṇa stayed awake all night, discussing the glories of His elder brother with Sumantra.

Early the next morning when Rāma awoke, He saw that some citizens of Ayodhyā were sleeping nearby. "Just see how much the citizens love us, Lakṣmaṇa," Rāma said. "They will not give up their determination to follow Me, trying to bring Me back to Ayodhyā. They have completely forgotten their homes and families. They should not be burdened by Kaikeyī's curse, as we are. Let us go before they awake."

Devising a plan, He told Lakṣmaṇa, "Let Sumantra drive the chariot in such a way that the citizens will become confused and unable to follow us any further."

After crossing the River Tamasa, Rāma instructed Sumantra to drive the chariot on a clearly visible path, while taking evasive measures that would mislead the citizens, and then return. Sumantra then drove off, and when he returned some time later, Rāma, Lakṣmaṇa and Sītā mounted the chariot and proceeded quickly down another path into the forest.

When the citizens awoke, they looked in all directions for their beloved Lord. Searching desperately here and there, they found the tracks of the chariot wheels, but after some distance, the tracks suddenly stopped. Unable to determine which way to go, the people gazed into the distance and wept.

With Rāma gone, the people reproached themselves, saying, "How can we return to Ayodhyā without Rāma? What will the women and children say when we fail to bring Him back? What is the use of living here without the beautiful moonlike face of Rāma? What is the use of a husband or children or even life itself? What good are household pleasures without the daughter of King Janaka and the lotus-eyed Rāma?"

With no alternative, the citizens returned to Ayodhyā, feeling extremely depressed. When the household women saw that the men had returned without Rāma, they reproached them with cruel, harsh words. Many simply sat down and wept. Due to shock, some of them were incapable of speaking or hearing.

Everyone in Ayodhyā began condemning Kaikeyī, swearing they would never live under her rule. Thus, life in Ayodhyā came almost to a standstill, appearing like a great

ocean whose water had dried up. The *brāhmaṇas* neglected their duties and mercantile people gave up conducting business. Householders no longer took the time to prepare meals, and the domestic animals let the grass drop out of their mouths, as though stunned. The cows would not give milk to their calves and mothers no longer felt happiness in greeting their sons. Even the stars in the sky assumed a stern aspect.

Feeling tormented with grief, no one in Ayodhyā could eat or engage themselves in entertainment. Indeed, everyone appeared to be almost lifeless, being absorbed in feelings of separation from Rāma.

As Rāma proceeded through various territories, villages and forests, He heard the people condemning Daśaratha and Kaikeyī for exiling Him. Finally, after crossing the Vedasruti and Gomati rivers, Rāma arrived at the River Syandika, which marked the southern boundary of the Kosala province.

Rāma stepped down from the chariot, and with folded hands, faced Ayodhyā to take leave of His birthplace. Many local inhabitants had followed Rāma, and when He asked them to return home, they cried loudly, unable to depart. Thus, Rāma drove swiftly away, hoping to minimize their anguish.

When they reached the Gaṅgā, Rāma asked Sumantra to stop the chariot under a large tree on the bank. The king of this territory was named Guha, a Niṣāda by birth and a close friend of Rāma's. When Guha heard of Rāma's arrival, he jubilantly came to meet Him along with his ministers and relatives.

Although born in a Niṣāda family, and belonging to a lower caste, King Guha had all the qualities of a great devotee. He was peaceful, self controlled, humble, tolerant, and charitable. In truth, he was superior to a *brāhmaṇa* because he was a fully surrendered devotee of the Lord. It is a great mistake to think that a man's caste is determined by his birth. That is not the Vedic conclusion. Rather, caste is determined by quality.

Seeing Guha approach, Rāma and Lakṣmaṇa came forward to greet him, and the Niṣāda king embraced Rāma with great affection. Feeling distressed at seeing the two brothers dressed in forest clothing, Guha said, "My dear Rāma, my kingdom is as much Yours as mine. Therefore, please make use of everything as if You were in Ayodhyā. I am honored to have You as my guest."

Guha brought sumptuous food, comfortable beds, and articles of worship to treat Rāma to a royal reception. Rāma was pleased to see this, and embraced Guha, saying, "At heart I accept all that you have offered Me. However, since I have taken a vow to wear only *kuśa* grass, tree bark and deer skin, and eat only fruits and roots, I cannot utilize these gifts. Therefore, please take away what you have brought, except for the food, which I can use to feed My horses, for they are the favorite steeds of Mahārāja Daśaratha."

At that, Guha gave the sumptuous feast to the horses. Rāma only took a little water, for He was fasting that day in honor of the Gaṅgā. That night Sītā and Rāma slept beneath a tree while Lakṣmaṇa and Guha guarded them. Although Guha requested Lakṣmaṇa also to take rest, He refused to do so while Rāma and Sītā were sleeping.

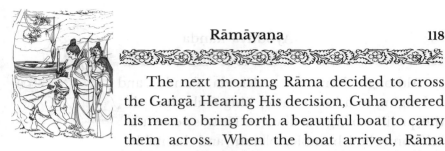

The next morning Rāma decided to cross the Gaṅgā. Hearing His decision, Guha ordered his men to bring forth a beautiful boat to carry them across. When the boat arrived, Rāma told Sumantra, "Please return now to Ayodhyā and serve Mahārāja Daśaratha. Try to remain composed so that you will be in a position to pacify the others. You have been of great help to us, but from now on we shall proceed by walking."

Sumantra pleaded with Rāma for permission to accompany Him to the forest. Rāma, however, insisted, "Please go and attend to My poor father. Do not be aggrieved, for we shall certainly return in fourteen years. Assure My parents of My well-being, and urge the king to install Bharata without delay. Please also request Bharata on My behalf to treat all of His mothers equally."

Unable to bear the thought of leaving Rāma, Sumantra argued, "When I return to Ayodhyā alone on this chariot, the people will become hundreds of times more unhappy. O Rāma, please allow me to accompany You. If You leave me aside, my life will become unbearable. I will surely enter fire or drown myself."

Rāma then replied, "I am sending you back to Ayodhyā so that Kaikeyī will be convinced that I have entered the forest. If you do not return with this chariot, then some fear will always remain in her mind that I might come back at any moment."

Turning to Guha, Rāma said, "I do not want to live in a forest surrounded by friends and servants. I shall go to an uninhabited place and live like a *ṛṣi*. Therefore, please bring

Me the milk-like extract of a banyan tree so that I can mat My hair."

When Guha brought the substance, Rāma and Lakṣmaṇa used it to make their hair matted, and thus they looked like forest-dwelling ascetics. Then, while bidding farewell to Guha, Sītā, Rāma and Lakṣmaṇa boarded the boat and departed.

When the boat reached midstream, Sītā offered prayers to Mother Gaṅgā, asking for their safe return to Ayodhyā.

Then, after the three disembarked onto the far shore, they continued their journey. Rāma then instructed Lakṣmaṇa to carefully protect Sītā by walking in front. Thus, Lakṣmaṇa walked ahead, Sītā stayed in the middle, and Rāma followed from behind.

When night fell they took shelter of a large tree. Both Rāma and Lakṣmaṇa stayed awake all night to protect Sītā. That night, as They talked, Rāma again urged Lakṣmaṇa to return to Ayodhyā to protect Their mothers from Kaikeyī's persecution. Indeed, Rāma became emotionally charged while thinking of His poor mother, and His face became covered with tears. While comforting Him, Lakṣmaṇa was able to convince Him that He could not live in His absence, and at last, Rāma permitted Him to stay.

The next morning Rāma, Sītā and Lakṣmaṇa set out again. After walking some distance they reached the confluence of the Gaṅgā and Yamunā Rivers. Desiring to meet the great *ṛṣi* Bharadvāja who lived there, Rāma approached his *āśrama,* and waited outside for permission to enter.

Soon a disciple of the *ṛṣi* came to greet Rāma, and escorted Him inside. Rāma saw Bharadvāja sitting in meditation, surrounded by many disciples. Rāma introduced Himself and then related the events surrounding His coming to the forest.

Thereafter Bharadvāja offered Rāma, Sītā and Lakṣmaṇa a nice reception and served them many varieties of foods prepared from roots and fruits. The *ṛṣi* then offered them comfortable accommodations, saying, "O Rāma, I have been expecting Your arrival since hearing of Your exile. I wish You

could spend the fourteen years here peacefully in my *āśrama*. With my students at Your disposal, You would not be inconvenienced."

Smiling, Rāma replied, "O best of *ṛṣis*, your offer is very kind. However, were I to reside here, I fear many people would come to see Me, since your *āśrama* is so close to Ayodhyā. Therefore, please tell Me of an isolated spot where I can stay to fulfill My vow of forest life."

Bharadvāja then suggested, "You can go to the Citrakūṭa Mountain, some sixty miles from here. After crossing the River Yamunā, look for the giant banyan tree named Śyāma. Then You will know You are proceeding in the right direction. The entire Citrakūṭa area is beautifully situated with cascading waterfalls and meandering streams. The cries of peacocks and cuckoos will enchant Your ears, and everywhere there is plenty of fruit and honey. Like the heavenly Gandhamādana Hill, it is a most suitable place for leading a life perfectly in the mode of goodness."

After spending the night at Bharadvāja's *āśrama,* Rāma, Sītā and Lakṣmaṇa took leave of the *ṛṣi* and departed. Later in the day, at the banks of the Yamunā, Rāma and Lakṣmaṇa prepared a large raft for crossing the river. Upon reaching midstream, Sītā offered prayers to Kālindī.

Reaching the far shore, they soon came to the banyan tree named Śyāma. Sītā offered respectful obeisances to the sacred tree and prayed for their safe return to Ayodhyā. Then, after waiting for some time, Rāma, Sītā, and Lakṣmaṇa passed the night on the bank of the Yamunā.

The next morning they resumed their journey. While walking through the forest, Sītā questioned Rāma about all

the varieties of plants and trees they encountered along the way. As Lakṣmaṇa walked in front, bow in hand, Rāma took great pleasure in describing the wonders of nature surrounding them.

In this way, Rāma, Sītā and Lakṣmaṇa finally approached the vicinity of Citrakūṭa Hill, where they were pleased to find an abundance of fruit, roots, sweet water and honey. When they came to the *āśrama* of Vālmīki, Rāma, Sītā and Lakṣmaṇa were happily received by the illustrious *ṛṣi.* Being invited to reside there, Rāma ordered Lakṣmaṇa to bring some logs and construct a small cottage. Thus, within a short time, Lakṣmaṇa had built a nice residence, with walls of wooden stakes and a thatched roof. At Rāma's request, Lakṣmaṇa performed the customary sacrifices to the demigods for consecrating their new dwelling. When Rāma entered the new cottage, He became happy, leaving aside the grief brought about by His exile.

Meanwhile, after the departure of Rāma, Guha had dispatched spies to observe Rāma unnoticed. When they sent news that Rāma had reached Citrakūṭa, Sumantra mounted his chariot to begin his painful journey back to Ayodhyā.

After two days, Sumantra arrived in Ayodhyā in the evening, and saw that the city had become nearly desolate. Everyone was deeply grieving due to separation from Rāma. Then, as word spread of Sumantra's return, thousands of citizens came forward into the street and crowded around him. Hoping to hear some news of their beloved prince, they anxiously waited for Sumantra to speak. In reply to their anxious inquiries, Sumantra explained, "The lotus-eyed Rāma has sent me back after reaching the banks of the Gaṅgā. Not allowing me to escort Him further, Rāma now

journeys by foot through the forest, with Sītā and Lakṣmaṇa."

Realizing that the Lord was not returning, some of the citizens fainted, and others wept. "Because we cannot see Lord Rāma, we are condemned," they said. "Alas, we have lost Him! But we can never forget how He used to glance at us affectionately and speak lovingly. When will we ever see Him again?" The people were grief-stricken as they recalled how Rāma used to tend to their welfare, just as a father looks after his children.

Sumantra then entered the royal palace to see the afflicted Daśaratha and relay the Lord's messages to him. Hearing Sumantra speak of Rāma, the king immediately fainted from feelings of separation. Trying to assist the king, Kauśalyā also swooned, and likewise had to be helped.

Before Sumantra could speak, the Queen said, "Why are you now lamenting? It was you who so unkindly banished your son to the forest. You value truth more than your own son, in whom all truth resides. Arise, O king, lest your followers begin to doubt the wisdom of your actions. If you continue to lament, your subjects will perish in the fire of separation from Lord Rāma."

Lashed by the sharp words of Kauśalyā, the king came to his senses. King Daśaratha then said, "O Sumantra, please fully describe whatever Rāma has said while departing. Where is He living? What is He eating? For all these years, He has been accustomed to luxury. How has delicate Sītā been able to live in the forest atmosphere? Surely her frail body cannot bear the scratch of a thorn or the scorching heat of the sun. And how is my beloved son Lakṣmaṇa? What are His

austerities? What is He eating? Have they sent me any message? O Sumantra, I can only survive on the strength of your reply."

Sumantra knew that Mahārāja Daśaratha's life could only be sustained by hearing about Rāma. Thus, he began to speak as follows: "At the time of our parting, Rāma instructed me to return to Ayodhyā to render service unto you and Bharata. Rāma's only concern is for your welfare, and thus, He wants to ensure that your promise to Kaikeyī is fulfilled. He also requested that I inform His mother, Kauśalyā, that He is faring well. In addition, O Kauśalyā, your son has requested that you remain constantly devoted to righteousness and worship your husband's lotus feet as you would those of a deity.

"Moreover, He has asked that you shun the pride born of position and seniority and treat Queen Kaikeyī as your superior. Likewise, my king, He requests you to install Bharata as heir apparent to the throne without delay. Even though young in years, He is still a king and deserves to be honored.

"Rāma also asked me to relay a message to Bharata, begging that He should look upon Kauśalyā and Sumitrā as He does His own mother.

"Moreover, O Emperor, I must inform you that poor Sītā just stands motionless, oblivious to everything, and sighing. She has never experienced adversity before, and she did not impart any message. As I was about to leave, however, she looked at the royal chariot and suddenly burst into tears. After offering obeisances, I left, but my horses wandered, for they were also blind with tears.

"O Emperor, as I returned to Ayodhyā, I saw that every moving and non-moving creature within the Kosala kingdom was in a pitiable condition due to separation from Rāma. Overcome by intense separation from Rāma, even trees, flowers, and fruits have withered up from grief. The rivers and lakes have dried up, the forest animals do not even move about, nor do reptiles search for food. In the ponds, the lotus flowers and the fish have perished. In the cities throughout your kingdom, the gardens are desolate, and the birds that used to sing in them have fled. Moreover, seeing this chariot arrive without Rāma, the citizens have been cast into a dazed, almost unconscious condition."

The stunned condition exhibited by the citizens of Ayodhyā occurs when a devotee experiences ecstatic tribulation, fear, astonishment, lamentation, or anger on behalf of the Lord. There are many instances of devotees becoming stunned when they thought they had lost the Lord's association. During Lord Kṛṣṇa's pastimes, the milkmaids of Vṛndāvana were frequently in a stunned condition, and the cowherd boys, elders, and cows were stunned when they thought that Kṛṣṇa was going to be killed by Kāliya or some other demon. Such a condition is symptomized by the inability to speak, the cessation of movement, a feeling of voidness, and an extreme awareness of separation from the Supreme Lord. Such ecstatic emotions are relished by great devotees who have no material desires and have surrendered everything to the Lord's lotus feet. Just like the residents of Vṛndāvana, the people of Ayodhyā were stunned due to transcendental love.

After hearing Sumantra's words, Mahārāja Daśaratha became even more overwhelmed with grief. In a fit of despair,

he declared, "You must take me to where Rāma is staying, or somehow bring Him here. Otherwise I shall die. I am merged in an ocean of grief. The two boons I granted to Kaikeyī are the shores of that ocean, and the term of Rāma's exile is its extent. My inward and outward breaths are the waves and whirlpools. That ocean is further agitated by the inflowing river of tears shed by Kauśalyā and others. The flaying of arms in agony is the leaping of the fish in that ocean, the disheveled hair is the seaweed, and our loud crying is its roar. Kaikeyī is the submarine fire that causes showers of welled up tears, and the words of Mantharā are the alligators that infest its waters."

After speaking, Mahārāja Daśaratha again fainted, and Kauśalyā, who had become almost mad with grief, writhed on the floor. In agony the Queen wailed, "O Sumantra, if you do not take me to Rāma at once I will surely die."

Sumantra could only hope to comfort the Queen by saying, "My Queen, since He is in the company of Sītā and Lakṣmaṇa, Rāma will pass His time quite happily, in spite of living in the forest."

Thus, even though Kauśalyā was the foremost of wives, she began to address Mahārāja Daśaratha as follows: "It is your fault that my son has been exiled, allowing these miseries to befall us. How could you be so cruel to your own son and His delicate wife? How will Rāma and Sītā bear having to lie down upon the bare ground? How will they be able to maintain themselves, eating only raw fruit and roots? How will they survive the freezing cold, the winds and torrential rains? How will they protect themselves from the ferocious animals that wander through the jungle at night in search of prey?

"Even if Rāma survives and returns to Ayodhyā after fourteen years, Bharata will never be willing to give Him back the throne. Indeed, even if Bharata were to offer it, Rāma would never accept something that had already been enjoyed by His younger brother. I am so unfortunate for having a wretched husband like you! The primary support of a woman is her husband. Since you are fully under the control of Kaikeyī, I am bereft of that shelter. The secondary support of a woman is her son, and since I am separated from Him, I am doomed."

Kauśalyā's lamentations were so painful to hear that Mahārāja Daśaratha lost consciousness again. Then Kauśalyā realized how her husband was suffering from her words, and her heart softened.

When the king regained consciousness, they reconciled, and he related the following story: "One who does not consider the good or bad reaction of a particular deed is certainly a great fool. One who cuts down mango trees to grow thorn bushes will undoubtedly repent at harvest time. By banishing Rāma to the forest, I have certainly followed this example.

"Long ago, when I was a young prince, I learned the art of piercing an invisible object with my arrow simply by hearing its sound. Once, as I was hunting at night on the banks of the River Sarayū, I heard a sound that I thought to be of an elephant drinking water. However, after shooting my arrow in that direction, I heard a loud scream, and a human voice called out, 'Who has so cruelly pierced me with his arrow, even though I am an innocent *ṛṣi*?'

"As that pitiful voice cried out in pain, I ran in the direction of the crying. Thus, I came upon a young ascetic boy lying upon the ground with my arrow stuck in his body. Seeing me before him, the boy said, 'My old and blind mother and father are waiting for me to bring them water. You have not only killed me, but them as well. Without my care they will be unable to continue living. Please go and confess to them that you have mortally wounded me. Before you leave, please pull out this arrow, for it is giving me great pain.'

Mahārāja Daśaratha continued: "I hesitated to pull out the arrow because I was afraid if I did so, the boy would die immediately. Seeing my reluctance, the boy assured me, saying, 'Do not fear, thinking you will be killing a *brāhmaṇa*. I was born of a *vaiśya* father and *śūdra* mother.'

"After hearing these words, I pulled out the arrow. When I did, the boy instantly gave up his life. I then filled his water pitcher and proceeded with a grief-stricken heart to the *āśrama* of the boy's parents. There, I saw the old, feeble, blind couple. Hearing me approach, they thought I was their son, and began to address me with affectionate words. This caused my heart great pain, but I took courage and explained to them how I had accidentally killed their son.

"'I am not your son,' I explained, 'but a *kṣatriya* named Daśaratha. I mistook the sound of your son collecting water for an elephant drinking. In my ignorance, I shot an arrow and killed your son. Your holiness, please tell me how I can atone for my sin.'"

Because Daśaratha was a learned man, he knew that he could not escape the reaction of a sinful deed. Thus,

he intelligently inquired about the proper means of atonement. Scriptures advise every intelligent man to atone for his sins before death to avoid suffering in the next life. One has to make restitution according to the gravity of the offense. Even though many people today question the existence of a future life, the stringent laws of karma—action and reaction—are at work, and no one is excused, not even on the plea of ignorance. When people break the laws of God and nature, they must reap the results, birth after birth, possibly descending to the lower species or to the hellish planets. In order to avoid this, Daśaratha immediately tried to counteract his sin.

"After hearing me, the old sage replied, 'Because you have voluntarily confessed your sin, I shall not curse you. If I were to do so, then you would die instantly. Since you killed my son out of ignorance, your life shall be spared. Now, please take me to where my son is lying.'

"I led the blind couple to where their son lay lifeless, and they began to caress his body and cry out pitifully. Then, as soon as they offered libations of water for their son's departed soul, King Indra descended to that spot on a celestial chariot.

"After assuring the aged parents that they would attain the same exalted destination as their son, Indra took the boy in his celestial form to the heavenly planets. The old ascetic then cursed me, 'Just as we are now experiencing great anguish upon the death of our son, you will have to feel the same grief due to separation from yours.' Then the old sage and his wife threw themselves upon their son's funeral pyre, thus giving up their lives and ascending to heaven.

"My dear Kauśalyā, today I am reaping the fruits of my horrible crime. I am dying of a broken heart. I can feel the power of my senses ebbing away like the flame of an oil-less lamp. I know that death will come to me very soon. O Queen, I have already become blind with grief. Please touch me so that I can be assured of your presence."

Mahārāja Daśaratha continued to lament in separation from Rāma, while remaining fully absorbed in His memory. When half the night had passed away, the king left his mortal body.

Because he so greatly loved his son, Rāma, the Supreme Personality of Godhead, King Daśaratha attained the Lord's abode in the spiritual sky, where Lord Rāma reigns eternally. Any devotee who always thinks of the Lord while eating, sleeping, working, or relaxing, attains the Lord's transcendental abode. Thus, although King Daśaratha had to endure the reaction of his past offense, he achieved his desired goal: eternal association with Lord Rāma.

The next morning, when the bards came to awaken the king, his servants stood outside the door with folded hands. However, when his consorts entered his room, they found his body without any sign of life. The women cried out in horror, waking Kauśalyā and Sumitrā with a start. When the two Queens saw that their king had passed away, they fell to the floor in agony. Hearing this uproar, Kaikeyī also came. When she understood that the king had died, she too began crying piteously.

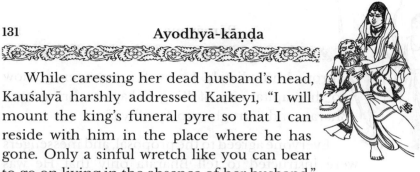

While caressing her dead husband's head, Kauśalyā harshly addressed Kaikeyī, "I will mount the king's funeral pyre so that I can reside with him in the place where he has gone. Only a sinful wretch like you can bear to go on living in the absence of her husband."

The ministers came and led Kauśalyā away, trying their best to pacify her. Thereafter, they preserved the body of Mahārāja Daśaratha in a vat of oil, since the funeral ceremonies could only be performed in the presence of a son.

Being bereft of their ruler, the citizens of Ayodhyā were plunged into gloom. No one was able to sleep that night. The people gathered in the streets, publicly reproaching Kaikeyī to vent their grief.

The next morning, the leading *brāhmaṇas* of Ayodhyā gathered at the court, urging the king's ministers to install one of the king's sons that very day. Addressing Vasiṣṭha, Vāmadeva, Mārkeṇḍeya, Kasyana, Gautama and other *ṛṣis*, the *brāhmaṇas* said: "A country without a king is doomed. In such a place, rogues and thieves take advantage of the situation and lawlessness prevails. In a kingdom without a ruler, ownership disappears, sons disobey fathers, charity is forgotten, and religious practice declines as the citizens exploit one another."

The *ṛṣis* replied, "What you say is perfectly correct. It is the king that makes the demarcation between good and evil in this world. Bereft of a good king, the subjects are just like cattle without a herdsman."

Vasiṣṭha suggested, "Since Bharata has already been selected as heir apparent, He should be installed upon the

throne immediately. Let swift messengers go now to the capital city of King Kekaya to bring back Bharata and Śatrughna to Ayodhyā."

Everyone agreed to the proposal, and messengers were instructed to tell Bharata only that He was urgently required at Ayodhyā. After traveling for several days, the messengers arrived at Kekaya's capital during the night. In the meanwhile Bharata had experienced a ghastly dream. He awoke in a most disturbed state, and seeing His despondency, Śatrughna and His other friends tried to cheer His spirits. Bharata, however, failed to find their joking words amusing. They then inquired from Him seriously about His inner disturbance.

Bharata explained, "Last night in My dreams, I saw My father, disheveled and dejected, fall from a mountaintop into a pool of cow dung. As he floundered in the mire, the king drank oil from his cupped palms and laughed hysterically, like a madman. Then, after the oil was spread over his body, the king began to eat rice that had been cooked in it.

"Suddenly the scene changed, and I saw that the ocean had become dry and the moon had fallen onto the earth. As the earth remained enveloped in darkness, Rākṣasas wandered its surface, while volcanoes erupted, spewing fire and lava. Then that scene evaporated, and I saw that the tusks of my father's elephant had been broken. Young, dark-skinned women began harassing the king, who was dressed all in black, and smeared all over with red sandalwood paste, adorned with a garland of red flowers, and seated upon an iron throne.

"Finally I saw a chariot drawn by donkeys swiftly carrying my father toward the south. After witnessing

this ghastly nightmare, I have concluded that My father, one of My brothers, or I Myself will surely die. Even now, although I know not why, I feel constant fear within My heart. My voice has become hoarse and my complexion has lost its luster. My mind is reeling, and I feel shame and hatred—all for no apparent reason. Indeed, the more I think, the more I am convinced this nightmare forebodes great evil."

While Mahārāja Bharata was speaking, the messengers from Ayodhyā entered the room. After offering their respects, they related their message: "O Prince, You are summoned to Ayodhyā by the ministers and Vasiṣṭha. Your presence there is urgently needed."

When Bharata asked them about the welfare of His parents, they replied as instructed, telling Him that all was well. Suddenly eager to depart, Bharata took leave from His maternal grandfather and uncle.

Upon His leaving, Mahārāja Aśvapati gave Bharata many valuable gifts. However, Bharata hardly considered them, because of the urgency conveyed in Vasiṣṭha's message, and the premonition in His dream.

Accompanied by Śatrughna, Bharata mounted His chariot and hurriedly departed, accompanied by a large army supplied for His protection. After passing through various territories in great haste, Bharata arrived at the outskirts of Ayodhyā on the seventh day of his journey.

Bharata could discern from some distance that the city did not have its usual cheerful aspect. When Bharata then entered the capital, He saw that everyone was grief-stricken.

Bharata then confided to His charioteer that the signs before Him indicated the demise of His father.

The entire city of Ayodhyā appeared neglected. Because the citizens had ceased performing their occupational duties, the entire place looked dirty and deserted. With tears in His eyes, Bharata entered His father's palace. Failing to find the king in his usual room, Bharata hurried to His mother's apartment. As soon as He entered her room, Kaikeyī jumped up from her seat, overjoyed to see her long absent son.

After Bharata bent down to touch His mother's feet, Kaikeyī lifted Him up and lovingly placed His head on her lap. Kaikeyī inquired about the welfare of her father and his kingdom. In reply, Bharata assured her that all was well. Then Bharata said, "I have hurried back because of Vasiṣṭha's summons. How is my father? Why do I not find him in his room?

Kaikeyī calmly replied, "The king, Mahārāja Daśaratha has passed away, my dear son."

Hearing this, Bharata fell to the floor grief stricken, and began crying aloud. Kaikeyī tried comforting Him, saying, "Dear Bharata, please do not become overwhelmed by sorrow. Pious and enlightened persons remain equipoised and do not give way to such lamentations."

Bharata then asked His mother how the king had died, and if he had left any message for him. Then He requested, "Please send someone for Rāma immediately, and inform Him of my arrival."

As if relating good news, Kaikeyī frankly replied, "Rāma has left the Kosala kingdom, being exiled to the forest. He now wears tree bark, and Sītā and Lakṣmaṇa have followed Him. Your father could not bear to live in separation from Kauśalyā's son, however, and thus he gave up his life while crying out, 'O Rāma! O Sītā! O Lakṣmaṇa!'"

When Bharata asked why Rāma had been exiled, thinking He may have killed a *brāhmaṇa*, Kaikeyī, determined to manipulate the events, replied, "In your absence, the king suddenly announced that he intended to install Rāma as the heir apparent to the throne the very next day. To save ourselves from becoming dominated by Kauśalyā and her son, I took advantage of two benedictions Your father had awarded me when I saved his life on the battlefield.

"With the first boon I demanded that You be installed on the throne, and with the second, I banished Rāma to the forest for fourteen years. Rāma was always Daśaratha's favorite, and without Him, he died of a broken heart. Therefore, You must accept the royal throne this very day, after performing the funeral ceremonies for Your deceased father. Please take heart and give up Your grief."

Bharata became fiery with rage. He rebuked His mother, saying, "O wicked woman, you must be the goddess Kālī herself, appearing to destroy the entire universe! You have killed My father and exiled Rāma, who is dearer to Me than life itself. Are you so perverse that you believe I will actually accept the throne from you, especially now? You are not My mother! You are My worst enemy! I pray that you go to hell for what you have done!

"Sinful woman, I will never allow you to fulfill your selfish ambitions. I will leave now for the forest and bring Rāma back to rule the kingdom. After Rāma is installed I will act as His eternal servant, for that is My natural position and highest aspiration.

"Are you so hard-hearted that you cannot understand how Kauśalyā must feel in the absence of her only son? Once, the celestial *kāmadhenu* named Surabhi happened to see that two of her sons had fallen to the ground unconscious. The two bullocks had worked very hard all day for a cruel farmer, plowing the fields in the hot sun. When Surabhi saw them in such a pitiful condition, tears fell from her eyes upon Indra's head. When Indra looked up to see the aggrieved Surabhi, he inquired of the cause of her distress. After Surabhi explained what had happened, Indra said, 'In the entire world, no one can be more dear to a mother than her son.'"

Bharata vowed, "O wretched woman, not only will I bring Rāma back from the forest, but I too, will spend fourteen years in exile just to keep My father's promise intact and save Rāma from the sin of abandoning His vow."

Saying this, Bharata fell to the floor unconscious, due to excessive grief and exhaustion. Then, after a long time, He recovered, and spoke to the ministers gathered there, "I have no desire to become emperor of the world, for I consider Myself a servant of My elder brother, Rāma. Being away in a distant place, I had no idea of My mother's wicked schemes. Please believe Me when I say that I had nothing to do with Rāma's exile. Kaikeyī's desires are not shared by Me."

Kaikeyī was not prepared for Bharata's reaction to her manipulations. When she saw that her plans were destroyed,

her illusion was suddenly dashed. She appeared to be awakening from a bad dream. Tears welled up in her eyes, and her heart filled with anguish.

Meanwhile, Kauśalyā heard Bharata's voice and went to meet Him. On the way, however, she fainted, just at the time when Bharata and Śatrughna were coming to see her. Thus, the two brothers saw Kauśalyā lying on the floor. Picking her up, They embraced her, tears streaming from Their eyes.

Seeing Bharata before her, Kauśalyā sarcastically remarked, "So, You have now come back to enjoy the kingdom You have always coveted. You must be very happy to see that everything has worked out so well, according to plan."

Upon hearing these words, Bharata was greatly pained. For some time He could not even reply. Then, regaining His composure, Bharata fell at Kauśalyā's feet, and with folded hands, said, "My dear mother, I had nothing to do with Rāma's exile. I had no idea what Kaikeyī was doing. Surely you know how much I love Rāma! Don't you see how aggrieved I am due to Rāma's exile and My father's death? To assure you of My innocence, I swear this oath, 'Whoever has helped in the nefarious plan to exile Rāma may reap the consequences of killing a king, a cow, a woman, a child, or an old person. May he become addicted to wine, women, meat and gambling. May godly men shun him and may he remain childless. May he incur the sinful reaction which affects the arsonist, the traitorous friend, and the unfair arbitrator. May his be the sin of refusing water to a thirsty man and he who shuns his wife when she approaches him when she is prepared for conception.' My dear mother, Rāma is My very

life and existence. He is My soul, and I have no purpose separate from dedication to His service."

Hearing this, Kauśalyā gave up her doubts, and became convinced of Bharata's innocence. After lifting Him up, she placed Bharata's head in her lap, crying as she caressed him. Bharata became overwhelmed by His stepmother's grief, and they passed the night together in commiseration.

The next morning, Vasiṣṭha told Bharata to give up His grief and cremate the body of His deceased father. Vasiṣṭha then accompanied Bharata to the cremation site. However, upon seeing the body of Mahārāja Daśaratha being taken from the vat of oil and placed upon an ornamental carrier, Bharata suddenly lost all composure and began sobbing uncontrollably. Vasiṣṭha again urged Bharata to calm Himself so that the funeral rites could be completed.

The procession wound its way to the crematorium. As the people walked before the carrier, they scattered flowers upon the road. Then the body was placed upon the funeral pyre and the fire lit, while *brāhmaṇas* chanted hymns from the Vedas. All of the king's consorts had arrived, riding upon palanquins according to their rank. The sound of their wailing filled the air.

Afterward, everyone went to the banks of the River Sarayū to offer water for the departed soul of Mahārāja Daśaratha. A ten-day contamination period was then observed, and Bharata performed other funeral rituals for two days. At the end of twelve days, Bharata distributed abundant charity to the *brāhmaṇas*.

At dawn on the thirteenth day, Bharata and Śatrughna went to the funeral pyre to collect the remaining bones and ashes so that they could be thrown in the river Sarayū. However, arriving at the crematorium and seeing the king's remains, the brothers again became overwhelmed with grief. Weeping profusely, Bharata and Śatrughna fell to the ground and cried out, "O dear father, where have you gone, leaving Us aside?"

Vasiṣṭha again comforted Bharata, saying, "My dear prince, You must control Yourself so that You can execute Your duties. Collect the bones and ashes of Your father's cremated body. After cleaning the funeral grounds, go to the River Sarayū and throw in the remains. The dualities of life and death, joy and sorrow, gain and loss are experienced by all embodied beings, and are thus unavoidable. Such overindulgence in lamentation does not befit a descendant of the Ikṣvāku dynasty."

Thereafter, the funeral rites were completed, and, returning to His palace, Bharata contemplated going to the forest to bring back Rāma, Sītā and Lakṣmaṇa. Śatrughna then addressed Bharata, "Rāma, who is the well-wisher of everyone, has been exiled to the forest on the whim of a selfish woman. My brother Lakṣmaṇa is certainly condemned. Was there nothing He could do to avert this disaster?"

Just then, the hunchback Mantharā appeared, and although she looked no better than a monkey, her body was smeared with sandalwood paste, and she wore a royal dress and valuable ornaments. Knowing her to be the real cause of Rāma's banishment, the doorman suddenly grabbed

Mantharā by the arm and dragged her before Bharata and Śatrughna, exclaiming, "Here is the wicked witch who incited Kaikeyī to banish Rāma. O Prince, she fanned the flames of jealousy within the Queen's heart, and thus became the murderer of Your father. Take her and punish her as You see fit."

Swelling with a desire for revenge, Śatrughna violently seized Mantharā and began to drag her along the ground. As Mantharā's ornaments broke, scattering jewels here and there, her other hunchbacked companions fled in fear from the furious Śatrughna. Śatrughna then vowed, "I shall now unleash My long held wrath upon both Mantharā and Kaikeyī, so that they will feel as much pain as they have caused others."

As Kaikeyī ran to the shelter of her son, Bharata restrained His younger brother by saying, "Śatrughna, women never deserve to be slain. I would have gladly killed Kaikeyī and Mantharā Myself, but I know Rāma would never have forgiven Me. Therefore, please restrain yourself." Śatrughna relented and released Mantharā, who then ran sobbing to Kaikeyī's feet.

In sparing Mantharā's life, Bharata showed both compassion and commitment to religious principles. Devotees of the Lord, being filled with all good qualities, are always compassionate. Although Mantharā had brought about the cruel banishment of Rāma, Sītā and Lakṣmaṇa, the death of Daśaratha, and great anguish for all the people, Bharata spared her life because of religious principles. Although she disregarded religious principles, they saved her life, just as they save the righteous who follow them.

The next morning, the bards came, eulogizing Bharata in expectation of His becoming king. However, their praises only aggravated His grief, and He ordered them to stop, saying, "I am not the ruler of Ayodhyā."

At that time, Vasiṣṭha, along with his disciples, entered the royal assembly and ordered messengers to summon Bharata, the ministers, the military commanders and other important citizens.

When Bharata arrived, He was cheered with the same enthusiasm previously offered His father. Vasiṣṭha then addressed Bharata as follows: "O Prince, because Rāma and Lakṣmaṇa have been banished to the forest and Your father has expired, life within the kingdom has become disrupted for want of a ruler. We know You are innocent of Kaikeyī's intrigues, and were selected by Mahārāja Daśaratha as his successor. All preparations have been made and the citizens are expectant. Please give Your consent so that we can install You upon the throne this very day."

Bharata became pained to hear this proposal. Restraining His tears, He replied to Vasiṣṭha, "O foremost of *ṛṣis*, you are well aware of our family tradition that the eldest son should assume the throne. I could never think of usurping the throne from Rāma, for I consider Myself to be His menial servant. I want to leave for the forest as soon as possible to persuade Rāma to return to Ayodhyā. If I am unsuccessful, I shall remain with Him like Lakṣmaṇa. Therefore, make ready a formidable army and have engineers construct the necessary roads so that we may proceed without impediment."

Upon hearing Bharata's impassioned plea, tears came to everyone's eyes. Everyone was pleased with His determination. Upon receiving their approval, Bharata also felt great relief, and shed tears of joy.

As news of Bharata's desire spread, everyone became joyful. Thereafter, the ministers summoned many engineers and laborers. Soon a huge work crew left the city to construct a broad highway into the forest. First, the workers cut down the trees and dug up the roots, leveled the ground and filled all the holes. Then they built bridges across the streams, and after paving the highway with concrete mixed with lime, they lined the road with flowering trees. Dams were then constructed to create artificial lakes. When everything was completed, the entire highway, which extended from Ayodhyā to the banks of the Gaṅgā, was sprinkled with sandalwood-scented water. Big tents were pitched at appropriate places to provide rest camps that were surrounded by fences and moats. Thus, the entire pathway, which appeared fit for use by the demigods, was completed in a very short time.

After the construction was thus completed, the citizens felt satisfied. The transforming effects of devotional service to the Lord are truly wonderful. Although previously the people were dejected because of separation from Rāma, they immediately felt relief as soon as they began to serve Him. There is no difference between serving the Lord and seeing the Lord. Indeed, serving Him is the proper way to approach Him. Rather than trying to see the Lord directly, we should serve Him so sincerely that He will want to see us.

The next morning Bharata ordered Sumantra to bring His chariot, and then departed with His huge army. The entire

party, led by Bharata, consisted of sixty thousand chariots driven by charioteers completely devoted to Rāma, a hundred thousand cavalrymen, and nine thousand elephants decorated like lotuses. Kauśalyā, Sumitrā and Kaikeyī also came, riding in separate chariots, hoping to bring Rāma back from the forest. Many other citizens also accompanied Bharata, being delighted at the prospect of seeing Rāma.

The citizens looked like denizens of heavenly planets. They wore their very best clothes with garlands of fragrant flowers, and their bodies were smeared with sandalwood paste. The chariots appeared like celestial airplanes, and the elephants moved inexorably forward, like clouds driven by the wind on a beautiful sunny day.

When the party arrived at the bank of the Gaṅgā, they stopped to spend the night. Bharata took the opportunity to offer libations of Gaṅgā water to His departed father.

When Guha saw Bharata leading a large army into the forest, he suspected that He intended to attack Rāma. Guha, therefore, warned his associates, "We are followers of Rāma, and must be prepared for danger. As a precaution, let one hundred soldiers guard each of our five hundred boats. Then, if necessary, we can prevent Bharata from crossing the Gaṅgā."

Taking many gifts with him, Guha went to meet Bharata, hoping to ascertain His true mentality. When Sumantra saw Guha approaching, he informed Bharata that the Niṣāda king was a friend of Rāma.

When Guha arrived, Bharata extended all hospitality, and inquired of the route to Bharadvāja's *āśrama.* Guha said,

"You can rest assured I shall guide You there so You won't experience the slightest difficulty. But please tell me frankly what Your intentions are for going to see Rāma. Coming with such a large army, it appears You have come to fight with Him."

Bharata replied, "My dear Guha, your accusation gives Me great pain. Please believe Me when I say that I have come just to persuade Rāma to return to Ayodhyā so that He may be installed on the throne."

Then, because night had already fallen, everyone prepared to take rest. Guha then approached Bharata as He lay upon His bed and told Him: "When Rāma came here with Sītā and Lakṣmaṇa, He lay upon a bed that we made from dried leaves. As Rāma and Sītā slept, Lakṣmaṇa and I stayed awake all night talking. Lakṣmaṇa could not bear to accept any comfort as long as Rāma was laying on the bare ground. The next morning, Rāma and Lakṣmaṇa matted Their hair with the sticky extract of a banyan tree and crossed the Gaṅgā."

Hearing that Rāma had matted His hair, Bharata became most aggrieved. He feared that His elder brother would not be willing to return to Ayodhyā. Overwhelmed with apprehension, Bharata suddenly fainted. Kauśalyā, who sat nearby, came to His aid. It was only after one hour that Bharata regained consciousness. When He saw His anxious stepmother, He assured her that His fainting was not caused by hearing anything untoward about Rāma.

At Bharata's urging, Guha continued to describe everything Rāma had done on His way to the forest. Guha then led Bharata, Śatrughna and Their mothers to where Rāma and Sītā had slept. He showed them the *kuśa* grass that

remained crushed by the weight of their bodies. Everyone was very sorry to see this, for they remembered how Rāma used to sleep comfortably, surrounded by royal opulence. Bharata was especially pained, for He considered Himself to be the cause of Sītā, Rāma, and Lakṣmaṇa's suffering. Bharata condemned Himself, and decided to immediately make His hair matted and lie down upon the ground, thus taking Rāma's place in exile.

The next morning, adorned with matted hair and tree bark dress, Bharata requested Guha to assist Him in crossing the Gaṅgā. Thereafter, the entire army of men and horses was taken across on the boats, while the elephants swam the river. After safely reaching the other side, Bharata disembarked, and with Guha's guidance, proceeded for the *āśrama* of Bharadvāja.

When Bharata drew near the great *ṛṣi's* hermitage, He left His army waiting at a distance of two miles, and proceeded on foot with Vasiṣṭha and Śatrughna. When Bharadvāja saw Vasiṣṭha enter his *āśrama,* he quickly rose up to greet him. He proceeded to ask of the welfare of Ayodhyā, wanting to know Bharata's true intentions. The *ṛṣi* said, "O Prince, please tell me what brings You to the forest. I pray You have not come with any intention of harming Rāma."

Bharata was extremely hurt by the *ṛṣi's* words. With tears in His eyes, He replied, "It is painful to see how people doubt My intentions. Please know that I have come to the forest only to try to convince Rāma to return to Ayodhyā so that He can rule the kingdom. O foremost of sages, please be gracious to Me and show Me where Rāma is staying."

Bharadvāja then replied, "O Prince, I already knew Your true mentality by dint of yogic power. I only tested You as a formality. Your elder brother, Rāma, is residing at the Citrakūṭa Mountain. Now please stay here for the night. You can resume Your journey tomorrow."

Bharata accepted Bharadvāja's hospitality. Then the *ṛṣi* requested Him to call for His entire army, wishing to entertain them also. After the soldiers arrived at his *āśrama,* Bharadvāja invoked Viśvakarmā and many other demigods, headed by Indra, Yamarāja, Varuṇa and Kuvera, requesting them to supply all the necessary objects for a first class reception for his guests.

Immediately thereafter, fragrant breezes began to blow, and, as fragrant flowers showered down from the heavens, celestial drums beat, accompanied by the singing of Gandharvas and the dancing of Apsarās. By Viśvakarmā's arrangement, the entire area within a forty mile radius became instantly carpeted with lush parks full of fruit-and-flower-bearing trees. Miraculously, four-room mansions and stables became manifested, as well as a royal palace, complete with every imaginable comfort, furniture, food, clothing and article of enjoyment.

Bharata entered the magnificent palace, accompanied by His priests and ministers. As He approached the royal throne, He meditated upon Rāma as if He were seated there. Thinking in this way, Bharata circumambulated the throne, and then offered obeisances. He then picked up a *cāmara* and sat in the seat intended for the chief minister, as everyone else took their respective places.

Meanwhile, by utilizing his mystic power, Bharadvāja created a river of sweet rice that flowed through his *āśrama*. Lord Brahmā and Kuvera each sent 20,000 women whose embrace caused a man to appear as if seized by a fit of madness. The chiefs of the Gandharvas came to sing of Rāma's glories for Bharata, and celestial trees were summoned by Bharadvāja to accompany them on various musical instruments.

While Bharata was thus being entertained, the soldiers were hardly neglected. Celestial girls sang to them with sweet voices and urged them to drink wine and eat sweet rice. Seven or eight girls were engaged in rubbing oil over each man's body and then bathing them with water. Other girls massaged the warriors' feet, while giving them wine in a secluded place. Even the horses were fed grains dipped in honey. When the men became intoxicated, they exclaimed, "This is heaven! We no longer want to continue our journey to the forest or return to Ayodhyā."

In this way, the soldiers became satiated with all manner of enjoyment in the company of the celestial damsels. Indeed, thousands of soldiers were seen running here and there while singing, laughing and dancing. Everyone was so amazed by the entertainment that it appeared to them as if they were enjoying a delightful dream. The night seemed to swiftly pass away.

With the appearance of dawn, the Gandharvas, Apsarās and celestial trees took their leave from Bharadvāja and returned to their respective abodes.

Bharata then took His mothers and approached Bharadvāja, asking him for directions to Citrakūṭa. Bharadvāja saw that one woman of the party appeared emaciated from grief. Just then another woman clasped his feet to offer respects, while a third stood with her head hung in shame. Seeing his concern, Bharata explained, "This is Kauśalyā, the senior widow of my father. This is Sumitrā, the mother of Lakṣmaṇa and Śatrughna. This other woman, who is vulgar, cruel, conceited and sinful, is Kaikeyī. Being the cause of Rāma's exile, she is the cause of all our present miseries."

Bharadvāja then told Bharata, "You should not consider Your mother to be actually guilty. There is a higher purpose behind Rāma's banishment to the forest. Thus, it is meant for the welfare and happiness of all living entities."

Thereafter, Bharata circumambulated Bharadvāja Ṛṣi and commanded his army to depart. As the regiments of infantry, horses, chariots and elephants marched forward, all the forest animals fled out of fear.

Finally, when Citrakūṭa Mountain was in view, Bharata commanded his sentries to look for Rāma's cottage. Some soldiers then saw a column of smoke rising in the distance, and excitedly informed Bharata. After ordering the army to set up camp, Bharata approached the cottage of Rāma on foot along with Vasiṣṭha, Sumantra and several others.

Having resided at Citrakūṭa for three months, Rāma was passing His time with Sītā, sitting on a big rock at the foot of the hill. Rāma was describing to Sītā the various roots that the *ṛṣis* ate, and pointed out the varieties of trees, flowers and wild animals that abounded there. Rāma always tried

His best to please Sītā and divert her mind from the grief of living in exile. While speaking to Sītā, Rāma pointed to the River Mandākinī, adorned with beautiful flowers, which served as the sporting ground for swans, cranes and other exotic birds. "Truly, O dear one," Rāma said, "there is no reason for us to be aggrieved, for we are residing together in this lovely place."

At just this time, Rāma noticed the dust being raised by Bharata's army coming in the far distance. Soon Rāma could hear the noises of the wild animals that were fleeing in fear. At this Rāma turned to Lakṣmaṇa and said, "Whatever is raising the dust is frightening the forest animals. Find out at once what is causing this disturbance."

Lakṣmaṇa then climbed a tall tree, and from there He could see the large army approaching. With great urgency He called down to Rāma, "Put out the fire immediately. A great army is approaching. Hide Sītā within a cave and gather Our weapons. We must prepare to meet them."

Rāma then called back to His brother, "Look out to see their chariot flags so We may know whose army is coming."

By the insignias, Lakṣmaṇa recognized that it was His brother's army, and shouted to Rāma, "It is Bharata! He must be coming to kill Us so He can be assured of enjoying unrivaled sovereignty. Indeed, they approach with great enthusiasm. We must make ready immediately, taking our bows to fight with them from the top of the hill. I think this is Our good fortune, for now we can fight with the person who has caused Our misfortune and suffering. We should not hesitate to kill Bharata outright. Afterwards I shall take

pleasure in killing Kaikeyī and all her relatives, just to purge the earth of the sins she has committed."

Checking the enraged Lakṣmaṇa, Rāma said, "Bharata is coming here in great eagerness to see Me. What, then, is the necessity of bows and arrows? My opinion is that Bharata has come to offer Me the kingdom. However, if You wish to kill Bharata so You may enjoy the royal throne Yourself, then say so, and I will tell Bharata to hand it over peacefully."

Thus admonished by Rāma, Lakṣmaṇa hung His head in shame, saying, "I was hoping Our father had come to see Us. However, since his familiar elephant is visible, though bereft of its usual white umbrella, I do not think he has."

Lakṣmaṇa then climbed down from the tree, and returned to the cottage with Rāma and Sītā. At this time Bharata entered the forest surrounding Citrakūṭa Mountain. When Bharata again spotted the column of smoke, He proceeded in that direction, hoping it would lead to Rāma's cottage.

As Bharata hastened there, Guha, Śatrughna and others followed, while Vasiṣṭha brought the three mothers. Finally, Bharata came to a clearing in the forest and saw the cottage with the gold plated bows of Rāma and Lakṣmaṇa, and a sacrificial altar in front.

When Bharata saw Rāma, He rushed forward with tears in His eyes, crying, "O Rāma! How painful it is seeing You with matted hair and clothing made of tree bark, and Your lotus feet pricked by the thorns in the forest! It is My fault that You cannot enjoy the royal comforts You are accustomed to, and instead must endure these hardships in the jungle!"

Coming forward to touch Rāma's feet, Bharata suddenly fainted and fell to the ground. Rāma quickly lifted Him up, and was disturbed to see that He was also wearing tree bark. After embracing Śatrughna, who had also fallen at His feet, Rāma embraced Sumantra and Guha. Then Rāma took Bharata on His lap, saying, "Dear brother, why have You come here, leaving Our father alone and unattended? Tell Me about Our mothers and the citizens of Ayodhyā. Are they all well and happy?"[6]

Rāma then inquired from Bharata in a way that was instructive to all present: "My dear Bharata, please know that a righteous kingdom will surely prosper. Are the *brāhmaṇas*, the elders and the demigods being properly respected? Are the women within the kingdom honored and protected? Are disputes being impartially judged? I hope You are avoiding the fourteen weaknesses of a king—atheism, hypocrisy, anger, procrastination, laziness, slavery to the senses, contempt for good advice, lack of vigilance, fondness for bad council, impractical planning, inability to keep a secret, attachment for foolish friends, negligence of religious observances, and failure to counteract enemies.

"My dear brother, are You aware of the three kinds of prowess: energy, authority and intelligence? Do You avoid

6. Śrila Prabhupāda explains: "The lotus feet of the Lord are always a subject matter for meditation for devotees. Sometimes when Lord Rāmacandra wandered in the forest of Daṇḍakāraṇya, thorns pricked His lotus feet. The devotees, upon thinking of this, would faint. The Lord does not feel pain or pleasure from any action or reaction of this material world, but the devotees cannot tolerate even the pricking of the Lord's lotus feet by a thorn."

the following four types of company: the gossipy, the foul-mouthed, the usurper of property and the unjust? Do You avoid making alliances with these sixteen kings: the child monarch, the senile, the frail and ill, those who have been overthrown, the overly aggressive, the cowardly, the greedy, the sensualist, the frivolous, those who are defeated in battle, those who frequently travel abroad, those with many enemies, those who are poverty stricken, those opposed to religious principles, those who are despised by their ministers, and the mentally disturbed?

"I hope you prefer to keep the company of one learned man rather than thousands of ignorant fools. One talented minister can give one immense benefit, whereas in times of necessity, thousands of fools can do nothing. O Bharata, if a king does not get rid of a physician who is simply adept at aggravating a disease, a servant who is intent upon bringing disgrace to his master, or a warrior who wants to become ruler himself, then they will surely kill him.

"Are the women protected and honored by You? Are they pacified with regard to their material needs? I hope that You do not place too much faith in women or confide Your secrets to them."

While observing Bharata's matted hair and forest clothing, Rāma could understand that He had accepted these austerities out of love for Him. Thus, after again embracing Bharata, Rāma inquired, "My dear brother, why have You relinquished the throne, coming to the forest dressed as a mendicant?"

Bharata replied, "O Rāma, My mother's intrigues were carried out without My knowledge. I know You are the rightful heir. Thus, I implore You to return to Ayodhyā and take up the rule of the kingdom. Practically the whole of Ayodhyā has come to a standstill, for everyone is morose because of Your absence."

While making His impassioned plea, Bharata held the lotus feet of Śrī Rāma, placing them on His head. Rāma then picked up Bharata, saying, "I know You took no part in banishing Me to the forest. Still, I have no desire to gain the throne by sinful means. O Bharata, You should not condemn Your mother or the king, for they were both acting within the bounds of propriety. Indeed, elders are free to do as they like with their dependents. Therefore, You should accept the royal throne and rule the kingdom. That was the desire of Your father. I am determined to spend fourteen years in the forest, for I consider the father's order to be the supreme religious principle."

Bharata, however, objected, saying, "In the presence of an elder prince, no one else can become the king. Therefore, You must come back to Ayodhyā and sit upon the royal throne, after offering water to the departed soul of Our father."

When He heard of His father's death, Rāma immediately fainted to the ground. Only when Sītā, Lakṣmaṇa and Śatrughna sprinkled water on His body did He regain consciousness. Then, after tearfully lamenting the loss of His father, Rāma declared, "Now I shall never return to Ayodhyā."

Although He appeared to lament like an ordinary man, in truth, Rāma remained transcendental. The Lord, His body, and His pastimes are never ordinary or material. In *Bhagavad-gītā,* Lord Kṛṣṇa proclaims that simply by understanding the transcendental nature of His appearance, activities, and disappearance, one can become liberated from the cycle of birth and death.

Lord Kṛṣṇa displayed a similar reaction when informed by the demon Śālva that His father Vasudeva had been killed. At that time, He almost fell unconscious from grief. Why do Lord Rāma and Lord Kṛṣṇa appear at times to be bewildered, although They are both the same Supreme Personality of Godhead? Lamentation and bewilderment characterize a conditioned soul. How can they be present in God, Who is full in all opulences, including knowledge and power? This is a controversial point. Factually, the Lord is never misled or illusioned. When playing the role of a human being, He presents Himself as a complete human being, exhibiting all the emotions of an ordinary man. All great sages who render the Lord transcendental loving service are liberated from the bodily conception. How, then, could the Lord Himself fall under illusion by identifying the soul with the body? Clearly, His grief is but another opulence, another facet of His supreme, unlimited, and inconceivable personality.

Thereafter, Rāma went to the banks of the Mandākinī Gaṅgā with His brothers and Sumantra to offer water for the benefit of his father. Then, upon returning to His cottage atop the Citrakūṭa Mountain, Rāma clasped the hands of His brothers, and all four of Them wailed in grief.

This loud sound reverberated through the valley. When Bharata's army heard the sound, they became aggrieved, for they knew it to be the brothers' lamentation for Their departed father. All the soldiers then rushed toward the sound, for they too, were anxious to see Rāma. When they reached the cottage, the warriors greeted Rāma with tears in

their eyes. In turn, Rāma welcomed each of them according to their position.

Meanwhile, while keeping the three widows of King Daśaratha in front, Vasiṣṭha hastened to see Rāma. When Vasiṣṭha and the widows arrived at the banks of the Mandākinī Gaṅgā, they saw the remnants of articles used as an offering by Rāma for His departed father. Kauśalyā was pained to see that the only food Rāma had at His disposal for an offering was the pulp of a forest fruit. Kauśalyā considered this unworthy for her husband, and with some amusement she thought, "This is the truth of the adage, 'The deities a man worships have to partake of the same food upon which he subsists.'"

When Vasiṣṭha and the three widows arrived at Rāma's cottage, they were distressed to see Him. He looked like a demigod that had fallen from heaven. Rāma quickly stood up and went to touch the feet of His mothers. Then, as He bowed before them, the three women wiped the dust from Rāma's back. Likewise, with tears in their eyes, Sītā and Lakṣmaṇa touched the feet of the mothers. Kauśalyā embraced Sītā while Rāma approached Vasiṣṭha to touch his feet. Rāma then sat down with His preceptor, as others also came around them. Bharata then told Rāma, "I want to return the kingdom of Kosala to You."

Although everyone present applauded this proposal, Rāma replied, "My dear Bharata, in this material world, no one can act independently. Under the control of eternal Time, everything ultimately meets with defeat. Thus, no wise man should lament for life's reversals. Union ends in separation, for as pieces of driftwood float together and

then disperse, family and society meet briefly and then depart for their separate destinations. As solid pillars gradually decay, causing a house to collapse, a man totters into old age and finally meets death. As a river cannot return to its source, everyone must follow the path of his father and forefathers. Why should one mourn for others when he himself is dying? A man's skin becomes wrinkled and his hair turns gray. What can he do? He rejoices when the sun rises and rejoices when it sets, not thinking he has died a little.

A sober and learned person should utilize his energy for following religious principles to attain a higher destination after death. There is no need to lament for Our father, for he has given up an old body to attain heavenly happiness. Bharata, You must return to Ayodhyā at once and execute Our father's order. I will remain here to carry out his will."

Bharata argued, "Our noble father had become too infatuated with women in his old age. Indeed, he seemed to confirm the popular notion that at the time of death one invariably becomes obsessed by something. Rāma, You should undo the harm that Our father caused due to that obsession and return to Ayodhyā. You are a *kṣatriya*, and Your duty is to act as a ruler, not as a hermit. You are a householder, the noblest of the four *āśramas*. Why are You abandoning the duties of family life? If You refuse to return to Ayodhyā, then so shall I. I will remain here in the forest with You, like Lakṣmaṇa."

Rāma replied, "Dear Bharata, you are wrongly criticizing Our father, saying he was impelled by lusty attachment for

Kaikeyī. At the time of Daśaratha's marriage to Kaikeyī, her father made him promise that her son would succeed him as emperor. Bharata, please go back to Ayodhyā now to keep Our father's promise intact. You must take the responsibility of ruling the kingdom, even if it is only for My sake."

Next the great *ṛṣi* named Jābāli began to speak. With the hope of inspiring within Rāma some desire to enjoy royal opulence and sense gratification, thus causing Him to return to Ayodhyā, Jābāli expounded the following atheistic philosophy: "O Prince, the living being is nothing more than the resultant combination of sperm and ovum. The father is the efficient cause of the living being and the mother is the material cause. But in reality, the only cause of creation is the chance interaction of atomic particles. When a person dies, he once more becomes dust. Thus, everything is only a combination of atoms and nothing more. What we call mother, father, son or daughter has no actual relationship with us. Rāma, why should You undergo suffering, just for the sake of Your so-called father? What is the use of performing funeral ceremonies? Can the dead eat your offerings? Only what we can directly perceive is the all-in-all. Therefore, my dear Rāma, You should enjoy that which is pleasing to the senses by accepting the kingdom from Bharata."

Hearing this diatribe, Rāma angrily replied, "Your views are impiety in the garb of piety. Thus, they are most dangerous. In the name of wisdom, you are preaching the grossest ignorance. Real knowledge leads to self-realization, whereas one who lives only for the pleasure of the senses becomes a slave to uncontrolled lust and greed. Truth is the highest principle of virtue. Thus, I will adhere to the

order of My father without being swayed by the aspiration for personal sense gratification.

"This earth is the field of action. When one attains the rarely achieved human birth, he should only perform pious activities. My father made a mistake by keeping you as a minister, because your views are atheistic. A non-believer like yourself is so condemned that the Vedas prohibit one from even seeing his face."

Jābāli then admitted, "In truth, I am a follower of the Vedas. I have firm faith in the existence of God. I was only speaking from that viewpoint in hope of persuading You to return to Ayodhyā."

At that, Vasiṣṭha intervened, since Rāma had become highly agitated by Jābāli's speech. "Jābāli spoke like an atheist only because he knew how much everyone wants You to return to Ayodhyā to sit on the throne. In the dynasty of Ikṣvāku, every great ruler of the past selected their eldest son to inherit the kingdom. The unbroken rule has been that for as long as the elder brother is alive, the younger brother cannot accept the throne. Therefore, we again implore You to return to Ayodhyā. You should consider that to deny my order would be an irreligious act. The instructions of the guru take precedence over those given by the mother or father."

Rāma, however, remained adamant, insisting that one's duty to his parents is inviolable. When Bharata realized that His attempt to persuade Rāma was futile, He became so sad that He ordered Sumantra, "Spread *kuśa* grass in front of the doorway of Rāma's cottage. I will sit there blindfolded,

foregoing all food and drink until Rāma relents and accepts the royal throne."

Sumantra, however, would not act without Rāma's order. Thus, Bharata spread the *kuśa* grass with His own hands and sat down in front of Rāma's cottage.

Rāma then said, "Dear brother, why are You adopting this attitude? Why are You stubbornly trying to oppose Me?"

Thus addressed, Bharata gave up the idea of fasting until death, but continued pleading, "Let me act as Your proxy by staying here in the forest for fourteen years while You return to Ayodhyā."

Just then a host of celestial *ṛṣis* appeared invisibly in the sky and applauded the wonderful conversation between the two brothers. Then, desiring to accelerate the death of Rāvaṇa, the *ṛṣis* said, "O Bharata, You should follow the advice of Your elder brother, Rāma."

Finally surrendering to the inevitable, Bharata produced a pair of wooden sandals inlaid with gold. He then requested Rāma to place His lotus feet on them. Rāma did as His brother asked, and then returned the sandals to Bharata. Then, with the sandals in hand, Bharata bowed to Rāma, saying, "After relegating the burden of ruling the kingdom to these sandals, I will remain outside Ayodhyā, wearing matted hair and clothing of tree bark. O Rāma, I shall subsist upon only fruit and roots while awaiting Your return. If, however, after fourteen years You do not come back to Ayodhyā, then I shall give up my life by entering fire."

Rāma sanctioned this statement and then embraced Bharata and Śatrughna, assuring Them He would return after the term of His exile had expired. With tears in His eyes, Rāma bid farewell to His brothers and urged Them not to neglect or hate Kaikeyī. Rāma then spoke sweet words to His mothers, although they were too upset to reply. Bharata then circumambulated Rāma, and at last, while imploring everyone to leave for Ayodhyā, Rāma turned His back and entered the cottage.

Placing Rāma's sandals upon His head, Bharata mounted His chariot. Along with Śatrughna, they set out, keeping the *brāhmaṇas* in front. When they arrived at the *āśrama* of Bharadvāja, the sage inquired whether Bharata had seen Rāma and if He had accomplished His mission. Bharata replied that Rāma was determined to observe His term of exile.

Vasiṣṭha brought forth Rāma's wooden sandals and requested Bharadvāja to empower them with the potency to fulfill the needs of the people of Ayodhyā. This was ceremoniously done by Bharadvāja, and thereafter Bharata clasped the *ṛṣi's* feet and took permission to depart.

Returning by the same path He previously followed, Bharata finally arrived at the outskirts of Ayodhyā. When He saw the city's desolate appearance, He said to Sumantra, "Without Rāma Ayodhyā has no life, just as the material body remains inert as soon as the living force passes out of it."

Upon entering Daśaratha's palace, Bharata broke down and cried, seeing its desolate appearance. Bharata then announced that He would retire to Nandīgrāma to live

as an ascetic. As the ministers praised His noble determination, Bharata called for His chariot and departed with Śatrughna. Out of spontaneous affection, all Ayodhyā's citizens followed Bharata to Nandīgrāma, a village just outside Ayodhyā.

Upon His arrival, Bharata first ordered His ministers to install Rāma's shoes upon a royal throne. Thereafter, remaining at Nandīgrāma with His army, Bharata submitted the state's affairs before Rāma's shoes, including all gifts presented to Him.

Bharata would often be seen holding the royal umbrella over Rāma's shoes, or fanning them with a *cāmara.* In this way, He ruled the kingdom for fourteen years, always feeling subordinate to Lord Rāma, who remained there in the form of His shoes.

Meanwhile, Rāma noticed that there was anxiety within the minds of the *ṛṣis* living in the vicinity of Citrakūṭa Mountain. Feeling that He might be the cause, Rāma humbly approached the chief *ṛṣi* and said, "I can see that something is disturbing the minds of the *ṛṣis* living here. Please tell me why, if you can, especially if I am at fault."

The old *ṛṣi* replied, "My dear Rāma, there could never be any fault on Your part. Our fear is caused by the Rākṣasas, headed by Khara, the younger brother of Rāvaṇa. Being envious by nature, Khara and the other Rākṣasas come before us in hideous forms and disrupt our sacrifices and pollute our bodies with impure substances. We shall move to another area before the Rākṣasas resort to violence. I plan to take my disciples to the *āśrama* of Aśva Muni, not far from here. If You like, You may also accompany me and take up residence there."

Rāma gave the *ṛṣi* permission to depart, but informed him that He would remain at Citrakūṭa. Later on, however, Rāma felt uncomfortable about staying there, since the memory of Bharata and His mothers haunted Him. Rāma also felt that the area had become contaminated by the stool of the horses and elephants of Bharata's army. Thus, He finally made up His mind to go elsewhere.

Rāma, Sītā and Lakṣmaṇa thus left Citrakūṭa for the *āśrama* of Atri Muni, where they were received affectionately, as if they were the *ṛṣi's* own children. When Atri called for his aged wife, Anasūyā, to welcome Sītā, the eternal consort of Lord Rāma approached the ascetic woman with great humility. Having greeted that hermitess, who was endowed with self-restraint, Sītā, full of joy, inquired after her health with joined palms.

Seeing the highly blessed and celebrated Sītā, who was given to the practice of virtue, the old lady thereupon comfortingly said to her, "Luckily enough you have your eyes fixed on righteousness. O Sītā, I am glad you are following your husband Śrī Rāma, who has been exiled to the forest. Worlds that are attended with great prosperity await those women to whom their husband is dear, no matter whether he lives in a city or in a forest, whether he is propitious or adverse. In the eyes of women who are blessed with a noble disposition the husband is the highest deity, no matter whether he is ill-mannered or licentious or entirely devoid of riches. I do not see for a woman a friend greater than the husband and more capable of yielding one's desired object at all places like the imperishable fruit of one's austerities, O princess of the Videha kingdom! Those evil women, however, whose hearts are swayed by desire, who lord it over their husband, having no sense of virtue and vice, and move about at will, do not follow him in the aforesaid manner. Indeed, fallen a prey to lust, women who belong to that category, O princess of Mithilā, meet with a fall from virtue and also reap infamy. Women like you, on the other hand, who are adorned with virtues like devotion to their

husband, and who know what is good and evil in the world, will dwell in heaven in the same way as those who have performed meritorious deeds. Therefore, remaining devoted to the service of this prince, looking upon Him as the foremost object of your worship and carefully serving Him, practice virtue in co-operation with your husband. Thereby you will easily attain fame as well as religious merit."

Appreciating Anasūyā's words, Sītā modestly replied as follows: "This instruction which you have given to me is no matter for wonder on your holiness' part. It is, however, already known to me how the husband is the adored of a chaste wife. Even if this husband of mine were ignoble and without any means of livelihood, I ought to have nonetheless conducted myself in the same way without any hesitation or scruple towards him: this was my duty. How much more worthy of devotion then is He who is deserving of praise by virtue of his excellences and excellent qualities headed by compassion, who has controlled His senses, who is constant in His love, whose mind is set on righteousness and who is as loving as a mother and father combined! Śrī Rāma, who is possessed of great might, conducted Himself towards the other consorts of the king (His stepmothers) in the same way as He did towards Kauśalyā (His own mother).

"Whatever was taught to me by my mother-in law while I was coming to the lonely forest stands inscribed on my heart. Nay, that lesson too which was actually imparted to me in the past by my mother while making over my hand (to the bridegroom at the time of marriage) in the presence of the sacred fire is still remembered by me. All that teaching has actually been renewed in my mind by your teachings,

O lady given to the practice of virtue! No austerity other than the service of her husband is enjoined on a wife. Steadfast in their vow of fidelity to their husbands, many exalted women are highly respected in the realm of gods by dint of their meritorious action."

Being pleased with Sītā, Anasūyā then said, "My dear child, I wish to offer you a benediction, using my ample stock of ascetic merit. Just tell me what you would like."

Sītā replied, "O great saintly lady, your presence is itself a most sufficient benediction."

Nevertheless, Anasūyā happily gave Sītā a celestial garland that never faded, celestial garments, ornaments and cosmetics that were all inexhaustible. Then, when Anasūyā requested her to narrate the story of her marriage to Rāma, Sītā replied as follows: "While my father, King Janaka, was once plowing the soil to prepare a sacrificial altar, I suddenly emerged from the earth, covered with dust. A celestial voice then announced that I should be accepted by the childless king. Thus, I was raised as the daughter of Mahārāja Janaka. Then, as I approached puberty, my father became anxious, since he could not find a suitable husband for such a divinely born girl. Finally, he decided to hold a *svayaṁvara*, wherein I would be allowed to marry anyone who could string the bow of Lord Śiva, given by Varuṇa to our ancestor, Devarāta.

"However, even the greatest of kings failed to lift the bow, what to speak of stringing it. However, Rāma arrived at Mithilā, along with Viśvāmitra, and He easily broke the bow in two after stringing it. But Rāma would not accept me as His wife until He received permission from His father,

Mahārāja Daśaratha. Thus, it was only after the arrival of the Kosala king that the marriage ceremony was performed."

After Sītā had told the story, and evening was approaching, Anasūyā requested Sītā to attend to her husband, after adorning herself with her newly acquired jewels. Rāma was pleased to see Sītā so exquisitely decorated, and that night they slept at Atri Ṛṣi's *āśrama*. The next morning, Rāma inquired from the *ṛṣi* about the path leading to the Daṇḍakāraṇya forest. The sage then gave Rāma directions, and warned Him, "That forest is infested with fierce and malicious Rākṣasas. They take pleasure in devouring anyone living there that neglects to rinse his mouth after eating or drinking, or who is inattentive in following any other religious injunction."

Thereafter, Rāma took leave of the *ṛṣi* and, accompanied by Sītā and Lakṣmaṇa, entered the dense forest, like the moon entering a mass of dark clouds.

Araṇya-kāṇḍa

As Rāma, Sītā and Lakṣmaṇa approached the Daṇḍakāraṇya forest, they beheld a delightful cluster of cottages inhabited by *ṛṣis*. Surrounded by towering trees laden with fruit and flowers, and resounding with the singing of birds and the chanting of Vedic mantras, the *āśrama* sanctified the hearts of all who beheld it. *Kuśa* grass and garments made of tree bark were spread everywhere, and deer and other wild animals roamed about freely without fear.

Rāma and Lakṣmaṇa loosened the strings on their bows and entered the hermitage. The *ṛṣis* greeted them pleasantly, and gave them a suitable grass hut to reside in. Then, after passing the night, Rāma took His leave from the sages and ventured even deeper into the forest, with Sītā walking in the middle, and Lakṣmaṇa behind.

As they walked along, a gigantic, hideous Rākṣasa suddenly appeared before them. Clad in a bloodstained tiger skin, he had sunken eyes, long sharp teeth, a jagged jaw, and a large, round protruding belly. From his spear dangled the heads of three lions, four tigers, two wolves, ten spotted deer and an elephant, all dripping with blood.

Appearing like death personified, the horrible monster roared ferociously and lunged forward, catching hold of Sītā. Then, after quickly retreating some distance, the Rākṣasa again roared loudly, "I shall take this woman for my wife and drink the blood of You other two."

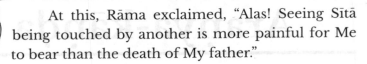

At this, Rāma exclaimed, "Alas! Seeing Sītā being touched by another is more painful for Me to bear than the death of My father."

Lakṣmaṇa, however, was in no mood for such talk. He reproached Rāma, saying, "How can You merely stand there, lamenting? Watch Me as I kill this Rākṣasa, and vent the anger I have held toward Bharata for so long."

The Rākṣasa called out, "Who are You, intruding into my forest?"

Rāma replied, "We are two *kṣatriyas*. Why do you dare obstruct Us like this, carrying off My wife?"

To this the Rākṣasa said, "My name is Viradha. I am the son of Java by his second wife Śatahrada. In reward for my severe austerities, Lord Brahmā benedicted me to become immune from all weapons. Therefore, I advise You to run away while You can, and leave this lovely woman for me. Otherwise, I will be forced to kill You."

At that Rāma and Lakṣmaṇa quickly took up Their swords and rushed at the Rākṣasa. However, even though They severely hacked his body, the wounded Rākṣasa picked up Rāma and Lakṣmaṇa in his arms and began carrying Them away, deep into the forest. Upon seeing this, Sītā cried out piteously, "O Rākṣasa, please leave these two aside and take me instead."

Hearing this, Rāma and Lakṣmaṇa decided to kill Viradha at once. Exhibiting super-human prowess, Rāma broke off the Rākṣasa's right arm while Lakṣmaṇa wrenched off his left. As Viradha fell to the ground, bereft of his senses, Rāma

and Lakṣmaṇa continued to beat him with Their fists. However, in spite of being smashed and kicked, the Rākṣasa did not die. Seeing this, Rāma told Lakṣmaṇa, "Since this demon cannot be slain in battle, let Us bury him alive. Quickly dig a pit while I guard him."

As Lakṣmaṇa dug, Viradha regained consciousness, and said to Rāma, "I now recognize You. In truth I am the Gandharva, Tumburu. Because of lusting after the Apsarā, Rambhā, I was cursed by Kuvera to become a Rākṣasa until a time that I would be delivered by You. Please bury me in this hole to release me from my curse. Thereafter, please go to meet the great *ṛṣi* Sarabhaṅga, who resides twelve miles from here. When You see him he will give You some very beneficial advice."

Lakṣmaṇa continued digging while Rāma kept His foot on the Rākṣasa's neck. Then, when Lakṣmaṇa had finished, Rāma threw the screaming demon deep into the hole and quickly covered him up with large stones. In this way, Tumburu gave up his Rākṣasa body and ascended to heaven, relieved of his curse.

Formerly, even great demons like Viradha were intelligent enough to understand that they were not the body but eternal spirit souls transmigrating from one body to another. Today, due to the influence of the age of Kali, even great scholars and religionists cannot understand this truth. In this age, people are short-lived, unintelligent, unfortunate and not philosophically inclined.

Therefore, Lord Caitanya has shown His special mercy by delivering the easiest and most sublime method of self-realization; the chanting of the Hare Kṛṣṇa *mahā-mantra*—Hare Kṛṣṇa, Hare Kṛṣṇa, Kṛṣṇa Kṛṣṇa, Hare Hare/ Hare Rāma, Hare Rāma, Rāma Rāma, Hare Hare—by which one immediately contacts the Lord and qualifies himself to ascend to the spiritual world and live in eternal bliss with Him.

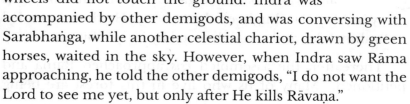

Rāma, Lakṣmaṇa and Sītā set out to see the great sage Sarabhaṅga. As they approached the *ṛṣi's āśrama,* they were amazed to see King Indra, seated upon a celestial chariot whose wheels did not touch the ground. Indra was accompanied by other demigods, and was conversing with Sarabhaṅga, while another celestial chariot, drawn by green horses, waited in the sky. However, when Indra saw Rāma approaching, he told the other demigods, "I do not want the Lord to see me yet, but only after He kills Rāvaṇa."

Indra ascended to the sky on his chariot drawn by 1,000 horses. Having witnessed this wonder, Sītā, Rāma and Lakṣmaṇa quickly went and touched Sarabhaṇga's feet. Then, after being welcomed by the *ṛṣi*, Rāma said, "O foremost of sages, if you are able to discuss the matter, please tell us the purpose of Indra's visit."

Sarabhaṅga replied, "Indra came here to take me to Brahmaloka, the destination I have earned by my performance of severe penances. However, I told the king of heaven that before departing from this world I wanted to see You, knowing that You were nearby."

Rāma requested Sarabhaṅga to designate a place for Him to dwell during the period of His exile. The *ṛṣi* replied, "O Lord, You should approach the great sage Sutīkṣṇa. He will provide You with a suitable residence in a most pleasant portion of the forest. O Rāma, as for myself, I have one request I beg You to fulfill. The time has come for me to quit my body. Therefore, I humbly request that I may do so in Your presence."

Saying this, Sarabhaṅga built a fire, and when he poured ghee upon it, the fire blazed brightly. Then, while chanting mantras, the *ṛṣi* entered the fire, burning his body to ashes. Immediately afterward, Sarabhaṅga rose from the fire in a youthful, dazzlingly effulgent body. He then ascended to Brahmaloka, and was welcomed by its inhabitants.

Thereafter, the assembled *ṛṣis* approached Rāma and petitioned, "Many of us who live in this forest are being

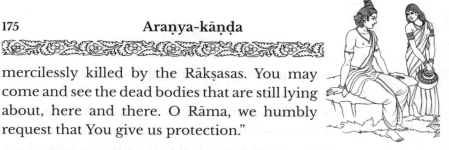

mercilessly killed by the Rākṣasas. You may come and see the dead bodies that are still lying about, here and there. O Rāma, we humbly request that You give us protection."

Rāma assured the *ṛṣis*, "As a *kṣatriya*, I am your servant. Thus, for your sake, I will kill the Rākṣasas."

Accompanied by the sages, Rāma proceeded to the *āśrama* of Sutīkṣṇa. After receiving Rāma's obeisances, the *ṛṣi* said, "I have been awaiting Your visit. O descendent in the dynasty of Raghu, before ascending to Brahmaloka, King Indra came here and informed me of Your imminent arrival." When Rāma asked the *ṛṣi* to designate a place for Him to reside, the *ṛṣi* offered Him the use of his own cottage. Rāma refused, however, saying, "If we were to remain here, by killing the deer we would become the cause of your unhappiness."

Rāma, Sītā and Lakṣmaṇa spent the night at Sutīkṣṇa's *āśrama.* The next morning, Rāma took His leave, bowing before the great sage. Sutīkṣṇa embraced Rāma, inviting Him to return to his *āśrama* after visiting the different hermitages in the Daṇḍakāraṇya forest.

Later that day, hoping to tactfully impart some advice to Rāma, Sītā said, "My dear husband, due to the powerful influence of material nature it is possible even for a great and noble man to gradually become degraded. Therefore, one should always be very careful to control his mind and senses, avoiding the addictions that result from material desire.

"There are three sinful activities that should especially be avoided: false speech, sexual relations with another's wife, and cruelty toward those who are not inimical. In Your character there is no trace of the first two faults, for You have

never uttered a lie, nor could You think of lusting after another man's wife. However, I see that You take the lives of many innocent animals. Thus, I can understand that there is still the contamination of enmity in You. I feel very unhappy when I see how the poor animals are being needlessly killed. My dear Rāma, simply by carrying a bow in Your hands You increase the killing propensity, just as putting fuel too near a fire makes it blaze higher.

"Please listen as I relate a story in this connection. Once, there was a great *ṛṣi* who performed such powerful austerities that King Indra became afraid of being overthrown. With a desire to obstruct the *ṛṣi's* advancement, King Indra came before him in the guise of a warrior. Indra handed the *brāhmaṇa* a sword, and requested, 'Please keep this for me very carefully until I return for it.' The *ṛṣi* consented, and thereafter, remaining true to his vow, he always kept the sword with him, even when he went into the forest to collect fruits and roots. As a result, the *ṛṣi's* mind gradually became tinged with the desire for cruelty. He gradually gave up his execution of austerities in exchange for a life of violence. In this way, the *ṛṣi* became degraded and attained a hellish destination after death.

"Therefore, my dear husband, since that *brāhmaṇa* was vanquished simply by the association of Indra's sword, I request that You keep Your bow in hand only to kill the Rākṣasas that are harassing the *ṛṣis*. Please do not kill even the innocent Rākṣasas, what to speak of other creatures.

"Although I know it is not my position to instruct You, I pray that You give my words careful thought. Afterwards, please do what You think is best."

Rāma replied, "Dear Sītā, I certainly appreciate your words, which are full of wisdom. I know that it is only because you love Me that you have thus advised Me, thinking only of My welfare. Unless one is dear, he is never given such frank counsel. O daughter of Janaka, the *ṛṣis* could easily kill the Rākṣasas themselves. However, they do not do so, for it would diminish their stock of acquired ascetic merit. For this reason I have promised to kill all the Rākṣasas in the Daṇḍakāraṇya forest. Even if I were to somehow renounce you or Lakṣmaṇa, I could never give up a promise to the *brāhmaṇas*."

Rāma, Sītā and Lakṣmaṇa arrived at a large beautiful lake. As they drew near, they heard the sound of singing, seeming to come from somewhere within the lake's waters. However, no one could be seen there. At that time a *ṛṣi* named Dharmabhṛta happened by, and Rāma asked him about the mysterious singing.

"This lake," the *ṛṣi* began, "is known as Pañcāpsarā, and was originally created by the sage Mandakarṇi with his mystic power. Once, Mandakarṇi Ṛṣi performed austerities on the shore of this lake for 10,000 years, subsisting only on air. The demigods became very fearful, thinking the *ṛṣi* was desirous of occupying one of their posts. Thus, they deputed five Apsarās to divert Mandakarṇi from his austerities. The *ṛṣi* indeed became captivated by the women, and married them all. After this the *ṛṣi* created a secret house within the water, and retired there to reside with his wives. The sound You are hearing is the music of the Apsarās. Even today they constantly serve the *ṛṣi*, who has regained his youth by utilizing his ascetic prowess."

Rāma, Sītā and Lakṣmaṇa went on, wandering from *āśrama* to *āśrama* within the Daṇḍakāraṇya forest. They would stay at each hermitage for a week, a month, or longer, sometimes even a year. In this way, ten years of Rāma's exile passed comfortably and contentedly. After this time the three wanderers returned to the hermitage of Sutīkṣṇa to reside.

While one day conversing with Sutīkṣṇa, Rāma said, "I have heard that the great sage Agastya lives somewhere in Daṇḍakāraṇya, but I could not find him within the vast forest. I would like to offer My respects to the *ṛṣi* and receive his blessings. Please direct Me to his āśrama."

After taking directions from Sutīkṣṇa, Rāma departed, accompanied by Sītā and Lakṣmaṇa. Then, as they came to the vicinity of Agastya Ṛṣi's *āśrama,* Rāma narrated the following history: "Once there were two Rākṣasa brothers named Vātāpi and Ilvala. Ilvala would take the form of a *brāhmaṇa*, and speaking in Sanskrit, he would invite some real *brāhmaṇas* to a memorial ceremony. Before the arrival of the *brāhmaṇas*, Ilvala would have Vātāpi take the form of a ram. Then, after cooking his brother, Ilvala would feed him to the invited *brāhmaṇas*. When Vātāpi thus entered the *brāhmaṇa's* stomachs, Ilvala would loudly call, 'O my brother, please come out now.' Being summoned, Vātāpi would tear open the *brāhmaṇa's* stomachs and come out, bleating like a ram. In this way, the two Rākṣasas killed thousands of *brāhmaṇas*.

Finally, at the request of the demigods, Agastya Muni went there as an invited guest. Agastya ate Vātāpi in the form of a ram, but then, when Ilvala called for his brother, the *ṛṣi* informed him, 'I have already digested Vātāpi and sent him

to the abode of Yamarāja.' When Ilvala heard this, he tried to attack Agastya in a fit of rage. However, the *ṛṣi* burnt him to ashes with his angry glance. Thereafter, because the Rākṣasas feared Agastya Muni, his *āśrama* remained free from attack."

When Rāma entered Agastya Ṛṣi's *āśrama,* sitting places were prepared and they were provided with a suitable welcome. After finishing their meal, Agastya presented Rāma

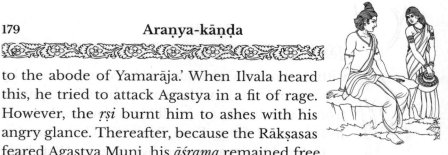

with the bow of Viṣṇu that had been constructed by Viśvakarmā, along with two inexhaustible quivers from Lord Indra, an infallible arrow, and a gold inlaid sword from Lord Brahmā. Then, turning to Sītā, Agastya praised her, saying, "You have earned eternal glory by voluntarily accepting such hardship for the sake of your husband. This is especially meritorious, since it has been the nature of women since the dawn of creation to love a man only for as long as he is prosperous."

Thereafter, Rāma asked Agastya to suggest a place for His residence. After some contemplation, the *ṛṣi* recommended He go to Pañcavaṭī, sixteen miles away, near the banks of the river Godāvarī. Then, just before Rāma's departure, Agastya confided, "I already know about Your entire life, by dint of yogic perception, which has been enhanced by my love for You."

After leaving the *ṛṣi's āśrama,* traveling on the way to Pañcavaṭī, Rāma, Sītā and Lakṣmaṇa came upon Jaṭāyu, the gigantic king of the vultures. Thinking at first that he may be a Rākṣasa, Rāma inquired about his identity. With mild words, Jaṭāyu replied, "My dear child, I was a good friend of Your father. Long ago, Kaśyapa married eight daughters of Dakṣa. From Vinatā, Aruṇa was born, and from Tāmasā, Syenī took birth. I am the son of Aruṇa and his wife Syenī, and my name is Jaṭāyu. My dear Rāma, please accept me as Your sincere servant. Since there are many fierce Rākṣasas inhabiting this forest, whenever You and Lakṣmaṇa leave Your cottage, I will watch over Sītā."

Because of Jaṭāyu's previous relationship with His father, Rāma respectfully bowed to Jaṭāyu. The vulture king then

accompanied them to Pañcavaṭī, keeping a watchful eye the entire time. Arriving at Pañcavaṭī, Rāma selected a suitable site for building their cottage, saying "It will be good to make our residence at a site near a lake or river, for water and greenery together create the ideal scenic beauty."

Rāma selected a site near the banks of the Godāvarī and an adjacent lake beautifully adorned with pink and blue lotuses. The land there was flat, giving an unobstructed view of the entire area. The cries of swans and waterfowl could be heard from the river, along with those of peacocks, echoing from caves of the nearby hills. After building a suitable cottage there, they consecrated it with flower offerings, and Rāma happily entered it.

As winter gradually set in, the morning sunshine became pleasing to the sense of touch. One morning, just after Rāma and Lakṣmaṇa had returned from bathing in the river, and were conversing about their religious duties, a Rākṣasī happened on the scene. Upon seeing Rāma, her heart immediately became saturated with love. With His glowing dark greenish-blue complexion and lotus-petal eyes, Rāma appeared to be the god of love himself in human form. The Rākṣasī, however, had an extremely ugly face, a large protruding belly, withered breasts, deformed eyes and copper colored hair. Whereas Rāma's body was youthful and well proportioned, muscular and bearing all the signs of royalty, the Rākṣasī's body was quite hideous and on the brink of middle age. Although she could change her form at will, she became so passionate upon seeing Rāma that she forgot to change her revolting appearance. She approached

Rāma, saying, "My dear handsome one, please tell me who You are and why You have come to the forest, dressed like a hermit. Indeed, You are dressed in the garb of an ascetic and are wearing matted locks of hair, yet You are wielding a bow and keeping a woman. Why have You come to this Rākṣasa-infested region? Please tell me who You are, and I will fulfill all Your desires."

In reply, Rāma briefly explained the incidents leading to His exile. He then asked the Rākṣasī who she was. The love-stricken demoness replied, "Hear the real truth, O lotus-eyed one. My name is Śūrpaṇakhā, the sister of Rāvaṇa, Kumbhakarṇa, Vibhīṣaṇa, Khara and Dūṣaṇa. I live in this forest and strike fear into the hearts of all creatures. Although my brothers are powerful, I surpass them all. I must frankly say, I have become overwhelmed with love for You. My mind is made up to have You for my husband. Give up Your ugly, deformed wife, for she is not worthy of a great hero like Yourself. I am very powerful, and can travel at will. Thus, I am a suitable partner for You. First, though, I will devour the flat-bellied Sītā and Your brother Lakṣmaṇa. Then we will be free to revel together in the hills and valleys of the beautiful Daṇḍakāraṇya forest."

As the Rākṣasī looked upon Him with love-filled eyes, Rāma laughed heartily at her proposal. Rāma then jokingly said, "I am already a married man, and certainly a young and beautiful girl like you could not tolerate living with a co-wife. My brother, however, who is an ever greater hero than Myself, is without a wife. Therefore, I suggest that you marry Him."

Śūrpaṇakhā took Rāma's words seriously, and left His side to face Lakṣmaṇa. Saturated with lusty desires, she said, "My dear handsome hero, You are indeed even more powerful and attractive than Your brother. Therefore, I consider You to be even more suitable for me. Come, make me Your wife, and we shall roam together through the forest, enjoying conjugal bliss."

Lakṣmaṇa smilingly replied, "O soft-skinned and lovely-limbed lady, you should know that I am simply the servant of My elder brother. Thus, if you were to marry Me, it would mean that you would be no better than His maidservant. I think you would be much better off by becoming Rāma's second wife, for in time He will surely discard the aging and misshapen Sītā and accept you alone. You have such a lovely face, always adorned with sweet smiles. Your ample breasts, slender waist and wide hips will make a man forget all other women. Who could resist you? Marry Rāma and He will cast aside His ugly wife."

Śūrpaṇakhā was too simple-minded to understand that Rāma and Lakṣmaṇa were joking with her. Thus, she again turned to Rāma, saying, "You are overly attached to the ugly Sītā. Thus, I will eat her up at once and forcibly take You as my husband."

Saying this, Śūrpaṇakhā rushed at Sītā. However, Rāma checked her, telling Lakṣmaṇa, "You should not joke with this Rākṣasī in a way that endangers Sītā. Now, disfigure her in a way that will teach her a lesson."

Upon Rāma's order, Lakṣmaṇa drew his sword, swiftly slicing off Śūrpaṇakhā's nose and ears as his elder brother

looked on. Śūrpaṇakhā screamed out in agony. Bleeding profusely, she fled into the forest. She quickly went to Janasthāna, where her brother, Khara, lived along with many other Rākṣasas. Frightened and smeared with blood, Śūrpaṇakhā threw herself at her brother's feet, weeping bitterly. Then as Khara looked on, his sister incoherently tried to explain what had happened.

Seeing his sister's disfigurement, Khara's heart became filled with horror and rage. Breathing like a trampled snake, Khara said, "O sister, please get up and calm yourself. Compose yourself so you can clearly tell me what has happened to you. Who has dared to injure you? Does he not realize that he has drunk poison by doing this? There is not a demigod, demon, Gandharva or *ṛṣi* who can harm you and escape with his life. Point out the culprit and I shall drink his blood with my sharp arrows."

Sobbing bitterly, Śūrpaṇakhā replied, "There are two brothers named Rāma and Lakṣmaṇa staying nearby in the Daṇḍakāraṇya forest. I do not know whether They are demigods or demons. However, since They have mutilated my face, I will only become satisfied after drinking Their blood!"

Khara then called for fourteen of the most powerful Rākṣasas and sent them out with Śūrpaṇakhā to kill Rāma, Lakṣmaṇa and Sītā.

As the Rākṣasas approached, Rāma was sitting in the cottage with Sītā, while Lakṣmaṇa guarded the doorway. Seeing the hideous man-eaters, Rāma ordered Lakṣmaṇa, "Stay here with Sītā while I fight these Rākṣasas."

Rāma then called out to the Rākṣasas, "We have come to this forest at the request of the *ṛṣis*, who seek our protection from your atrocities. We are living a life of austerity, eating only fruits and roots. Why have you come here to disturb us? Turn back now, if you at all value your lives."

Surprised at being challenged so courageously, the Rākṣasas stared at Rāma with blood red eyes, saying, "Our master, Khara, is very angry with You, and has ordered us to kill You. How can You hope to fight with so many of us? In a moment we shall crush You with our weapons and You will be dead!"

The Rākṣasas rushed at Rāma with uplifted weapons. However, with fourteen arrows, Rāma cut their weapons to pieces. With fourteen more, He pierced their hearts. Thus, like trees whose trunks had been severed, the Rākṣasas fell to the ground dead, bathed in their own blood.

Shaking with fear, Śūrpaṇakhā fled back to her brother's abode, and informed him of the slaughter. "You tried to comfort me by sending these Rākṣasas to kill Rāma and Lakṣmaṇa. But they have killed all the Rākṣasas with ease. Now you must go yourself to kill Rāma and Lakṣmaṇa. If you do not gain revenge for what They have done to me then I will give up my life out of shame." Saying this, Śūrpaṇakhā fell to the ground, overwhelmed with grief, and began beating her belly, bursting into tears.

Hearing his sister's harsh words, Khara became enraged, uttering a vow, "Give up your sorrow, my sister. I promise to kill Rāma and Lakṣmaṇa this very day so that you may drink Their blood!"

Hearing this, Śūrpaṇakhā became somewhat pacified. Khara then ordered his brother, Dūṣaṇa, to bring his chariot and weapons and to assemble their army of 14,000 Rākṣasas. Then Khara mounted his chariot and departed for the Daṇḍakāraṇya forest with his Rākṣasa army.

As the Rākṣasas proceeded, dark clouds showered rain mixed with blood upon them, causing Khara's horses to fall down on the road. A vulture came and perched upon Khara's flag standard, while a dark red aura dimmed the light of the sun. Then, as jackals howled frightfully, darkness set in, and Rāhu covered the sun, although not in an eclipse. All the while, Khara's left arm trembled violently and his voice became hoarse and faint. Still, despite witnessing all these harbingers of evil, Khara laughed, saying, "O Rākṣasas, because of my great prowess, I do not care for any of these so-called inauspicious omens."

Meanwhile, all the great demigods and *ṛṣis* assembled in the sky to witness the impending battle. As the Rākṣasas approached, Rāma described to Lakṣmaṇa the auspicious signs He had perceived: "My arrows are feeling joyful, My bow is stirring with delight, and My right arm is throbbing. My dear brother, take Sītā at once to a mountain cave and watch over her carefully while I massacre these Rākṣasas."

After Lakṣmaṇa and Sītā had departed, Rāma put on His suit of blazing golden armor. Then, when the Rākṣasas advanced toward Him, while roaring ferociously, Rāma summoned His all-devouring anger and assumed a dreadful form.

As the Rākṣasa army surrounded Rāma, Khara released 1,000 arrows, while other Rākṣasas showered innumerable weapons, such as clubs, spears, swords, and axes. Rāma, however, easily cut those weapons to pieces with His arrows. Even though deeply cut and bleeding, He appeared not to feel any pain. Rāma then released thousands of arrows at the Rākṣasas, cutting off their bows, flags, shields, armor, and bodily limbs. Indeed, many of the Rākṣasas fell down dead, along with their elephants and horses, their chariots smashed to pieces.

At that, the Rākṣasas became further enraged, and countered by showering their weapons upon Rāma in even greater profusion. Rāma, however, again cut their weapons to pieces with His arrows, and killed many Rākṣasas by piercing their hearts. He severed many of their grotesque heads from their gigantic trunks. Upon seeing this, the remaining Rākṣasas fled in fear to the shelter of Khara.

In great anger, Dūṣaṇa suddenly rushed at Rāma. Many Rākṣasas followed him, encouraged by his valor. In response, Rāma took up the best of Gandharva weapons. Thus, from His bow came many thousands of arrows which soon covered the sun, engulfing the battle scene in darkness. From those arrows thousands of Rākṣasas were cut to pieces, and their dismembered corpses collected in tall heaps.

Dūṣaṇa then rallied his army, urging the remaining 5,000 Rākṣasas to attack Rāma. In the fight that ensued, Dūṣaṇa fought heroically, and when Rāma saw that the brother of Khara successfully counteracted His arrows, He became extremely angry. Taking up a blazing arrow, Rāma cut Dūṣaṇa's bow in half. Then, with four more arrows, He

killed the Rākṣasa's horses. With another arrow, Rāma severed the head of Dūṣaṇa's driver, and with three more arrows, pierced the Rākṣasa's chest. Although in great pain, Dūṣaṇa jumped down from his disabled chariot and took up a spiked club. He then rushed headlong toward Rāma, intent on killing Him. However, with just two arrows, Rāma quickly severed Dūṣaṇa's arms, and then firing one more, He killed the terrible Rākṣasa.

Seeing Dūṣaṇa fall, the remainder of his army rushed toward Rāma, seeking revenge. Working at the speed of mind, Rāma released 5,000 arrows in a steady stream, like so many blazing meteors. Thus, the 5,000 Rākṣasa soldiers soon lay slaughtered on the ground.

Seeing this great massacre, Khara ordered his few remaining soldiers to attack. Rāma, however, made short work of them. Thus, the Daṇḍakāraṇya forest became a sea of reddish mud from the blood of the 14,000 slain Rākṣasas, with only Khara and Triśira remaining alive.

As Khara prepared to attack Rāma, his general, Triśira, begged him for permission to fight first. Khara agreed, and thus, the three-headed Rākṣasa came toward Rāma, showering Him with arrows. When some of the arrows pierced Rāma's forehead, Rāma became enraged, and quickly retaliated by killing Triśira's horses and driver and knocking down his flag. Then, as Triśira attempted to jump down from his disabled chariot, Rāma pierced his heart with a fiery arrow, and cut his three heads off with three more.

Khara rallied the few remaining Rākṣasas that had survived, and fearfully attacked Rāma. During the fierce

duel that ensued, the streams of arrows so completely covered the sky that the sun became invisible. Then, bringing his chariot close by, Khara dexterously cut Rāma's bow in two. Next, Khara released 1,000 arrows that shattered Rāma's armor, which fell to the ground in pieces.

Although His arms were deeply cut, Rāma calmly strung the bow of Lord Viṣṇu. Rāma then cut down Khara's emblem, but the Rākṣasa retaliated with four arrows that bathed Rāma in His own blood. Becoming more enraged, Rāma quickly released six arrows that pierced Khara's head, arms and chest. Then, with thirteen more, Rāma killed Khara's four horses, severed the driver's head, cut off His opponent's bow, and smashed his chariot. The last arrow, which appeared as dazzling as lightning, pierced Khara's chest, making him fall back senseless.

Khara, however, quickly recovered, and jumped down from his ruined chariot. Then he stood before Rāma, club in hand. Rāma chastised him, saying, "You cruel and sinful Rākṣasa. Since you have dedicated your life to giving pain to others, you are thoroughly condemned. To punish you, I shall now strike off your head this very hour."

This merely enraged Khara further. He screamed at Rāma, "You vile wretch, those who are actually heroes do not brag about their prowess."

Khara hurled his gigantic mace at Rāma. The blazing club burned to ashes all the trees and bushes that stood in its path. However, Rāma's arrows easily broke the club to pieces as it soared through the air. Then the two again exchanged harsh words, and Khara, looking for a weapon to attack Rāma

with, uprooted a huge tree. Whirling it around and around, Khara released the tree at Rāma, shouting, "You are killed!"

Rāma, however, easily cut the tree to pieces. Then, desiring to end the battle, Rāma released 1,000 arrows. With blood flowing from nearly every pore of his body, Khara made a final rush toward Rāma. As he did, Rāma selected a blazing arrow, which entered Khara's chest and burst into flames. Finally, the Rākṣasa fell to the ground, dead.

The demigods became overjoyed, witnessing Rāma's victory from their airplanes in the sky. As they beat on drums and showered flowers, the demigods glorified Rāma for His astonishing feat of killing all the Rākṣasas single-handedly in such a short time.

Great *ṛṣis,* headed by Agastya, appeared before Rāma and said, "When Indra previously visited Sarabhaṅga, it was to arrange for Your killing these Rākṣasas. That is why the *ṛṣi* advised You to dwell in this region."

Thereafter, Sītā and Lakṣmaṇa came out from the cave they were sheltered in, and upon seeing Rāma safe and sound, Sītā ran to embrace Him with great joy.

One Rākṣasa named Akampana, who had somehow escaped the massacre, went to Rāvaṇa's abode in Laṅkā and informed Rāvaṇa of the death of his two brothers. Upon hearing the news, Rāvaṇa became red with rage, shouting, "Who dares to offend me in this way, bringing about his own death? No one can save him now, not even Indra, Yamarāja or Viṣṇu. Tell me at once! Who has dared to make me so angry?"

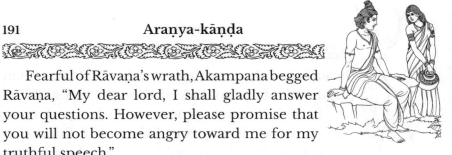

Fearful of Rāvaṇa's wrath, Akampana begged Rāvaṇa, "My dear lord, I shall gladly answer your questions. However, please promise that you will not become angry toward me for my truthful speech."

Thus, after gaining Rāvaṇa's assurance, Akampana explained: "The 14,000 Rākṣasas, including your two brothers, were killed by a human being named Rāma, the son of King Daśaratha."

Rāvaṇa then inquired, "Was this Rāma accompanied by all the demigods?"

Akampana replied, "Oh no, my lord! This Rāma killed all the Rākṣasas single-handed, without even taking help from His younger brother. Indeed, Rāma is so powerful that He accomplished this awesome task in a very short time—less than two hours! No one could stand before Rāma. When He became enraged, it appeared as if the entire universe would be destroyed."

Rāvaṇa angrily declared, "I shall go to Janasthāna at once and kill this Rāma and Lakṣmaṇa. Then we will see what kind of heroes They really are!"

But Akampana warned Rāvaṇa, "Please do not act hastily, underestimating the power of Rāma. He is capable of annihilating the entire universe—and again recreating it. Even if the demigods and demons all combined together, I do not think they could kill Rāma. Therefore, O lord, do not consider attacking Him with force. There is, however, another way that I think could provide the means for Rāma's death. The wife of Rāma, named Sītā, is incomparably

beautiful, with a face that is lovelier and fairer than thousands of moons. Indeed, she is the very emblem of feminine attractiveness, and the perfection of womanly chastity and behavior. I think that without Sītā, Rāma could no longer bear to live. Therefore, I suggest that you go to kidnap her."

Rāvaṇa immediately liked this idea, and after reflecting momentarily, he responded, "Your suggestion is brilliant! I shall go to Pañcavaṭī tomorrow on my chariot and carry Sītā away by force with great pleasure."

After dismissing Akampana, Rāvaṇa went to the hermitage of Tāṭaka's son, Mārīca. After receiving Rāvaṇa with great respect and washing his feet, Mārīca inquired, "O lord of the Rākṣasas, your surprise visit here fills my mind with misgiving. I know that you would not have come personally unless the matter were most important."

Rāvaṇa replied, "You are certainly correct. A human being named Rāma has completely annihilated my army of Rākṣasas posted at Janasthāna. Rāma's brother Lakṣmaṇa had disfigured my sister, Śūrpaṇakhā, causing Khara and Dūṣaṇa to retaliate. I considered my two brothers invincible, but they have been slain along with all their soldiers. I need your help, Mārīca, because I plan to kidnap Rāma's wife, Sītā."

With great shock and horror, Mārīca responded, "Whoever has given you this idea is your worst enemy in the guise of a friend. O Rāvaṇa, if you try to carry out this foolish plan, it will only result in your destruction, for Rāma has inconceivable prowess, on the level of Lord Viṣṇu Himself. Rāma is like a fathomless ocean. Crocodiles are

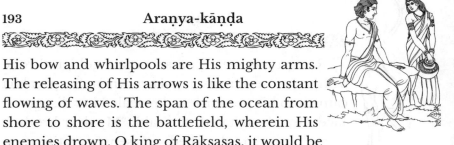

His bow and whirlpools are His mighty arms. The releasing of His arrows is like the constant flowing of waves. The span of the ocean from shore to shore is the battlefield, wherein His enemies drown. O king of Rākṣasas, it would be far better for you to control your wrath and return to Laṅkā. Enjoy yourself there along with your wives, and let Rāma enjoy with His wife in the Daṇḍakāraṇya forest. Otherwise, you will bring disaster down upon your own head."

Taking Mārīca's advice, Rāvaṇa returned to his magnificent palace at Laṅkā. Meanwhile, Śūrpaṇakhā, having witnessed the slaughter of all the Rākṣasas at Janasthāna, went to Laṅkā to see her brother, Rāvaṇa.

Rāvaṇa had ten heads and twenty arms, and his body bore many scars from former conflicts, including those inflicted by Lord Viṣṇu's Sudarśana *cakra*. Once, Rāvaṇa had attacked Bhogavatī, the capital of the Nāgas. After defeating the serpents Vāsuki and Takṣaka, he took away Takṣaka's wife by force. Then, after conquering Kuvera, Rāvaṇa took possession of his Puṣpaka chariot. Then, simply out of spite, he destroyed some of the heavenly gardens.

Long ago, Rāvaṇa had performed severe austerities, and at the end of 10,000 years, he began offering his ten heads in sacrifice to Lord Brahmā. Being pleased with Rāvaṇa, Lord Brahmā awarded him immunity from death at the hands of all living creatures, except human beings. After receiving this benediction, the puffed-up Rāvaṇa began killing *brāhmaṇas* and disrupting their sacrifices. Thus, he became a thorn in the side of the demigods, who fervently prayed to Lord Viṣṇu for his destruction.

Rāvaṇa was seated on an ornate golden throne within his seven-story palace when Śūrpaṇakhā came into his presence and revealed her disfigured face. Greatly agitated, she said, "My dear brother, are you so absorbed in sense gratification that you fail to recognize the grave danger at hand? When the king is only interested in his own vulgar enjoyment and doesn't pay attention to state affairs, everyone comes to despise him. Haven't your spies reported how Rāma single-handedly slaughtered 14,000 Rākṣasas at Janasthāna, including your two brothers? You are a useless king, and I predict that you will not remain on the throne for long."

Rāvaṇa became inflamed by the prodding from his sister, especially as she did it in front of his ministers. Barely controlling his anger, he inquired from her, "Who is this Rāma, and what is His strength? Was it He that deformed you like this? Speak now, for I want to know everything!"

Śūrpaṇakhā replied, "With His long, powerful arms and large eyes shaped like lotus petals, Rāma appears to be the god of love himself. His complexion has a dark greenish-blue hue, and He is strongly built like a lion. His bow is as effulgent as a rainbow, and when He stretches it to full length, He shoots golden arrows that resemble venomous snakes, releasing them so fast that you can't tell whether He is pulling out the arrow or shooting it. Although He is the most heroic *kṣatriya,* He has dressed Himself in tree-bark and deerskin and keeps matted hair.

"He killed the entire army of Rākṣasas at Janasthāna with a volley of arrows. He has such exceptional strength that He

has even subdued Khara and Dūṣaṇa. I'm sure He could divert the current of a river, or bring down the stars and planets from the heavens.

"Rāma's younger brother is Lakṣmaṇa, and He was the one who cut off my nose and ears, under His elder brother's instruction. The wife of Rāma is named Sītā, and she is exactly like the goddess of fortune. She has large dark eyes, and the beauty of her face surpasses that of many, many moons. Her smooth skin is the color of molten gold, and her slim waist, graceful hips and full breasts make her incomparably beautiful. O Rāvaṇa, there is no other woman like Sītā. If you were to see her you would fall madly in love, for she would make a perfect wife for you. I intended to capture her to bring to you, but instead I was disfigured by Lakṣmaṇa. Now, my dear brother, you should go and kidnap Sītā—that is, if you truly are as powerful a hero as you think."

When he heard about the lovely Sītā, Rāvaṇa became fully determined to possess her. He again mounted his chariot, and after crossing the sea, went to the *āśrama* of Mārīca, who was dressed like a *ṛṣi*, engaged in performing austerities. Mārīca inquired from Rāvaṇa respectfully, "O king, what is the reason for your early return to my residence?"

Rāvaṇa replied, "After hearing of Rāma's slaughtering the Rākṣasas at Janasthāna, I have not found a moment's peace. I have, therefore, made up my mind to kidnap Sītā, and I want you to help me. To this end, I have devised a very clever plan. I want you to take the form of a golden deer, freckled with silver spots. Afterwards, go out into the forest and play in front of Sītā. She will surely become captivated by such a wonderful creature and desire to have it as her pet.

After you prance playfully before her, lead Rāma astray. Once you have done this, I will come and kidnap Sītā, taking her back to Laṅkā. Thereafter, when Rāma becomes aggrieved and emaciated due to separation from His beloved wife, I will easily be able to slay Him."

Upon hearing the name of Rāma, Mārīca became greatly fearful. His mouth dried up, and staring with unblinking eyes, Mārīca addressed Rāvaṇa with folded hands, "O lord, if you try to carry out this plan, it surely will cause the destruction of all the Rākṣasas and your kingdom of Laṅkā. Because of your lusty nature and ignorance of Rāma's prowess, you are foolishly rushing toward your own doom. Please hear from me of Rāma's supreme potency before you act blindly, and bring about your own destruction.

"Previously, I used to wander about the earth, club in hand, feeling very proud of my superhuman strength. I subsisted upon the flesh of *ṛṣis* in the Daṇḍakāraṇya forest. Out of fear, Viśvāmitra approached King Daśaratha to solicit Rāma's help for protecting his sacrificial performances. Thereafter, while Rāma guarded Viśvāmitra's sacrificial arena, I ignorantly went there with the intention of disrupting the proceedings. However, with just one arrow, Rāma hurled me 800 miles into the ocean, and then killed the other Rākṣasas accompanying me. When I regained consciousness, having thus been spared by Rāma, I returned to Laṅkā, but was still not cured of my false pride. Taking the form of a large carnivorous stag with a flaming tongue, I returned to the Daṇḍakāraṇya forest and roamed about, drinking the blood of the *ṛṣis*. As it happened, I again came upon Rāma, who was wandering in the Daṇḍakāraṇya forest

with Lakṣmaṇa and Sītā. With the bitter memory of my past defeat in my mind, and considering how Rāma had accepted a life of renunciation, I was determined to gain revenge. However, when I rushed at Him, Rāma released three arrows. My two companions were killed instantly, and I fled for my life. I think my life was spared only because Rāma's arrows do not kill one who flees from the battlefield.

"Ever since that time, I have been consumed with fear of Rāma. As a result, my inclination for violence and fighting has vanished. Having given up all malice toward others, I have taken to an ascetic life of yoga practice. However, I have failed to obtain peace of mind, for whenever I happen to glance upon a tree, I think that it is Rāma, dressed in tree bark. Thus, the entire forest appears to have become transformed into innumerable Rāmas. Because of this, whenever I look anywhere, I become terrified. Sometimes I see Rāma in my dreams, and I immediately wake up, my heart thumping in terror. Indeed, I have become so afraid of Rāma that whenever I hear a word beginning with the letter "r," such as *ratha* or *ratna*, my heart trembles with fear.

"O King, for your own welfare, as well as for mine, I advise you to forget kidnapping Sītā. Aside from fearing Rāma, why should you perform such a sinful act? There is no offense more punishable than the abduction of another's wife. Remain satisfied with your thousands of wives and save your dignity, fortune, kingdom and life itself."

Having listened patiently, Rāvaṇa replied, "Now *you* must listen, Mārīca. I did not come for your advice. I came to obtain your help in executing my plan to kidnap Sītā. As

my minister it is your duty to give advice only when asked, and to obey my orders without question. I have made up my mind, and nothing can deter me. I want you to take the form of a deer to charm Sītā. Then, when she begs Rāma to capture you, lead Him deep into the forest and call out, 'O Sītā! O Lakṣmaṇa!' When He thinks that His brother is in difficulty, Lakṣmaṇa will leave Sītā aside to go help Him. Just perform this small service, and in return, I will reward you with half of my kingdom. However, if you refuse, then I shall kill you myself this very day. It is your choice. You may take certain death at my hands, or possible death at the hand of Rāma. Make up your mind!"

Mārīca, however, boldly declared, "Flatterers are quite easy to come by, my lord. Rare is that person who will speak unpleasant words for the benefit of others. A minister should always give good advice, even if uncalled for, especially when the king is misguided. Unfortunately, however, one who is about to die is never willing to take good advice. O king, if we carry out your plan, I am certain that both of us will end up dead. Still, I would rather die at the hands of an exalted enemy on the battlefield than be killed by you here. Therefore, let us depart at once."

Rāvaṇa was pleased that Mārīca saw the wisdom of his ultimatum. He embraced Mārīca, and they mounted Rāvaṇa's aerial chariot and departed. After flying over numerous forests, rivers, towns and fields, they landed in the Daṇḍakāraṇya forest, near where Rāma, Sītā and Lakṣmaṇa were residing.

Upon descending from the chariot, Mārīca immediately transformed himself into a beautiful deer. Then, going to

Rāma's cottage, he began to prance playfully, to and fro.

Mārīca's deer form had numerous jewel-like silver spots, with the tips of its horns appearing like sapphires. Its mouth appeared like a pinkish lotus flower, its tail like a rainbow, and its ears were bright blue. Indeed, the magical deer appeared to have been constructed from many varieties of valuable jewels.

With a dazzling luster, the deer seemed to illuminate the entire area surrounding the cottage. Sometimes it nibbled at the grass and sometimes it frolicked among the trees.

At that time, Sītā was gathering flowers. Seeing her, Mārīca in the form of a deer leapt, ran, crouched and turned, eager to attract her attention. All the other deer in the area, fled away on catching the scent of the disguised Rākṣasa.

The magical deer came close to Sītā, and bounded in front of her. Sītā became captivated with wonder and enchantment, for she had never before seen such a wonderful deer. With wide open eyes, she called out, "O Rāma, O Lakṣmaṇa, come quickly!"

As Sītā stood with eyes fixed, Rāma and Lakṣmaṇa also beheld the magical deer. Lakṣmaṇa, however, was wary. "This might be a trick," He said. "The Rākṣasa Mārīca is known to take such animal forms just to entice and waylay kings who come to the forest to hunt."

Sītā interrupted Lakṣmaṇa, for her intelligence had already become deluded by watching the magical deer, created by the Rākṣasa's mystical prowess. "O Rāma," she said, "please catch this deer, for it has caught my fancy.

Such a deer would make a lovely pet for me, and provide a welcome diversion from our dreary forest existence. Please go quickly, and catch this deer. I will take it back with us when we return to Ayodhyā at the end of our exile. Surely it will delight Bharata and our mothers. Please, Rāma, I want so much to have it to play with. It is so lovely, and its smooth skin shines like the moon. O, my husband, if You cannot capture it alive, at least find and kill it so that I may have its beautiful jewel-like hide for a rug. Perhaps You think me a foolish woman, but I must have this deer. I have become completely enchanted by its beauty."

Rāma was delighted to have the chance to fulfill Sītā's desire, and He, too, was captivated by the deer's mysterious beauty. He told Lakṣmaṇa, "Sītā is enthralled with this deer, and I must bring it for her. Look at its tongue, which darts like a flame, or lightning from a cloud. Nowhere is such a deer to be found, not even in the heavenly gardens. This deer's splendor will cost it its life. I will make a carpet of its spotted, golden skin so Sītā and I can enjoy sitting together upon it. And if, as You say, the deer is actually Mārīca, then killing it will be beneficial for all the *ṛṣis* that reside in this forest. O Lakṣmaṇa, stay here with bow in hand until I return. Keep a careful watch over Sītā."

Rāma took up a sword, bow and two quivers, whereupon Mārīca suddenly vanished from sight. As Rāma entered the forest, the deer once again came into view, then ran away swiftly, while frequently looking backwards. Again, the deer came close to Rāma, as if tempting Him to capture it. As Rāma rushed toward the deer, however, it disappeared from sight.

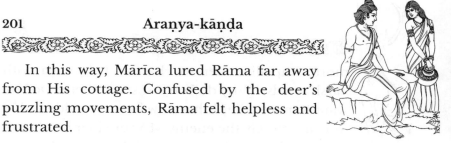

In this way, Mārīca lured Rāma far away from His cottage. Confused by the deer's puzzling movements, Rāma felt helpless and frustrated.

Finally, feeling exhausted from the chase, Rāma rested for a while beneath a tree. Then, once again, the deer suddenly appeared close by. However, just when Rāma rose up to capture it, the deer mysteriously vanished.

Out of frustration, Rāma gave up the idea of trying to capture the deer alive. Thus, when it next appeared at some distance, Rāma pulled out a blazing arrow of Lord Brahmā and released it to kill the deer. Mārīca jumped high, trying to avoid Rāma's arrow, but it pierced his heart, nonetheless. As Mārīca fell to the ground, mortally wounded, he assumed his real form as a Rākṣasa. Then, remembering Rāvaṇa's instructions, Mārīca imitated Rāma's voice, and called out in great distress, "O Sītā! O Lakṣmaṇa!"

Mārīca then gave up his life, and upon hearing his call, Rāma became dejected, wondering, "What will Sītā and Lakṣmaṇa think?" A terrible fear entered Rāma's heart, as He rushed back to His cottage.

Meanwhile, when Sītā heard the voice of Mārīca, she thought that Rāma was crying out for help. In panic, she turned to Lakṣmaṇa, urging, "Go quickly to Rāma and find out what has happened! That was Rāma crying out for help! He needs you. O Lakṣmaṇa, my heart is throbbing and I can hardly breathe. I think the Rākṣasas must have overwhelmed Rāma!"

With Rāma's order to guard Sītā firmly in mind, Lakṣmaṇa did not move away. His seeming indifference upset Sītā even

more, impelling her to chastise Lakṣmaṇa with harsh words, "Why do You just stand there? Do You want Rāma to die? It has now become evident that You are merely the enemy of Your elder brother in the guise of a friend. I think You wish Rāma to die so You may enjoy me as You like. Otherwise, You would surely rush to His rescue. Go quickly, Lakṣmaṇa! What is the use of me remaining alive and safe while my husband is in danger?"

As Sītā sobbed and trembled with fear, Lakṣmaṇa replied, "Try to control yourself. Rest assured, no one can ever harm Rāma. Neither the Rākṣasas, nor Indra, nor all the demigods can harm Him. I am convinced the voice you heard was the conjuring trick of Mārīca, made to frighten us. Rāma has ordered me to protect you. Therefore, I must stay here and obey Him."

Sītā was by now almost deranged with anxiety, and Lakṣmaṇa's words only aroused her anger more. Her eyes red with rage, Sītā raved, "You shameless and wicked man! I think You are enjoying Rāma's misfortune. Otherwise, why would You speak so casually? You have only been pretending to be Your elder brother's humble servant. The real reason You have accompanied Rāma to the forest was to look for an opportunity to kill Him and fulfill Your lusty desires to enjoy me. Perhaps You are Bharata's agent! In any case, You will never obtain the fulfillment of Your sinful desires! Do You really think I would accept You after having been the wife of lotus-eyed Rāma? I would rather die! Indeed, without Rāma, I could not bear to live for a moment."

Sītā's words pierced Lakṣmaṇa's heart as if they were sharp arrows. With folded hands, the horrified Lakṣmaṇa

replied, "O princess of Mithilā, you are like a deity to me. Thus, I cannot speak harshly in reply. I know that it is the nature of women to create trouble and discord between friends. Indeed, women are so fickle and hard-hearted that when they become obsessed with some desire, they give up all sense of morality. O daughter of King Janaka, you have goaded me with your sharp words, and so I will go to Rāma as you demand. However, because I see terrible omens, foreboding great evil, I fear that when I return with Rāma, We will no longer find you here."

With great agitation, Sītā said, "If Rāma is killed then I shall jump off a cliff, drown myself, or take poison. I would rather die than be touched by another man!"

Inflamed with rage by Sītā's harsh words, Lakṣmaṇa was torn between duty and His inner desire to see Rāma. Thus, as Sītā continued to malign him, Lakṣmaṇa reluctantly departed, allowing Rāvaṇa his eagerly awaited opportunity.

Dressed in saffron cloth, his hair tied in a knot on top of his head, wearing wooden sandals and carrying an umbrella over his right shoulder and a staff and waterpot in his left hand, Rāvaṇa came before Sītā in the guise of a wandering mendicant. Sitting inside her cottage, Sītā was crying, shedding tears of grief in Rāma's absence, as Rāvaṇa appeared at her doorway.

Out of fear, the wind ceased blowing, the leaves on the trees in the forest stopped fluttering and the waters of the Godāvarī became hushed. While chanting Vedic mantras, Rāvaṇa approached Sītā. As he stared at her, his heart became pierced by Cupid's arrows. Then, hoping to charm

her, Rāvaṇa spoke to Sītā. "Who are you, O lovely lady, residing all alone within this terrible forest? Are you the goddess of modesty, Hrī, the goddess of fame, Kīrti, the goddess of mystic powers, Bhūti, or the goddess of love, Rati? Perhaps you are Lakṣmī herself, now bereft of your lotus flower. Your smooth white teeth are like a row of

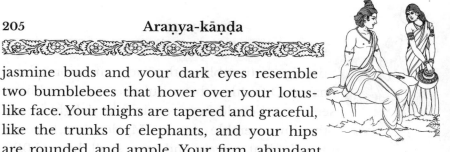

jasmine buds and your dark eyes resemble two bumblebees that hover over your lotus-like face. Your thighs are tapered and graceful, like the trunks of elephants, and your hips are rounded and ample. Your firm, abundant breasts seem to touch each other, and their nipples are pointed and prominent. Beneath them is a waist so slim that a thumb and index finger can circle it perfectly. No mortal or celestial woman can equal you in beauty, which has ravished my heart, like a swelling river that floods its banks.

"O dark eyed lady, why do you remain here when you could prosper elsewhere? You should reside in a palace, adorned with the finest dresses and jewels, attended by countless servants. Are you the wife of one of the Rudras, Maruts or Vasus? O sweet smiling one, choose a worthy husband and leave this jungle that abounds with ferocious animals."

Even though addressed so boldly, Sītā offered her guest a proper reception, not wishing to offend a *brāhmaṇa*. After offering him a seat and water to wash his feet, Sītā gave her guest a meal and explained, "Dear sir, my name is Sītā, the daughter of the noble-minded King Janaka of Mithilā. At the age of nine I was married to my beloved husband, Rāma. Later, at the urging of his wife, my father-in-law King Daśaratha installed her son Bharata as heir apparent, banishing Rāma to the forest for fourteen years. Please tell me your name and ancestry and why you have come to the Daṇḍakāraṇya forest."

No longer able to control his emotions, Rāvaṇa excitedly replied, "I am Rāvaṇa, the king of the Rākṣasas. Even great

demigods tremble at the mere mention of my name. O faultless, beautiful one, now that I have seen you, I could never again take delight in my other innumerable consorts. My dear Sītā, become my principal queen and you shall have 5,000 maidservants awaiting your command. Leave this forest and enjoy with me in the beautiful gardens of Laṅkā."

Hearing Rāvaṇa, Sītā became enraged. She contemptuously replied, "I am completely devoted to Rāma, who is as steady as a rock, as grave as the ocean, and sheltering like a banyan tree. I am devoted to Rāma, who is mighty-armed and broad-chested, whose face resembles the full moon, and who is self controlled and virtuous. Rāma is a lion among men, and you, who are like a jackal, want to possess me, a lioness.

"Would you dare touch the sun or lift up Mount Mandara? Would you pierce your eyes with a needle, or carry a blazing fire in your garment? Would you attempt to swim across the ocean with a boulder tied to your neck? Then why do you dare consider running away with Rāma's wife?

"Rāma is Garuḍa, and you are but a crow. Rāma is the ocean, and you, a small puddle. Rāma is nectar and you are stale gruel. He is sandalwood, and you are mud. He is gold, and you are iron. Rāma is a swan, and you are no better than a vulture. You may kidnap me, but as long as Rāma lives, you could no more enjoy me than a fly that flounders in ghee."

Although speaking boldly, Sītā was shaking with fear. Thus, to further intimidate her, Rāvaṇa said, "Listen, my lovely lady. I am the half-brother of Kuvera, the lord of wealth. After vanquishing him, I took away his Puṣpaka

chariot, and now he hides himself near Mount Kailāsa. The demigods are all afraid of me, and wherever I go, the sunshine becomes like moonshine, the wind calms itself, and rivers stop flowing. Forget Rāma, for He is a mere mortal, doomed to soon perish. Come with me and enjoy heavenly delights. I passionately yearn for you. Do not disappoint me."

Sītā then replied, "If you are truly Kuvera's brother, then why do you act with such wicked intentions? The ravisher of Indra's wife may survive, but whoever tries to molest me is doomed!"

Finally, Rāvaṇa lost all patience. In a fit of rage, he revealed his gigantic form as a fierce Rākṣasa, with ten heads, twenty arms and sharp teeth. The king of Rākṣasas then declared, "If you wish to have a husband who is renowned throughout the three worlds, then accept me. Serve me and I shall never displease you. Why are you so fond of Rāma, who has been banished to the forest?"

Rāvaṇa then grabbed Sītā by the hair with his left hand. As if summoned, Rāvaṇa's golden chariot came close by, and, placing his right hand upon her thigh, the king of the Rākṣasas took the frightened Sītā in his arms and ascended into the sky. As they ascended, Sītā screamed out, "Rāma! Rāma! Come and save me. Punish this wretched Rāvaṇa!"

In desperation, Sītā called out to the trees, the river, birds and animals, begging them to inform Rāma that she had been abducted. Just then, Sītā saw Jaṭāyu, sleeping while perched atop a tree. Sītā called out to him, "Jaṭāyu, please help me. Please go now and tell Rāma that I have been kidnapped by the evil Rāvaṇa!"

Hearing Sītā's cries, Jaṭāyu awakened, and seeing how she was being roughly handled by Rāvaṇa, he challenged the king of the Rākṣasas, saying, "O Rāvaṇa, I am Jaṭāyu, the king of the vultures. How can you dare lay your hands on the wife of another? Beware, for you are carrying a poisonous snake in your arms! I am now 60,000 years old and without weapons, and you are young with many weapons, but I will not allow you to carry away Sītā. I warn

you—give up your evil intentions, or else prepare to be thrown from your chariot like a ripe fruit falling from a tree!"

Thus challenged, Rāvaṇa angrily rushed toward Jaṭāyu. As the fighting began, it appeared that two great mountains were striking one another. Rāvaṇa threw many weapons at Jaṭāyu, while the giant vulture gouged Rāvaṇa with his taloned feet. Although many powerful arrows pierced Jaṭāyu, the sight of Sītā crying upon Rāvaṇa's chariot enabled him to tolerate the pain.

Jaṭāyu warded off the onslaught of arrows with his wings, and managed to break Rāvaṇa's bow with his feet. Gaining this advantage, Jaṭāyu quickly cut off Rāvaṇa's armor, and with his sharp claws he killed the mules yoked to the chariot. He smashed the chariot to pieces while simultaneously decapitating Rāvaṇa's driver with his beak. His chariot broken, Rāvaṇa fell to the ground while tightly clasping Sītā in his arms. As they witnessed this wonderful display of prowess, all the creatures watching applauded Jaṭāyu's valor.

However, Jaṭāyu was old, and soon became exhausted. Rāvaṇa rose up into the sky, holding Sītā with one hand, and bearing a sword in another. Condemning Rāvaṇa, Jaṭāyu suddenly swooped down upon his back, and began pulling at his hair so hard that the Rākṣasa king's lips quivered with indignation. Pressing Sītā tightly to his left thigh, Rāvaṇa struck back at Jaṭāyu with the palm of his hand. Jaṭāyu, however, dodged the blow, and then tore off Rāvaṇa's ten left arms with his powerful beak. Rāvaṇa's arms, however, were immediately replaced by new arms. Leaving Sītā aside, the king of the Rākṣasas began beating Jaṭāyu with his fists and feet.

The fighting continued for nearly an hour. Finally, in desperation, Rāvaṇa took up his sword and cut off Jaṭāyu's wings, feet, and flanks, causing him to fall mortally wounded to the ground. Greatly distressed, Sītā rushed to where Jaṭāyu lay, embracing him with tears in her eyes. Rāvaṇa, however, quickly grabbed Sītā by the hair and carried her off, as she cried out in grief, "Rāma! Rāma!"

Sītā's cries caused the entire universe to fall out of order. Everything became enveloped in darkness. In empathy with Sītā's grief, the wind no longer blew, and the sun lost its luster. Lord Brahmā, however, who could perceive the entire incident through divine eyes, declared, "Our purpose is now accomplished!"

Thereafter, as Rāvaṇa rose into the sky, Sītā's ornaments broke apart, her jewels falling to the ground. The pearls from her necklace slipped from her breast like the pure water of the Gaṅgā falling from the sky. Overwhelmed with fear and grief, Sītā continuously struggled to free herself from Rāvaṇa's grip, reproaching him again and again for his vile, cowardly act.

As Rāvaṇa sped towards Laṅkā, all creatures appeared to lament: "There is no dharma, there is no truth, there is no gentleness." Her loose hair waving in the wind, her mark of *tilaka* erased and her face devoid of cheer, Sītā moaned, "O Rāma! O Lakṣmaṇa!"

Just then, Sītā saw five monkey chiefs sitting atop a mountain. Unnoticed by Rāvaṇa, she took off her silk upper cloth and some jewels, and dropped them in the midst of the forest-dwellers, hoping they would inform Rāma. As the

monkeys stared with unblinking eyes, Rāvaṇa carried Sītā away toward Laṅkā.

Like many other powerful materialists, Rāvaṇa risked everything to gain the object of his desire. While carrying Sītā across the ocean to his kingdom, he relished the thought of having successfully abducted her, and he eagerly anticipated making her his queen. Blinded by lust, he failed to realize that the object of his desire was actually death personified for him. The goddess of fortune always serves the lotus feet of the Supreme Lord, and when materialists try to enjoy her, she manifests to them as Durgā, the deadly material nature. As the mistress of this world, Durgā rides a tiger and carries a trident whose prongs are the threefold miseries of material life (miseries arising from the body and mind, miseries inflicted by other living entities, and miseries imposed by higher powers in the form of natural disasters). Indeed, no one, not even the greatest scientist or conqueror, can counteract the sufferings meted out by Durgā.

Thinking himself more powerful than God, Rāvaṇa dangerously ignored reality. After crossing the ocean, Rāvaṇa took Sītā into the

inner apartments of his palace. There, he ordered his fierce Rākṣasī attendants, "Watch over Sītā most carefully and let no one see her face without my permission. Let her have gold, jewels, the best clothing, ornaments and food—whatever she may desire. However, take heed of my warning: anyone who dares to utter one harsh word toward her will die by my hands!"

After this, Rāvaṇa called for eight powerful Rākṣasas, saying, "Ever since Rāma killed all the Rākṣasas at Janasthāna, I have felt an intolerable enmity toward Him. Indeed, I will not sleep peacefully until Rāma is killed. Go now to Janasthāna, and after spying on Him, bring back any information that you may gather."

Then again Rāvaṇa went to see Sītā, being overwhelmed with desire. Upon entering her quarters, he found her in a distressed state, surrounded by numerous Rākṣasīs. Bathed in her own tears, Sītā appeared like a wind-buffeted boat at sea, or a doe strayed from its herd and surrounded by dogs.

Although she was unwilling, Rāvaṇa forced Sītā to accompany him on a tour of his palace. The opulent palace resembled that of the demigods, with thousands of servants waiting to carry out Rāvaṇa's desires. Many rooms had cages with exotic birds, and the palace walls were covered with intricate designs of precious jewels. The couches were made of ivory inlaid with gold. Musicians played sweet and melodious songs, and lotus flowers and fountains adorned the palace gardens and ponds.

As she viewed the spacious and fabulously decorated rooms, each containing thousands of women adorned with untold valuable jewels, Rāvaṇa explained, "Laṅkā is inhabited

by 32 crores of Rākṣasas, excluding the aged and infants, and 1,000 of these are my personal servants. If you are wise, O lovely Sītā, you will fulfill my ardent desire and become my principal queen. Become my mistress and rule over all this opulence. I am tormented by love for you, and shall be devoted to you alone. Please grant me your favor and look upon me with affection, for youthful beauty is fleeting. You should enjoy life with me and forget the insignificant Rāma."

Sītā covered her moonlike face and began shedding silent tears. Rāvaṇa then continued, "Do not be afraid that our union goes against religious principles. I love you more than life itself. I fall at your feet and beg you to grant me your favor. Let this plea, which has arisen from love's anguish, not go in vain. Never before has Rāvaṇa bowed down before any woman."

Rāvaṇa thought that by speaking of his love for her, Sītā would soon be subdued. However, Sītā fearlessly replied, "My heart remains for Rāma alone. Why should I, a swan sporting with her mate within a lotus-filled lake, prefer a duck meandering on the shore? You can do whatever you like to me. Because of your vile, sinful lust, you will soon meet your death at the hands of Rāma."

After being harshly rebuked by Sītā, Rāvaṇa became enraged, saying, "I will give you just twelve months to surrender to me. At the end of that time, if you still resist me, I will have my cooks cut you to pieces and serve you as my breakfast."

Rāvaṇa then turned to the Rākṣasī attendants and ordered, "Transfer Sītā to the *aśoka* grove. Keep a careful

watch over her and try to win her over to my side by whatever means is required. Threaten her, flatter her, do whatever it takes, but tame her as one would an elephant."

Arriving at the beautiful *aśoka* grove, replete with trees full of fruits and flowers, Sītā became overwhelmed with anguish. Due to being constantly intimidated by the deformed Rākṣasīs, she soon fainted out of fright.

At that time, Lord Brahmā summoned Indra, and said, "Sītā has been kidnapped by Rāvaṇa and taken to Laṅkā. This is our good fortune, for it surely means the imminent destruction of the Rākṣasa king. Still, there is the danger that Sītā may die due to separation from Rāma. Therefore, I want you to go and give her this heavenly sweet rice to eat."

Thereafter, Indra went to the *aśoka* grove at Laṅkā along with Nidrā Devī, the goddess of sleep. After Nidrā had put all the Rākṣasas to sleep, Indra, in the dress of a *brāhmaṇa*, approached Sītā and said, "I am the heavenly king, come to render assistance to Lord Rāma. Please take this celestial sweet rice, for it will make you immune to hunger, thirst, and bodily miseries for many years to come."

Sītā doubted that the *brāhmaṇa* was Indra, and requested him to reveal his celestial form. Upon her request, Indra assumed his true form. When Sītā observed that his feet did not touch the ground, his garland was not faded and his clothes were completely free from dust, she became convinced of his identity and accepted the sweet rice.

Sītā first offered the food by praying for Rāma to accept it. As soon as she ate it, she became freed from all bodily

pangs. Their mission accomplished, Indra and Nidrā Devī vanished from the scene.

Whenever the Lord's devotee is in great difficulty, the Lord sees to his protection. A devotee never worries for his own protection or well being. Knowing that Kṛṣṇa or Rāma is always attentive to his needs, he concentrates on his service to the Lord. In the wonderful reciprocation of love, the devotee always thinks of his Lord, and the Lord always thinks of His devotee.

After killing Mārīca, Rāma hastened back to His cottage. Along the way He thought, "The Rākṣasas certainly want to take revenge against Me for slaughtering their entire army at Janasthāna. Mārīca's tricks were probably part of a plan to lure Me away and devour Sītā. I pray that Lakṣmaṇa did not leave Sītā alone after hearing Mārīca cry out, perfectly imitating My voice."

Rāma's apprehension increased upon hearing the frightful cry of a jackal at His back. Then birds and other wild animals began to pass Rāma on His right side, uttering frightful cries. Moreover, His left eye twitched, His left arm throbbed convulsively and His heart thumped. While observing these inauspicious signs, Rāma met Lakṣmaṇa coming from the cottage. Taking Him by the left hand, Rāma immediately began to reproach Him, saying, "How could You disobey My order, leaving Sītā unprotected? From all the inauspicious omens that have appeared, I can understand that she has either been killed or kidnapped. Oh, Lakṣmaṇa, how could You leave Sītā all alone?"

As the two rushed back to the cottage, Rāma suddenly tripped on the forest path. Overwhelmed by fear of losing Sītā, and angry with Lakṣmaṇa for leaving her unprotected, Rāma began to lament like a deranged person: "If Sītā is dead then I shall kill Myself, for I cannot bear to think of living without her. Oh, Lakṣmaṇa, how could You betray Me like this and leave dear Sītā unprotected?"

Lakṣmaṇa hoped to explain, saying, "Sītā became a madwoman after hearing Your cries for help. She spoke harshly, accusing me of leaving You to die so I could enjoy with her. Then she accused me of being Bharata's accomplice, Your enemy in disguise. Hoping to prove her accusations false, I came here to Your aid."

Rāma angrily replied, "There is no excuse for leaving Sītā unprotected. You are fully aware that I am unconquerable and do not lack prowess for defending Myself from Rākṣasas or anyone else. You should not have become provoked by a woman's anger and disobeyed My order. O Lakṣmaṇa, You have made a great mistake. Such behavior is unworthy of You."

Rāma and Lakṣmaṇa finally reached Their cottage, only to find it deserted. Rāma then began searching all around for Sītā. Failing to find her, His face appeared withered and dark from grief. Afflicted with transcendental madness from feelings of separation, Rāma began questioning the trees: "Have you seen My beloved Sītā pass this way, dressed in yellow silk and decorated with flowers in her hair?"

Rāma then began asking the forest animals and birds if they had seen Sītā. Receiving no reply, He became more

morose. Then, imagining that Sītā had suddenly appeared before Him, Rāma cried out, "O dearly beloved, why are you running away from Me and hiding Yourself? Why do you not speak to Me?"

Rāma then imagined that Sītā had been devoured by the Rākṣasas, and envisioned her delicate bodily features. Rāma and Lakṣmaṇa continued to comb the surrounding mountains and forests, refusing to give up hope of finding Sītā. However, when Sītā could not be found, Rāma became discouraged and sat down in despair. Regardless, Lakṣmaṇa encouraged Him to continue searching. Thus, They roamed across many mountains, forests and plains.

Finally, Rāma could go no further, and He gave way to intense grief. Standing motionless, seeming bereft of reason, He breathed hotly, and His eyes filled with tears. Rāma became indifferent to Lakṣmaṇa's assurances that They would find Sītā. Tormented by love, Rāma cried out helplessly, "Sītā! Sītā!" again and again. As if deranged, Rāma cried, "My darling, have you hidden yourself just to play a joke with Me? I beg you to please come out, for My suffering is intolerable."

There are many instances of devotees weeping in separation from the Lord. The milkmaids of Vṛndāvana spent their whole life wandering in search of Kṛṣṇa. Lord Caitanya, as the perfect devotee, also adopted the mood of separation as the highest expression of love of God. Still, one may ask why Rāma, as the Supreme Lord, wept for His beloved like an ordinary man. Indeed, being the omniscient Lord, He certainly knew her whereabouts.

The Lord enacts His pastimes for several reasons. Foremost, He comes to teach us that He is never impersonal but always the Supreme Person. Thus He gives pleasure to His devotees and teaches mental speculators and mystic yogis that the Supreme Absolute Truth is a person, captured and controlled by love. Secondly, He comes to establish dharma, the way of

righteousness. He also comes to annihilate the demons. By weeping over His abducted wife, Lord Rāma establishes dharma, right conduct. He shows us, by negative example, the condition of a man too attached to women.

This incident also shows that a woman should always be protected, lest she be exploited by Rākṣasas like Rāvaṇa. Vedic living has no scope for a woman's being independent. However powerful a woman may be, she cannot protect herself independently.

Still, this is for the instruction of the materialists. On the spiritual side, Rāma, being the Supreme Personality of Godhead, is not subject to material conditioning. The separation Rāma experiences from Sītā is understood as transcendental conjugal love in separation. This is an activity of the Supreme Lord's pleasure potency, and belongs to the mellow of conjugal love in the spiritual world.

Although repeatedly called for, Sītā did not appear. Rāma became convinced she had been devoured by the Rākṣasas. Lakṣmaṇa was also sick at heart. Rāma then said, "O Lakṣmaṇa, please go to the banks of the Godāvarī, for perhaps Sītā has gone there to collect flowers."

Thereafter, when Lakṣmaṇa returned from the Godāvarī without Sītā, Rāma personally went to the river and began asking the trees and animals about her. However, due to their fear of Rāvaṇa, none of the creatures dared reply, although Rāma noticed that the deer were looking at Him with meaningful intention. Rāma then questioned the deer and tried reading their minds through their eyes. The deer seemed to reply by turning their heads upward and to the

south, as if indicating that Sītā had been carried away through the sky in that direction. Lakṣmaṇa could understand the deer's message, and suggested They walk toward the south in hope of finding some clue.

After setting out, They soon came to a trail of scattered flowers, which Rāma recognized as those He had given Sītā. Addressing a nearby mountain, Rāma asked, "Where has Sītā gone after passing this way?"

Receiving no answer, Rāma became enraged, saying, "O mighty hill, if you do not reply to Me, I shall shatter you to pieces with My arrows!"

There was only silence as Rāma glowered at the peak with hot eyes. Rāma then prepared to release His arrows at the mountain when Lakṣmaṇa pointed out Sītā's footprints beside those of a giant Rākṣasa. Following the footprints, Rāma and Lakṣmaṇa soon came upon Rāvaṇa's broken bow and quiver, portions of his shattered chariot, along with pieces of Sītā's broken ornaments. Then, when drops of blood were found, Rāma concluded that Sītā was indeed devoured by the Rākṣasas, for it appeared that two man-eaters had fought over her at that spot.

Gazing upon the dead mules, smashed chariot and scattered weapons, Rāma vowed, "No Rākṣasa shall escape My vengeance, for today I will destroy them all in retaliation for Sītā's murder. Why have the useless demigods not done something to save My helpless wife? If the demigods do not deliver Sītā to Me at once, as revenge for their negligence and the crime of the Rākṣasas, I shall destroy the entire universe!"

Rāma's eyes were red-hot with anger, and His lips, tightly pressed together, trembled with rage. Then, taking His bow from Lakṣmaṇa, Rāma placed a terrible arrow, meant to destroy the entire universe, upon the string. Terrified, Lakṣmaṇa joined His hands in supplication, pleading, "Rāma, by nature You are gentle, self controlled and the well-wisher of all living entities. Therefore, please control Your wrath and do not act hastily. It appears to Me that there was only one Rākṣasa involved in this fight, for there is but one broken chariot. Let us continue to search for Sītā. If We still do not find her, then You can act as You see fit. My dear brother, You must practice forbearance, since suffering is inevitable. If You cannot tolerate life's miseries, how can the common man be expected to do so? You should only consider how Your enemy can be killed. There is no need to destroy the entire universe."

While speaking this way, Lakṣmaṇa lovingly massaged His brother's lotus feet, and gradually pacified Rāma. After withdrawing the arrow from His bow, Rāma assented to Lakṣmaṇa's suggestion to search the entire area of Janasthāna thoroughly.

Thereafter, while combing the forest, Rāma and Lakṣmaṇa came upon the fallen Jaṭāyu, lying in a pool of blood. Rāma thought he was a Rākṣasa disguised as a bird, who had devoured Sītā and was now resting. Thus, as Rāma approached, He fitted an arrow to His bow, ready to release it. However, upon drawing near, Rāma understood that it was Jaṭāyu, and that he had been fatally wounded while trying to rescue Sītā from the clutches of Rāvaṇa. Understanding the situation, Rāma threw His bow aside and embraced Jaṭāyu.

Seeing the plight of His servant, Rāma became doubly aggrieved.

Rāma anxiously asked, "O Jaṭāyu, please tell Me everything you know about Sītā and her abductor."

The dying Jaṭāyu related all that had happened, and commented, "Rāvaṇa took Sītā away at the time of day known as *vinda*. If a person loses something at that time, he will surely reclaim it very soon. My dear Rāma, do not be overly aggrieved because of Sītā, for You shall certainly regain her after killing the Rākṣasa king in battle." Then, as Jaṭāyu described Rāvaṇa's exalted lineage, he gasped his last breath, uttering, "Rāma! Rāma!"

Rāma told Lakṣmaṇa, "I am more saddened by the death of Jaṭāyu, who gave his life for My sake, than by the kidnapping of Sītā. Go and bring some wood so We may cremate his body. Let it be known that Jaṭāyu will attain the highest destination as a reward for his service to Me."

Lakṣmaṇa prepared the funeral pyre, and Rāma placed Jaṭāyu's body upon it and lit the fire. The brothers made offerings for the benefit of Jaṭāyu's departed soul and chanted Vedic mantras. Rāma and Lakṣmaṇa then went to the banks of the river Godāvarī to offer oblations of water, and then took bath. Thus completing the funeral ceremonies, Rāma and Lakṣmaṇa again fixed Their minds upon the task of finding Sītā, and continued to wander the forest.

Traveling toward the southwest, They reached an untrodden land overgrown with trees and bushes. After passing through that region with great difficulty, They left the Daṇḍakāraṇya forest and entered the Krauñca forest. After passing through that, Rāma and Lakṣmaṇa entered another

dense jungle. There, They were suddenly confronted by a huge Rākṣasī, standing before a large cave. The ghastly Rākṣasī, with her long, sharp teeth, large protruding belly and hard skin, quickly stepped forward, catching Lakṣmaṇa by the hand, saying, "My dear handsome hero, please come with me and revel in this delightful forest." Then the Rākṣasī embraced Lakṣmaṇa, saying, "I am Yours! Take me as Your beloved wife."

In reply, Lakṣmaṇa angrily drew his sword and cut off the Rākṣasī's ears, nose and breasts. Bleeding and screaming with pain, the Rākṣasī fled. Then, Rāma and Lakṣmaṇa continued on as before.

Suddenly Rāma said, "My left arm is throbbing and My mind feels perturbed. O Lakṣmaṇa, We should prepare for imminent danger."

A moment later, They heard the frightful cry of a *vañjulaka* bird, and Lakṣmaṇa remarked, "This indicates that victory will be ours."

After Rāma and Lakṣmaṇa proceeded some distance into the forest, a loud noise was heard, as a storm suddenly began brewing. Searching out the source of the noise, Rāma and Lakṣmaṇa proceeded cautiously, swords in hand. Before long they came upon a huge Rākṣasa with no head, neck or legs, and a gigantic mouth located in the middle of his belly. The Rākṣasa was as big as a mountain, with sharp bristling hair all over his body. On his chest were two fiery eyes, and his long arms stretched out for eight miles, enabling him to easily catch large animals to eat. Although Rāma and Lakṣmaṇa retreated to a distance of two miles after seeing the monster,

the Rākṣasa suddenly captured Them in his grasp, squeezing so tightly that They were made helpless. Although Rāma did not feel threatened, Lakṣmaṇa felt despondent, saying, "O Rāma, You should offer Me as a sacrifice to this Rākṣasa in exchange for Your own life. After that, You can continue Your search for Sītā."

While Rāma encouraged Lakṣmaṇa not to be afraid, the Rākṣasa said, "My name is Kabandha. It is very fortunate that You have come to my forest, because I have been hungry for a long time. Since You are the food which Providence has provided for me, I think that You will have a very difficult time keeping Your precious lives."

Lakṣmaṇa then told Rāma, "We should quickly save Ourselves by cutting off this Rākṣasa's arms with Our swords."

Hearing this, Kabandha became furious, and immediately opened his fearful mouth wide, hoping to devour Rāma and Lakṣmaṇa at once. However, before Kabandha could do so, Rāma severed his right arm and Lakṣmaṇa cut off his left. Thus, the Rākṣasa fell to the ground, bathed in his own blood. In an anguished voice, Kabandha asked, "Who are You?"

Lakṣmaṇa replied, "This is Rāma, a *kṣatriya* in the line of Ikṣvāku. I am His brother, Lakṣmaṇa. We have come here searching for Rāma's wife, Sītā, who has been kidnapped by the king of the Rākṣasas, Rāvaṇa."

Kabandha was overjoyed to hear the name of Rāma. The Rākṣasa then said, "I am so fortunate! You have come here to redeem me! Please listen as I explain how I acquired this ghastly form. In my last life I was the son of Dhanu. By performing great austerities, I satisfied Lord Brahmā and was

granted the benediction of a long duration of life. After receiving this boon, however, I became very proud, thinking my archenemy, Indra, could no longer harm me. Thereafter, when I attacked the king of heaven on the battlefield, he hurled his thunderbolt at me. When the thunderbolt struck me, my head and legs were forced into my body. Finding myself in such a wretched condition, I begged Indra to kill me. However, he refused, saying that to do so would falsify the words of Lord Brahmā. At last, when I asked Indra how I could survive without a head, he placed my mouth in the middle of my belly and made my arms eight miles long. Indra then declared, 'When Rāma and Lakṣmaṇa come before you, you will regain your heavenly form.'"

Kabandha continued, "Ever since that time I have been catching creatures with my long arms and stuffing them into my mouth, hoping that one day I would catch Rāma mentioned by Indra. Then once I harassed a certain *ṛṣi*, who cursed me to retain this horrible form for eternity. I tearfully begged the *ṛṣi* to prescribe some end to my plight. He confirmed that I would regain my original form after being cremated by Rāma. Now, I have been delivered by You, and after my death, I will direct You to a powerful ally who will help You to attain Your desired goal."

Rāma then explained, "My wife Sītā has been kidnapped by Rāvaṇa, the king of the Rākṣasas. However, I only know his name. I know nothing else about him, concerning his appearance or place of residence. I will throw you into a big pit and cremate your body so that you can attain your desired destination. In return, give Me some information about this Rāvaṇa."

Kabandha then said, "I am very sorry, but I do not know anything about Rāvaṇa. After being cremated, however, I will inform You of a person who has traveled throughout the three worlds. He will be able to assist You in locating the king of the Rākṣasas."

Thereafter, Rāma and Lakṣmaṇa took Kabandha into a mountain cave and placed his body upon the funeral pyre that Lakṣmaṇa had prepared. Because it was so fat, when the body began to burn, it looked just like a huge lump of burning ghee. Then, from out of the fire arose Kabandha in his original celestial form, dressed in fine garments and decorated with ornaments and garlands. After taking his seat upon a celestial chariot pulled by swans, Kabandha said, "O Rāma, political misfortune can be overcome in six ways: by making peace, by fighting, by assassination, by building up superior arms and fortifications, by sowing dissension, and by seeking the help of others. Just as You are now placed in the height of adversity from the loss of Your wife, so will You be able to retrieve her with the help of someone in a similar condition. That person is the monkey king, Sugrīva, who has been exiled by his brother, Vāli, the son of Indra. O Rāma, You should make friends with Sugrīva, who was begot by Sūrya in the wife of Ṛkṣarāja, for he is also in need of a benefactor. He is now living along with four other monkeys on Ṛṣyamūka Mountain, which is near Lake Pampā.

"First go to Lake Pampā. It is a beautiful site that abounds with exotic birds. These birds live without fear of human beings, for they have never been injured by them. You should feed these birds, and the fish in Lake Pampā, and then meet the ascetic woman Śabarī who resides there.

"The entire area is beautified by ever-fresh flowers, produced from the perspiration from the bodies of Mataṅga Ṛṣi's disciples as they brought fruits, roots and flowers from the forest. The great sage Mataṅga gave up his body at Lake Pampā long ago. Thereafter, the ascetic woman Śabarī attended to his disciples. Although these *ṛṣis* have also long since ascended to higher worlds, Śabarī still resides there, awaiting Your audience before departing for Brahmaloka.

"Near Lake Pampā is the Ṛṣyamūka Hill where Sugrīva lives in a large cave, always fearful of being attacked by Vāli. Sugrīva is loyal, intelligent, generous, wise, brave and powerful. You would do well to make an alliance with him, for he knows all about the Rākṣasas. His followers can wander over the earth until they find Sītā."

Saying this, Kabandha took permission from Lord Rāma and ascended to heaven. Then, following Kabandha's directions, Rāma and Lakṣmaṇa set out. On the second day They arrived at Lake Pampā, where They saw the *āśrama* of Mataṅga Ṛṣi.

When Rāma and Lakṣmaṇa entered the hermitage, Śabarī got up and greeted Them with folded hands. Then, after touching the lotus feet of Rāma and Lakṣmaṇa, Śabarī honored Them with varieties of food and drink, and water to wash Their feet. When Rāma inquired about her spiritual practices, Śabarī, who was a perfected soul, replied, "Just by seeing You, I have achieved the fruition of all my austerities. When You came to Citrakūṭa, the *ṛṣis* I was serving all went to heaven in celestial chariots. Before departing, however, they assured me that You would come here, and that after

receiving You, I would also attain a heavenly destination."

At Rāma's request, Śabarī took Him and Lakṣmaṇa on a guided tour of the beautiful area surrounding Lake Pampā. Afterwards, Śabarī requested Rāma's permission to cast off her mortal body, so that she could rejoin the sages she had so faithfully served.

Being very pleased with Śabarī, Rāma granted her desire. Thus, after building a fire, the old ascetic lady, dressed in black deerskin and tree bark and wearing matted hair, leapt into the blazing flames. The next moment Śabarī rose up to heaven like a flash of lightning, adorned with celestial jewels and garlands.

Having thus witnessed Śabarī's spiritual prowess, Rāma and Lakṣmaṇa went to bathe in Lake Pampā, created from the waters of the seven seas. Thereafter, feeling enlivened and ever hopeful of finding Sītā, Rāma anxiously departed with Lakṣmaṇa, eager to find Sugrīva.

Kiṣkindhyā-kāṇḍa

The spring beauty surrounding Lake Pampā awoke within Rāma memories of His loving pastimes with Sītā, thus intensifying His transcendental grief. Rāma constantly thought of Sītā and wondered if she was able to live without Him. Rāma bitterly lamented: "O Lakṣmaṇa, it is now the month of Caitra, and this lake is so lovely with its deep blue waters. This is the season of love, when all the trees become resplendent with blossoms, their petals raining down to decorate the beautiful green forest carpet. Without Sītā, however, life seems meaningless. That which pleased Me when she was present, now pains Me. When I hear the cuckoos call, I think of Sītā's sweet voice. When I see the pink lotus flowers swaying on the crests of the waves, I think of Sītā's eyes. The gentle fragrant breeze reminds Me of Sītā's honey-scented breath. O Lakṣmaṇa, the pain of this cruel spring is unbearable, for I can no longer bear to live without Sītā. You should return to Ayodhyā and serve Bharata, while I stay here and give up My life."

Trying to instill some hope in Rāma, Lakṣmaṇa replied, "My dear brother, there is no reason to suppose that Sītā does not still live. Wherever Rāvaṇa may be, in heaven, on earth, within the ocean or the nether regions, We shall find him and vent Our wrath. Give up this useless melancholy and fix Your mind on finding Sītā. It is by earnest endeavor that We shall succeed—not by lamenting."

Being thus admonished by Lakṣmaṇa, Rāma gave up His depression. While conversing, They reached the vicinity of the Ṛṣyamūka Hill. From a distance, Sugrīva could see Rāma

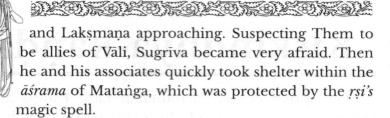

and Lakṣmaṇa approaching. Suspecting Them to be allies of Vāli, Sugrīva became very afraid. Then he and his associates quickly took shelter within the *āśrama* of Mataṅga, which was protected by the *ṛṣi's* magic spell.

But in spite of such security, Sugrīva was so restless and frightened that he kept wandering from one hilltop to another, unable to sit still for a moment. Hanumān then said to his distracted master, "You should give up this paranoia of Vāli. Being a fickle-minded monkey, you hastily come to conclusions that surely will be rejected after more careful consideration."

Sugrīva replied, "Whether They are agents of Vāli or not, these persons are certainly frightening. Indeed, these two warriors look like chiefs of the demigods, and are armed with bows and swords. Certainly Vāli is very cunning and has many friends. Therefore, I want you find out why They have come here. Observe Them carefully, noting Their speech and Their expressions. Find out who They are and what They want. If you purposefully glorify me in Their presence, you shall be able to detect if they are friends or enemies."

As he also had the suspicious mind of a monkey, Hanumān concealed his real form and appeared before Rāma and Lakṣmaṇa as a mendicant. Then, after falling flat to offer his obeisances, Hanumān said, "O great heroes, please tell me how it is that such exalted personalities as Yourselves have come to this desolate region. Your strongly built bodies indicate that You are warriors, although You are dressed as ascetics. My name is Hanumān, minister of Sugrīva, who has been banished from his kingdom by his elder brother, Vāli. I am the son of Vāyu, and I can go

anywhere at will and assume any form that I please. Sugrīva has sent me here to extend his friendship and hospitality."

Rāma then told Lakṣmaṇa, "This Hanumān is a minister of Sugrīva, the noble king of the monkeys whom we have been searching for. He appears to be most courteous, and speaks very poetically. In his eyes, limbs, attitude and expression there is nothing displeasing or duplicitous. He has depth, confidence, and power. Likewise, his speech reflects a mature unification of heart, voice and intelligence. Even an enemy would be charmed by his words! O Lakṣmaṇa, please explain to Hanumān the events that have brought Us here today."

Lakṣmaṇa said, "It is Our good fortune to meet you. We have been searching for Sugrīva and are eager to make an alliance of friendship with him. This is Rāma, the son of Mahārāja Daśaratha, and I am His younger brother, Lakṣmaṇa. Rāma's father desired to install Him as heir apparent to the royal throne, but due to political intrigue, Rāma was banished to the forest instead. Recently Rāma's beloved wife, Sītā, was kidnapped by the Rākṣasa king Rāvaṇa. Overwhelmed by grief, We have been searching for Sītā in the forest. While wandering here and there We happened to come upon a fierce Rākṣasa named Kabandha. By killing Kabandha We relieved him of a terrible curse. In return, while ascending to heaven, he advised Us to make an alliance with Sugrīva. That is why We have now come. We are ready to do whatever is beneficial for you and your noble king."

As Lakṣmaṇa described Their plight to Hanumān, His voice and tear-filled eyes reflected His inner anguish. Seeing this, Hanumān replied, "Like You, Sugrīva is also

bereft of his kingdom and wife. I am certain that he and his followers will help You in Your campaign to find Sītā. Please come along with me and meet Sugrīva, for he has been very anxious to know the reason for Your coming here." Saying this, Hanumān assumed his true form as a gigantic monkey. Then he took Rāma and Lakṣmaṇa upon his shoulders and departed for the Ṛṣyamūka Mountain.

Upon arriving there, Hanumān first went to Sugrīva and informed him of Rāma's friendly intentions. Satisfied, Sugrīva took the form of a mendicant and went out to meet Rāma and Lakṣmaṇa. As he approached, Sugrīva extended his hand as an offering of friendship. With great pleasure Rāma extended His hand in return, and then feelingly embraced the monkey chief.

Afterwards, to formally unite the two friends, Hanumān lit a sacred fire between Rāma and Sugrīva. After ceremoniously circumambulating the fire, Rāma and Sugrīva looked upon each other in a spirit of firm friendship.

Sugrīva then said, "My dear Rāma, from this day on, Your happiness shall be my happiness, Your sorrow shall be my sorrow, and vice versa."

Sugrīva then placed a flower-laden branch on the ground for Rāma to sit upon, and Hanumān did the same for Lakṣmaṇa. After all were seated, Sugrīva explained, "My dear Rāma, I pass my life in constant anxiety because of my brother Vāli. After Vāli forcibly took my wife and kingdom, I took shelter within this forest. However, I am haunted by the fear that my elder brother may come here and attack me at any time. I do not know a moment's peace."

Rāma gently smiled and replied, "Service is the real fruit of friendship. Therefore, it is My duty to dispose of Vāli and assist you in regaining your kingdom and wife."

Sugrīva then said, "Hanumān has told me about Your exile and the kidnapping of Your wife. As a friend it is my vow to help You recover her, whether she is in heaven, on earth, or in the nether regions. O Rāma, I am sure I saw Sītā as she was being carried away by a powerful Rākṣasa, crying out, 'Rāma! Rāma!' She saw me seated atop this hill with my associates and threw down her upper garment and some jewels, which we later collected."

Rāma was eager to see these articles, and asked Sugrīva to retrieve them. Sugrīva then went to the cave he stored them in, and brought them out for Rāma to examine. Immediately recognizing the cloth and ornaments, Rāma cried out, "O darling! O dearly beloved!" As tears fell from His lotus eyes, Rāma began wailing pitifully, and then lost consciousness.

After coming to His senses, Rāma said, "O Lakṣmaṇa, these articles were worn by Sītā. Do you recognize them?"

Lakṣmaṇa replied, "I have never looked at Sītā above her ankles, so I cannot say whether the cloth is hers. I do, however, recognize the ankle bells, because I used to bow to her lotus feet every morning."

Rāma then inquired about Rāvaṇa and Sugrīva replied, "Unfortunately, I have not heard of Rāvaṇa. However, You may rest assured that I will help You find him. O Rāma, You should not lament excessively for the loss of Your dear wife. A person can never become happy simply by grieving. Indeed, such sorrow actually diminishes one's strength and puts his life in danger. Although I am a foolish monkey and in a similar situation, I do not lament as much as You."

Hearing Sugrīva's words, Rāma became a little pacified. He then embraced Sugrīva again and the two sat together comfortably. When Sugrīva brought up the topic of his fear of Vāli, Rāma said, "O Sugrīva, rest assured that I will kill Vāli this very day. First, however, I would like to know how such enmity developed between you two brothers."

Sugrīva replied, "It is only unto a true friend that one can give full vent to his grief. As it happened, when my father

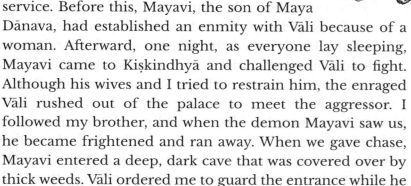

died, Vāli, being the elder prince, became the king of Kiṣkindhyā and I engaged in his service. Before this, Mayavi, the son of Maya Dānava, had established an enmity with Vāli because of a woman. Afterward, one night, as everyone lay sleeping, Mayavi came to Kiṣkindhyā and challenged Vāli to fight. Although his wives and I tried to restrain him, the enraged Vāli rushed out of the palace to meet the aggressor. I followed my brother, and when the demon Mayavi saw us, he became frightened and ran away. When we gave chase, Mayavi entered a deep, dark cave that was covered over by thick weeds. Vāli ordered me to guard the entrance while he went into the cave to fight the demon.

"Thereafter, an entire year passed, and although I remained there guarding the entrance, I saw no sign of my brother. Suddenly, I observed blood mixed with foam oozing from the cave, and could hear the noise of many demons, but not my brother's voice. I concluded that Vāli must have been slain. I then blocked the entrance to the cave with a huge boulder and offered water for the benefit of my departed brother's soul. When I returned to Kiṣkindhyā, the ministers installed me upon the royal throne, and I began ruling the kingdom righteously.

"It came to pass that after some time, and much to the surprise of everyone, Vāli returned to Kiṣkindhyā, having slain the demon. When my brother saw me seated upon the royal throne he became enraged, and immediately arrested the ministers, throwing them in chains. I could have fought with my brother, but out of respect, I bowed down to him and placed the royal crown at his feet, hoping he would become pacified. Vāli, however, remained angry, and continued to

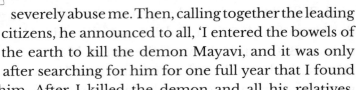

severely abuse me. Then, calling together the leading citizens, he announced to all, 'I entered the bowels of the earth to kill the demon Mayavi, and it was only after searching for him for one full year that I found him. After I killed the demon and all his relatives, the blood from their bodies flowed, practically filling up the cave, and making it very difficult for me to get out. When I finally reached the mouth of the cave, I discovered it was blocked by a huge boulder. I called out for Sugrīva again and again, but received no answer. Finally I kicked out the boulder, freeing myself, and returned to Kiṣkindhyā. Much to my surprise, I saw Sugrīva sitting upon the royal throne. I could then understand that his intention was to shut me up within the cave to gain control over the kingdom.'

"Thereafter, Vāli took away all my possessions, including my wife, and banished me from Kiṣkindhyā, leaving me with only a single cloth. Since that time I have been residing upon this mountain, along with my closest friends."

Rāma then said, "My dear Sugrīva, rest assured that I will kill Vāli so that you can recover your wife and kingdom."

Even after hearing Rāma's assurances, Sugrīva remained doubtful whether Rāma was powerful enough to slay Vāli. To further illustrate his elder brother's prowess, he told the following story: "Once there was a great demon named Dundhubhi, who wandered over the earth in the form of a buffalo. Upon reaching the seashore, Dundhubhi challenged the ocean to fight. The ocean personified then appeared and said, 'O best of the Asuras, I am not a competent match for you. I suggest that you approach Himavān, the presiding deity of the Himālayas and father-in-law of Lord Śiva.'

"Thinking the ocean to be afraid of fighting with him, Dundhubhi went to the Himālayan Mountains and began tearing down its peaks and cliffs. Himavān then appeared upon one mountaintop and said, 'I am the shelter of great *ṛṣis* who are nonviolent and equipoised. I am not at all adept at warfare. Therefore, O greatest of the demons, please leave us aside, and do not create any further disturbance.'

"The angry demon then asked who he could fight with instead, and Himavān described my brother Vāli, the son of Indra. Thereafter, Dundhubhi went to Kiṣkindhyā, and, while bellowing loudly, he began tearing up the ground with his hooves, uprooting great trees, and damaging the city's gates with his horns.

"Vāli immediately went out and challenged the arrogant demon to fight. After a brief exchange of harsh words, Vāli grabbed Dundhubhi by the horns, whirled him around, and dashed him to the ground, causing blood to flow from the demon's ears. A fierce duel then ensued, as each struck the other forcefully. However, after a short time the demon began to weaken. Seeing this, Vāli lifted Dundhubhi into the air and smashed him on the ground with all his strength.

"As blood poured profusely from every hole of his body, the demon gave up his life. Then, Vāli lifted up Dundhubhi's dead body and hurled it four miles away. However, as the corpse flew through the air, drops of blood fell from its mouth and landed on the ground at Mataṅga Ṛṣi's *āśrama.* This angered the great *ṛṣi,* who wondered who could have done such a thoughtless and stupid act. When Mataṅga came to know that the demon had been killed by Vāli, he

pronounced the following curse: 'If that monkey ever comes within four miles of my *āśrama,* he will instantly die. If any of his ministers come here they will remain as statues for thousands of years.'

"Although Vāli tried to pacify the *ṛṣi,* he was unable to, and has been afraid to approach this place ever since. Over there you can see the bones of the great demon. You can just imagine how powerful Dundhubhi must have been. How then, can You hope to defeat Vāli?"

Lakṣmaṇa then laughed, realizing that Sugrīva doubted Rāma's ability to kill Vāli. He asked, "What feat could Rāma do that would prove His prowess and set your mind at ease?"

Sugrīva replied, "Once, at this place, Vāli pierced seven large trees with seven arrows. If Rāma could split one of these trees with a single arrow and then kick the remains of Dundhubhi a distance of 200 bows' lengths, I would consider Him a suitable match for Vāli."

Hearing this, Rāma effortlessly lifted the skeleton of Dundhubhi with His big toe and sportingly flung it a distance of 80 miles. Even so, Sugrīva said, "When Vāli threw Dundhubhi's body it was heavy with flesh and blood. Moreover, he was greatly fatigued from fighting. Since the carcass is now much lighter, it is impossible to judge who is more powerful, You or Vāli."

At that, Rāma took up His bow and released a powerful arrow that pierced all seven trees, entered the earth, went down to the bottom of the universe, and after one hour returned to His quiver. Sugrīva was struck with wonder, and reverently bowed at Rāma's lotus feet. Rāma then embraced Sugrīva and suggested, "Let us now go to Kiṣkindhyā. You

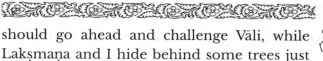

should go ahead and challenge Vāli, while Lakṣmaṇa and I hide behind some trees just outside the city gates."

When Sugrīva arrived at Kiṣkindhyā, he let out a loud roar, challenging his brother. As Vāli heard it, he immediately rushed out, excited with rage, just like the sun emerging from behind a hill. In great anger, Vāli and Sugrīva struck each other with their fists. However, as Rāma watched the fight, He could not discern which of the two was Vāli, for the two brothers looked exactly alike. Thus, Rāma refrained from discharging His arrows, causing Sugrīva to think that He was unwilling to help him. Indeed, Sugrīva was getting the worst of the fight, and finally ran away, barely alive, battered and soaked in his own blood. As Vāli chased Sugrīva, he taunted, "Coward, run for your life. This time I shall spare you."

Sugrīva then took shelter in the forest by Mataṅga's *āśrama,* and soon thereafter, Rāma, Lakṣmaṇa and Hanumān arrived. Sugrīva reproached Rāma, "If You did not intend to kill Vāli, why did You encourage me to challenge him? It would have been better for You to say, 'I am not willing to kill your elder brother.'"

Rāma then explained that He could not distinguish who was who in the fight, since they appeared identical. "It was for this reason, "Rāma said, "that I hesitated to discharge My arrow." He told Sugrīva to mark himself with something that would distinguish him from his brother.

Thereafter, Sugrīva again set out for Kiṣkindhyā, accompanied by Rāma, Lakṣmaṇa, and Hanumān. When they reached the outskirts of the city, Sugrīva strode forward, challenging his brother with loud roars, while the others

concealed themselves behind trees and bushes.

Vāli was inside the ladies' apartments when he heard Sugrīva summon him. In a fit of rage he rose up from his seat, storming out of the room in heavy strides. In great anxiety, Vāli's wife Tārā, clung to her husband, imploring him, "My dear lord, please cast aside your anger, and consider the matter carefully. You have already beaten Sugrīva severely. Thus, it is quite suspicious that he should return so soon, roaring with confidence. I must conclude that to dare act so boldly, Sugrīva must now be accompanied by a strong ally. Our son Aṅgada has received information from his spies that Rāma and Lakṣmaṇa have come here and made an alliance of friendship with Sugrīva. Since Rāma is inconceivably powerful, comparable to Lord Viṣṇu Himself, you should not risk creating enmity with Him. Please settle this by making Sugrīva the heir apparent, and thus establish friendship with Rāma."

Being destined to die, Vāli could not accept sound advice. Thus, he replied, "I cannot tolerate such arrogance from my younger brother. As for Rāma, I have no quarrel with Him. He is a virtuous *kṣatriya*, and I have no fear that He would harm a person that bears no enmity."

Saying this, Vāli stormed out of the city, hissing with rage. He confronted Sugrīva, and a fierce struggle ensued. As before, Vāli eventually began to gain the upper hand. Then Sugrīva signaled Rāma, indicating that his strength was waning.

Seeing that Sugrīva was near the point of collapse, Rāma fitted a powerful arrow onto His bowstring. He released

the arrow, and it flashed through the air like lightning, piercing Vāli deeply in the chest. However, even though bathed in his own blood and lying on the ground, Vāli did not immediately give up his life, for he was wearing a gold chain given to him by his father, King Indra.

Coming from their hiding place, Rāma and Lakṣmaṇa approached the fallen Vāli, who began chastising Rāma, saying, "I heard You were a righteous hero and king,

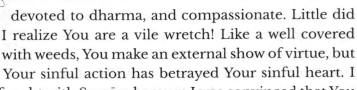

devoted to dharma, and compassionate. Little did I realize You are a vile wretch! Like a well covered with weeds, You make an external show of virtue, but Your sinful action has betrayed Your sinful heart. I fought with Sugrīva because I was convinced that You would not attack me. How could anyone claiming to be a *kṣatriya* and a hero kill someone engaged in fighting with another and with whom he has no enmity? I never harmed or insulted You. I never attacked Your kingdom. What merit have You acquired by striking me unfairly? How will You ever justify this action in front of righteous men? If You would have fought honestly, then it would be You lying here, not I! You shot Your arrow at me from behind, like a snake attacking a sleeping man. I challenge You to justify this shameful act!"

Rāma replied, "Your accusations show that you are actually ignorant of true morality. Monkeys are by nature frivolous because of their uncontrolled minds. Because you are a monkey, and your advisors are also monkeys, you cannot understand dharma.

"The entire earth, with its mountains, forests and rivers, is ruled over by the dynasty of Ikṣvāku. The kings of the Ikṣvāku dynasty have complete authority over all men and animals, and have the power to punish or reward whomever they please. It is you who have acted sinfully, under the sway of lust and greed. You have taken Rumā, the wife of your younger brother, and enjoyed her as your wife. It is for this sinful act that you deserve to die at My hands. Death is the proper punishment for one who has sexual relations with his daughter, daughter-in-law, sister or the wife of a younger brother. If a king does not punish a sinner, then he

himself becomes sinful. It is for this reason that I promised to kill you and thus enable Sugrīva to regain his wife and kingdom. Aside from this, it is an accepted practice that while hunting, *kṣatriyas* release their arrows at inattentive animals from a hidden position. Therefore, since you are only a monkey, My act does not bear the slightest fault."

Being enlightened by these words, Vāli felt shame for his abominable actions. With folded hands, he replied, "Whatever You have said is certainly true. I only dared to denounce You because I was overly proud, ignorant of my own sins. My dear Rāma, I implore You to give protection to my only son, Aṅgada, begot by me through my wife Tārā. He will certainly become grief-stricken upon hearing of my death. Please excuse my harsh words spoken in ignorance." Rāma assured Vāli that He would take care of Aṅgada.

Meanwhile, Tārā came running from the palace with her son. She was surrounded by Vāli's ministers, but when the monkeys saw Rāma they began to flee in fear. Tārā tried to restrain them, but they urged, "Do not go out to see Vāli. Protect your son within the fortifications of Kiṣkindhyā and prepare to install him on the throne."

Tārā answered, "I do not care for sovereignty. The kingdom and its royal opulence are now useless without my husband."

Crying and beating her breast in lamentation, Tārā went to where Vāli lay upon the ground, in the grip of approaching death. Tārā embraced her dying husband, and Vāli's other wives surrounded them, plunged in grief. Tārā's only desire was to follow her husband, and she made up her mind to

fast until death. At this, Hanumān went to her and pleaded, "O Queen, please get up. Do not succumb to grief. You must perform the funeral ceremonies for your husband and protect Aṅgada after installing him upon the throne."

Vāli then said, "My dear Sugrīva, I beg you to forgive me for all the wrong I have done toward you. Accept the kingdom from me now and take care of my son, Aṅgada, for he shall always remain faithful to you."

Saying this, Vāli handed Sugrīva the celestial gold chain he had received from Indra. Then, turning to Aṅgada, he said, "My dear son, now that I am departing you should always remain obedient to Sugrīva. Always act after due consideration and accept the dualities of pleasure and pain with an equipoised mind. Avoid excessive attachment and hatred, for both lead to degradation."

Thus, after speaking to Aṅgada, Vāli, who was deeply wounded by Rāma's arrow, gave up his life. Then, as Tārā continued to embrace her dead husband, wailing in grief, Nīla came and extracted the arrow from Vāli's chest. Tārā then told Aṅgada, "Bow down to your father's feet." As the young prince did this, he too became overwhelmed with grief.

Upon seeing Tārā's anguish, Sugrīva became despondent, and with a sorrowful voice, said to Rāma, "I have found that the fulfillment of my desire has produced the opposite of what I anticipated. Instead of happiness, I feel repulsion toward the kingdom, and even life itself. To atone for my sin, I will give up my life in the fire. My dear Rāma, these other heroic monkeys will help You search for Your beloved wife, Sītā."

Rāma became dejected hearing Sugrīva speak this way. As tears came to Rāma's eyes, Tārā approached Him, saying, "I know that my husband will be very unhappy without me, even if he now resides in heaven. Therefore, please kill me also, so I may rejoin him. If You consider killing a woman to be sinful, then just think of me as nondifferent from Vāli."

Rāma turned to Sugrīva, saying, "Your tears of sorrow are sufficient bereavement for the departed soul of your brother. This world is moving under the direction of eternal time, and all living entities make their appearance and departure. Under the direction of the Supreme Personality of Godhead, Time never oversteps its limit. Thus, one should not lament for that which is inevitable."

In this way, Sugrīva became pacified. With Lakṣmaṇa's help, he began to arrange for the cremation of his brother's body. Soon thereafter, a palanquin was brought from Kiṣkindhyā. Sugrīva placed Vāli's body on it and led the funeral procession to the banks of a nearby mountain stream. As the funeral pyre was being built, Tārā placed Vāli's head upon her lap, while continuing to weep bitterly, giving pain to all who saw her. Finally, the other women came and raised Tārā up, allowing Sugrīva and Aṅgada to place the body of Vāli on the funeral pyre. After the cremation, the relatives brought water from the river Tuṅgabhadrā, and made offerings for the departed soul of the heroic monkey king.

When the funeral ceremonies were completed, Hanumān requested Rāma to accompany Sugrīva to Kiṣkindhyā to install him on the royal throne. Rāma, declined, however,

saying, "Hanumān, I suggest that you officiate at Sugrīva's coronation and have Aṅgada installed as heir apparent. Since the monsoon season is nearly upon us, it is not a suitable time to search for Sītā. All the monkey chiefs may stay in Kiṣkindhyā for four months, while Lakṣmaṇa and I pass Our time residing in a mountain cave. When autumn arrives, we can begin an all-out search for the kingdom of Rāvaṇa."

Sugrīva then entered Kiṣkindhyā and was welcomed by the citizens. The bathing ceremony at his coronation was performed by the foremost of monkeys, including Mainda, Dvivida, and Hanumān, as well as Jāmbavān, the king of the bears. Sugrīva accepted his wife Rumā back, and installed Aṅgada as heir apparent to the royal throne.

For four months, Rāma and Lakṣmaṇa dwelt within a mountain cave. Feeling intense separation from Sītā, Rāma could not find any pleasure in the scenic beauty of the mountainous region. He was unable to sleep at night, and constantly shed tears of anguish.

One day Rāma said to Lakṣmaṇa, "After evaporating water from the ocean for nine months, the sky now sends forth heavy showers of rain. Dark clouds as large as hills range across the sky in clusters, creating a mood of melancholy. The golden lightning, as it streaks inside a blackish monsoon cloud, appears like Sītā in the arms of Rāvaṇa.

"The lush, green grass, spotted with various flowers and restless birds, provides a colorful dress for mother earth. Bees are humming, frogs are croaking, and the rumble of

thunder and patter of the rain provide musical accompaniment. Surely Sugrīva is able to enjoy all this, for his objective has been fulfilled. But without Sītā, I am like the riverbank that erodes from the river's constant current."

Lakṣmaṇa would try to encourage Rāma, pointing out that the purpose of a grieving man was never fulfilled. Regardless, the dark skies and frequent rains that nourished the tropical jungle only intensified Rāma's longing for Sītā.

Rāma assumed that when He had helped Sugrīva to regain his kingdom, Sugrīva would remember his obligation to assist Him find Sītā. But when autumn arrived and the skies became clear, Sugrīva did not come forward to meet Rāma. Having achieved his goal, and now without cause for fear, Sugrīva had begun to spend his time completely absorbed in enjoying the company of young women in private, especially his wife Rumā and the newly acquired Tārā. Thus, he even neglected to fulfill his obligation of managing the state administration.

When Hanumān saw how Sugrīva had become a slave to sensuality, and thereby becoming negligent in his duties, he approached the king and advised, "You must keep your promise and fulfill your obligation to Rāma. Only out of respect for you, has Rāma not personally come here to remind you. However, you must remember that it is only by His grace that you have been allowed to prosper. It is now time for you to summon the more than ten million monkeys under your command and begin an all-out search for Sītā."

Hanumān's speech momentarily brought Sugrīva back to his senses. Sugrīva then called Nīla and ordered, "Let

my proclamation be broadcast to all the monkey warriors: All must proceed here for duty within fifteen days, or else face the death-sentence." Giving this command, Sugrīva returned to his inner apartments.

The beauty of autumn only heightened Rāma's anguish in separation from Sītā. When He could understand that Sugrīva was simply wallowing in a life of sensuality, Rāma became yet more depressed. Lakṣmaṇa also became despondent from witnessing Rāma's grief, and tried his best to cheer Him.

One day Rāma decided, "Now that autumn has arrived, the ground is dry and firm, the air crisp and cool. This is the perfect time to initiate a military campaign. Unfortunately, Sugrīva is not to be seen. It appears that he has forgotten all sense of duty, being fully absorbed in the pleasure of the association of women. Therefore, Lakṣmaṇa, I want You to go to Kiṣkindhyā and admonish Sugrīva in My name, saying, 'O king of the monkeys, one who acts like you is the most vile of persons. I am astonished that you are not afraid of neglecting Rāma, the slayer of your elder brother. I hereby warn you that if you neglect your promise to help Rāma find Sītā, then He will personally come to Kiṣkindhyā and kill you, along with all your relatives.'"

When Rāma exhibited His anger, born of intense transcendental frustration, Lakṣmaṇa also became incited with rage. Picking up His bow, Lakṣmaṇa declared, "If that rascal Sugrīva does not jump to execute Your command, then I shall kill him Myself this very day!"

As Lakṣmaṇa quickly departed, Rāma tried to restrain His brother's anger. "First speak to Sugrīva in a conciliatory

tone, for I am sure that will be enough to bring him to his senses," Rāma said.

In a mood of great indignation, Lakṣmaṇa entered Kiṣkindhyā, a beautiful city built within a large cave. As He rushed like a mad elephant toward Sugrīva's palace, Lakṣmaṇa knocked down the trees that stood in his path. When the many fierce monkeys guarding the palace entrance saw Lakṣmaṇa approach, His lips trembling in rage, they began gathering weapons by uprooting large trees and tearing down mountain peaks. When Lakṣmaṇa saw the monkey guards arming themselves in this way, He became so ferocious that the monkey guards became panic-stricken and fearfully ran away.

Sugrīva's ministers rushed to Sugrīva to inform him of Lakṣmaṇa's arrival in such an angry mood. Sugrīva, however, was fully absorbed in sexual activities with Tārā, and did not pay much heed to his ministers.

As the ministers ordered the monkeys to arm themselves in preparation for battle, the enraged Lakṣmaṇa met Aṅgada and told him to inform Sugrīva of his arrival. At that, Aṅgada went into Sugrīva's chamber and, clasping his uncle's feet, informed him of Lakṣmaṇa's presence. However, Sugrīva had fallen asleep in a drunken state, and failed to rise. Only when numerous monkeys began to clamor loudly around Sugrīva did he finally arise. Out of fear of Lakṣmaṇa, Sugrīva came to his senses. As Sugrīva opened his blood-shot eyes, his ministers informed him, "Lakṣmaṇa is now waiting for you outside the palace gates in a highly agitated state. We urge you to go out immediately, offer your obeisances and submit to Him. Pray this will appease His anger!"

Having finally realized the gravity of the situation, Sugrīva hastily arose from his bed, wondering why Lakṣmaṇa would be angry with him. Hanumān then reminded Sugrīva, "O king, due to becoming absorbed in sense gratification, you have not even noticed how the time has passed. Autumn has long since arrived, yet you have neglected to fulfill your promise to help Rāma in His search for Sītā. Lakṣmaṇa has now come here to remind you. I suggest you approach Him with folded hands, and hope that you may somehow appease Him."

On Sugrīva's order, Aṅgada escorted Lakṣmaṇa into the palace. All the monkeys who previously had taken up weapons now stood with folded hands to greet Lakṣmaṇa. When Lakṣmaṇa came to the inner apartments of Sugrīva's palace, He could hear the voices of women singing to the accompaniment of musical instruments, mixed with the jingling sound of their ornaments. Indeed, upon seeing all the young, beautiful women, Lakṣmaṇa became somewhat ashamed, due to His vow to shun the company of others' wives. Although He restrained Himself from entering, Lakṣmaṇa announced His arrival by twanging His mighty bow. Sugrīva trembled upon hearing that sound, and told Tārā, "I wonder why Lakṣmaṇa is angry. I think it would be better for you to go out first and try to appease Him."

Tārā came before Lakṣmaṇa, her dress loosened and her eyes rolled from intoxication. Lakṣmaṇa's anger subsided, and He humbly looked downward toward her feet out of respect. Tārā then inquired, "My dear prince, why are You so angry with Sugrīva?"

Lakṣmaṇa sharply replied, "Your husband has neglected his obligation to Rāma, preferring instead to pass his days in

his inner apartments, dallying with women."

Tārā then pleaded to Lakṣmaṇa, "You must forgive Sugrīva, for he has lost his good intelligence under the sway of lust. Even great *ṛṣis* sometimes hanker for sense gratification, what to speak of a fickle-minded monkey. Please do not think that Sugrīva has forgotten his obligation to Rāma. He has already called for millions of monkeys to assemble here to begin the search for Sītā. Please come in and talk to Sugrīva Yourself."

Lakṣmaṇa entered the inner apartments of the palace. When He saw the fabulous opulence and bevies of beautiful women, his anger again became aroused. Sugrīva was seated upon a couch, embracing Rumā. However, upon seeing Lakṣmaṇa enter, he hurriedly stood up with folded hands, as did all the ladies present. Lakṣmaṇa then chastised Sugrīva, "You have simply made empty promises, proving yourself to be a false friend. Therefore, you are most abominable. One who receives help from a sincere friend and does not repay that service is considered hard-hearted, and must be killed. Indeed, once, when Lord Brahmā saw such an ungrateful person, he exclaimed, 'The means of atonement has been prescribed for the killer of a cow, a drunkard, a thief, or for one who has broken a sacred vow, but there is no expiation for an ungrateful soul!' I warn you, Sugrīva! If you do not begin helping Rāma immediately, you will meet your brother Vāli in the abode of Yamarāja this very day!"

Tārā then replied for her husband. "O Lakṣmaṇa, Sugrīva is not a liar, nor is he hard-hearted. He has not forgot what Rāma did for his sake. His only fault is losing all sense of time because of overindulgence in sense gratification. We have heard that in Laṅkā, the abode of Rāvaṇa, there are

100 thousand crores of Rākṣasas. Since it would not be possible to kill Rāvaṇa without slaying them first, Sugrīva has summoned innumerable monkey warriors from all corners of the earth. He has not yet met with Rāma or initiated the search for Sītā because he is awaiting their arrival. Sugrīva has set a fifteen-day time limit. Thus, thousands of monkeys, bears and baboons are expected to begin arriving at Kiṣkindhyā this very day."

Hearing this, Lakṣmaṇa gave up His anger. Sugrīva humbly threw aside his garland and said, "I could never repay Rāma for all that He has done for me. He is my master and my Lord. I will follow Him wherever He goes and do whatever He orders. I fully admit that I was at fault, and humbly beg Your forgiveness."

Pleased, Lakṣmaṇa replied, "Kindly forgive my angry mood as well. I think it would be best for you to go now and see Rāma. He will be encouraged by your sincerity."

Sugrīva then ordered Hanumān, "Summon again all the monkeys from the Himālayan, Mahendra, Mandara and Kailāsa mountains. Arouse all who are prone to sense indulgence and procrastination. Tell them that anyone who does not respond to my order within ten days will be killed!"

Hanumān immediately dispatched the monkey leaders in all directions. Then within the same hour, millions of monkeys began pouring into Kiṣkindhyā. After presenting themselves to Sugrīva, the monkeys were dismissed. Then Lakṣmaṇa again requested Sugrīva to go and meet with Rāma. Thus, Sugrīva had a palanquin brought forth, and he and Lakṣmaṇa were carried to Rāma's dwelling, accompanied by innumerable monkeys.

Thereafter, as Lakṣmaṇa and Sugrīva stood before Rāma with folded hands, Rāma gazed upon the army of monkeys with great pleasure. Sugrīva then fell flat before Rāma, submitting himself as a fully surrendered soul at His lotus feet. Rāma then mercifully lifted up Sugrīva and embraced him, without any trace of resentment for Sugrīva's past negligence.

After offering the monkey king a seat, Rāma instructed Sugrīva about royal duties: "A king should understand the proper times for dharma, *artha* and *kāma*, and then enjoy life accordingly. When a king gives up the Vedic regulations, being overly attached to sense gratification, thus indulging himself irregularly, he is considered fallen. My dear Sugrīva, now is the time for you to endeavor to find Sītā, as you have already vowed."

Sugrīva replied, "My dear Rāma, please rest assured: I am eager to help You, as are all the monkeys who have assembled here."

Rāma again embraced Sugrīva, reconfirming their friendship. Thereafter, a huge dust cloud began forming, because of the great hoards of monkeys converging upon Kiṣkindhyā in response to Sugrīva's order. The cloud covered the entire sky, so that the sun became veiled. All the great leaders of the monkeys, and Jāmbavān, the king of the bears, came before Sugrīva with their millions of followers. The entire surrounding forest and mountain area became completely covered by the monkeys. Pointing out the different groups of monkeys, Sugrīva said to Rāma, "My dear Lord, You should consider these monkey warriors as Your own army. From now on, please order them as You see fit."

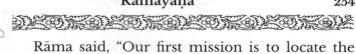

Rāma said, "Our first mission is to locate the abode of Rāvaṇa and ascertain whether Sītā is still alive. My dear Sugrīva, you should organize the search parties. When Sītā is found, I will give the necessary orders."

Sugriva immediately called for the monkey king Vinda and ordered, "I want you and your soldiers to search everywhere in the eastern direction, including the seven oceans and seven islands. Beyond the ocean of milk there is an ocean of fresh water, wherein lies the subterranean fire. Thirteen *yojanas* from the eastern shore of the fresh water ocean is the mountain called Jātarūpaśila, which is made entirely out of golden rocks. It is there that Lord Ananta Śeṣa resides, supporting the entire earth. This marks the outer boundary of the eastern quarter. I am giving you one month to search this entire area. Anyone who reports back later than that will be executed for neglecting the royal order."

Next, Sugrīva dispatched Aṅgada, Nīla, Hanumān, Jāmbavān, Mainda, Dvivida and others to the south, making the son of Vāli their leader. After describing the southern region, Sugrīva instructed the monkeys, "Eight hundred miles beyond the northern shore of the salt ocean is an island that I think must surely be the residence of Rāvaṇa. Further to the South is Bhogavatī, the capital of Rasātala, which is presided over by Vāsuki. Then, beyond the Ṛsabha mountain, which marks the furthest boundary of Bhū-maṇḍala, is the abode of Yamarāja. Do not search the Pitāloka or anywhere beyond, for no earthly being can go there."

Sugrīva then dispatched Suṣeṇa and his followers to the west. He instructed them, "In the middle of the salt ocean is Prāgjyotiṣapura, the city of Narakāsura, and the western

limit is where the sun sets. Beyond that there is no information as to what exists, so you should not go there."

Finally, Śatabali was dispatched to the North, and Sugrīva informed him, "You will first come to the land of the Mlecchas, and then the Himālayan Mountains. Beyond these mountains is 800 miles of desolate land. After that is Mount Kailāsa, where Kuvera resides. Beyond Kailāsa is Krauñca Mountain, then Uttara-Kuru province, and finally, the northern salt-water sea, in the middle of which is a golden mountain called Somagiri. Therein, Lord

Viṣṇu, Brahmā and Śiva reside. When you see that mountain, you should turn back, for it is not possible to go beyond that."

Sugrīva considered Hanumān to be the most capable of finding Sītā. To encourage him, Sugrīva said, "O Hanumān, of all the powerful monkeys, you are exceptional. There is no one capable of obstructing you on this earth, in the sky, in heaven or in the nether regions. Not only do you have super-human strength, but you are courageous, intelligent and resourceful. Therefore, I am especially counting on you to find Sītā."

Hearing these words and observing Hanumān's self-confidence, Rāma also became convinced that Hanumān would be the one to find His beloved wife. Taking His ring, Rāma handed it to Hanumān, saying, "My name is inscribed on the inside. When you locate Sītā, give her this ring. She will then become convinced that you are My envoy. My dear Hanumān, I have full confidence that you will be able to carry out this important mission on My behalf."

Accepting the ring, Hanumān touched it to his head and bowed down before Rāma. He then departed while the other monkeys began scouring the earth for Sītā. Rāma and Lakṣmaṇa consented to remain in Their mountain cave for the next month. After the monkeys had departed, Rāma asked Sugrīva, "How have you acquired such extensive knowledge of the earth's geography?"

Sugrīva replied, "After Vāli returned to Kiṣkindhyā and banished me, even though I voluntarily surrendered the kingdom to him, he remained angry and continued to chase after me. Thus, out of fear for my brother, I continually

wandered over the surface of the entire earth seeking shelter. Finally, after some time, Hanumān informed me of Mataṅga's curse, and I took shelter of Mataṅga's *āśrama.*"

As the monkeys searched for Sītā, they spread out during the day to comb their allotted areas, and at night regrouped to take rest. Before one month had elapsed, Vinata, Śatabali and Suṣeṇa returned, having thoroughly scoured their assigned regions. With sad faces, they reported to Sugrīva that they had not been able to unearth even a single clue about Sītā's location. Sugrīva sat next to Rāma as the monkeys came and related to Him their experiences. Everyone concluded that Hanumān was their only hope.

As the party led by Aṅgada thoroughly searched throughout the desolate Vindhya mountain range, they became tormented by hunger and thirst, for that entire region was devoid of water. Then, when the monkeys left the mountains and entered the adjoining forest, they were disappointed to find that the trees did not even bear leaves, what to speak of fruit and flowers. Because all the streams in that area were dried up, it was also bereft of birds and other animals.

The forest had once been the home of the great sage Kaṇḍu. When his son died prematurely at the age of ten, the *ṛṣi* became so angry that he cursed the entire forest to become unfit for the habitation of man or beast.

While roaming in this desolate forest, the monkeys came upon a ferocious Rākṣasa. Although the demon was fearless, having received a benediction from the demigods, he was

killed by Aṅgada, who thought him to be Rāvaṇa. However, when Aṅgada's party searched the entire area and failed to find any clue concerning Sītā's whereabouts, they became disappointed.

Time passed quickly. As Aṅgada urged the monkeys on in their search around the Vindhya mountain range, the allotted one month came to an end. Oppressed by hunger and thirst, the monkeys searched for water. Then Aṅgada and Tāra sighted a cave where moist creepers grew thickly and aquatic birds flocked. They hastened to the cave, hoping to find water within.

The cave was deep and dark, and as they cautiously entered it, they made a chain by holding hands. Finally, after proceeding for eight miles, the monkeys could see a light deep within the cave. Proceeding further, they came upon a grove of golden trees. Soon they came upon golden palaces, beautiful ponds and lovely gardens. In the midst of this heavenly grove, the monkeys beheld an ascetic woman dressed in black deerskin and glowing with great spiritual effulgence. Hanumān approached her with folded hands and said, "Kindly tell us who you are and to whom this cave belongs. Why does everything have such a golden appearance? We are very tired and thirsty. We have been wandering about through waterless regions for a long time."

The woman replied, "My name is Svayamprabhā, the daughter of Meru-sāvarṇi, the superintending deity of Mount Meru. I am a friend of the Apsarā Hemā, and I remain here guarding this hermitage. This cave, named Ṛkṣabila, is the creation of Maya Dānava. After performing austerities here, Maya Dānava received a benediction from Lord Brahmā that enabled him to possess all the mystic powers known

to Śukra. Thereafter, Maya Dānava continued dwelling here. However, later on, when Maya became attached to Hemā, Indra drove him from these regions with the help of his thunderbolt. Lord Brahmā then gave this cave to Hemā. Please make yourselves feel at home and kindly tell me the purpose of your coming to this inaccessible region."

According to Vedic etiquette, one must always welcome a guest. First, one should offer him a sitting place and

refreshment; afterwards, one can inquire about his well being. Even if the host is very poor, he can at least offer a clean sitting place and a glass of water. In such a pleasant atmosphere, a guest is sure to feel peaceful and happy. Thus Svayamprabhā heartily welcomed her visitors.

As Svayamprabhā offered her guests her hospitality, Hanumān narrated the entire story of Rāma's exile and their search for the kidnapped Sītā. Hanumān then said, "We cannot thank you enough for your kind reception. Is there any service we can perform in return?"

Svayamprabhā replied, "Because I am engaged in performing austerities, I have nothing to ask from others."

Hanumān then said, "Our master, the monkey King Sugrīva, has allotted us one month to find Sītā. That time has already expired, and we therefore feel doomed. Is there any way you can help us?"

Svayamprabhā replied, "It is nearly impossible for anyone who has entered this cave to get out alive. However, I shall assist you by utilizing my mystic powers. But you must close your eyes, for no one can leave here while looking about."

Thereafter, the monkeys kept their eyes tightly shut. Suddenly they felt themselves being transported out of the cave. When they at last opened their eyes, they saw that everyone had been carried out of the cave. Looking about, they could see that all the trees were now in full bloom. Apparently spring had arrived. The monkeys became very depressed, thinking of how so much time had somehow

mysteriously elapsed. Aṅgada then suggested, "We should all sit down and fast until death, for that would be more noble than being killed by Sugrīva for our negligence."

All the assembled monkeys agreed that there was no question of them returning to Kiṣkindhyā without first obtaining some information about Sītā. Tāra then proposed, "Let us take shelter within this inaccessible cave, for we could all live there without fear of being discovered."

Aṅgada remained silent, as if ready to approve this plan. However, Hanumān said, "My dear prince, I consider you to be endowed with the eight attributes of intelligence: an inclination to hear what others have to say, the capacity to hear what others have to say, the ability to comprehend the basic meaning of what others have to say, good memory, capacity to reason in favor of a proposition, capacity to reason against a proposition, deep insight into the meaning of what others say, and true wisdom. Above and beyond all this, you are endowed with the fourteen excellences that characterize great personalities: a sense of time and place, firmness, ability to endure all kinds of hardship, knowledge of all subjects, expertise, vigor, ability to guard secrets, consistency, heroism, ability to judge one's own strength in comparison to that of the enemy, appreciation for the services rendered by others, compassion for surrendered souls, indignation in the presence of unrighteousness, and steadiness in duty."

In this way, Hanumān employed the first political expedient by flattering Aṅgada. Then he utilized the third by causing some dissension among the monkeys, making them argue about what should be done. Finally, he intimidated Aṅgada by saying, "If you go through with your foolish plan

to live within this cave then you shall soon meet with disaster. The other monkeys will not remain faithful to you for very long under such conditions. Moreover, eventually Lakṣmaṇa will find out where you are and destroy the cave along with you and the other monkeys. However, if you return to Kiṣkindhyā, Sugrīva will certainly forgive you. Because you are the only son, he will later install you on the throne."

Aṅgada countered Hanumān by arguing, "You overestimate Sugrīva and forget that he is enjoying his elder brother's wife. Sugrīva purposefully neglected his promise to Rāma and took action only after being threatened by Lakṣmaṇa. Therefore, whoever wants to can return home. I, however, shall remain here, fasting until death."

After saying this, Aṅgada sat down on *kuśa* grass and wept. The other monkeys surrounded him, likewise determined to give up their lives. Just then, Sampāti, the elder brother of Jaṭāyu, came out of his cave and perched on top of a mountain in sight of all the monkeys. Being overjoyed, he said aloud to himself, "By the grace of providence I have got some food after such a long time. When the monkeys begin to fall down dead from starvation, I shall eat them one by one!"

Hearing this, Aṅgada became agitated. Addressing Hanumān, he said, "What a horrible fate we now face! This is all the doing of the evil Kaikeyī. First she caused the destruction of the great soul, Jaṭāyu, then Vāli, and now she will become the cause of our deaths as well."

This was the first time Sampāti had heard of Jaṭāyu's death, and so he requested, "Please tell me all the details

about the passing of my younger brother. I have become very pleased in hearing Jaṭāyu's name glorified by you, although I am distressed to hear of his death. O best of the monkeys, I wish to beg one favor from you. Long ago, the rays of the sun burned my wings, and now I cannot fly. Would you kindly help me to come down from this mountain peak?"

Since only moments earlier, Sampāti had expressed his desire to eat them, the monkeys could not readily put much faith in his words. However, they reasoned, "We are going to die in any case by fasting. Therefore, even if this gigantic vulture eats us alive, it only means that our suffering will end more quickly."

The monkeys went and helped Sampāti down from the mountaintop. As they went down, Aṅgada told the entire story of Rāma's exile and the heroic death of Jaṭāyu. In turn, Sampāti related his own history in a tearful voice: "Long, long ago, Jaṭāyu and I wanted to test our prowess by challenging the king of heaven. After soaring high into the sky, up to the heavenly planets, we defeated Indra in battle. Then, having become very proud, we decided to rise up even higher. Thereafter, as we approached the sun, Jaṭāyu grew faint from the great heat. To save Jaṭāyu I covered him with my wings. In the process, my wings became burned and I fell down onto the Vindhya Mountains."

Aṅgada then interrupted, saying, "If you are actually the elder brother of Jaṭāyu and our well-wisher, then give us information about the abode of Rāvaṇa."

Sampāti replied, "Because I am now very old and my wings are burnt, I am unable to physically serve Lord Rāma.

But at least I can do so with my power of speech. I was told that a young lady was carried away by Rāvaṇa, and while crying out, 'Rāma! Rāma!' she dropped some of her ornaments to the ground. I know that this Rāvaṇa is the king of the Rākṣasas, and his kingdom, Laṅkā, is situated on an island, one hundred *yojanas* from the southern shore. Because I am a descendent of Vinatā, my vision extends for more than one hundred *yojanas*. Thus, I can see the golden city from here. My dear monkeys, you will be able to find Sītā in Laṅkā, guarded by the Rākṣasīs. Now, please grant me one favor. Take me to the ocean so that I can offer water for the departed soul of my brother."

The monkeys were overjoyed to hear about Sītā. Thus, casting aside their vow to fast until death, they took Sampāti to the ocean and quickly returned. Jāmbavān then asked him, "How did you come to learn that Sītā had been abducted by Rāvaṇa?"

Sampāti explained, "After my wings were burnt and I fell into the Vindhya Mountains, my son Supārśva began to take care of me and bring my food. Once I was very hungry, and when Supārśva returned home without food, I chastised him. My son told me, 'While searching for flesh today, I happened to see a giant Rākṣasa carrying away a young woman through the air. I wanted to bring both of them to you to eat, but the Rākṣasa asked me in a very friendly manner to allow him to pass by. I could not refuse his request. Afterwards, the Siddhas came and informed me that he was Rāvaṇa, and said that it was fortunate for me that the Rākṣasa had not killed me.'"

Sampāti could see that the monkeys were now confident of his friendship. He continued narrating his life story. "After I fell onto the Vindhya Mountains, I remained unconscious for six days. When I came to my senses, I went to see the great sage, Niśākara, who was living nearby, and was known to my brother and me. When I met the *ṛṣi,* he asked me how my wings had been burnt and I explained the entire incident. I told him that after falling from the sky and not hearing from my brother, I contemplated committing suicide by jumping from a mountain peak. As I stood before him, tears flowing from my eyes, Niśākara told me, 'Do not despair, for I give you the

following benediction—when, at a future date, you give information to the monkeys about Sītā, your wings will reappear, along with renewed energy.'

"Saying this, the sage Niśākara retired to his cottage, and I crawled back to my place in the Vindhya Mountains. Since then, I have simply waited for your arrival. After 8,000 years passed, the *ṛṣi* Niśākara gave up his body and went to heaven. In his absence, I had begun to doubt the validity of his words."

As Sampāti spoke to the monkeys, a pair of wings sprouted from his body, and he felt a surge of youthful energy. With great delight, Sampāti encouraged the monkeys to resume their search for Sītā. As Sampāti soared into the sky, the monkeys headed south, rejuvenated with new hope.

However, when the monkeys reached the shore of the ocean, they became dejected upon seeing its vastness, thinking themselves incapable of crossing over to Laṅkā. Aṅgada encouraged the monkeys, saying, "Despondency is useless, for it has never caused an action to bear fruit. Indeed, despair is the root of failure. It is as deadly as a poisonous snake. Now, whoever can leap 100 *yojanas* to rescue Sītā from the clutches of Rāvaṇa, please step forward, so we can become freed from Sugrīva's wrath."

Since no one responded to Aṅgada's call, he began asking the monkeys individually how far they could jump. Some monkeys said that they could jump 10 *yojanas*, or 20, 30, 40, or 50. Mainda said he could jump 60 *yojanas* and Dvivida claimed 70. Suṣeṇa declared he could easily jump 80 *yojanas*, while Jāmbavān explained, "Formerly I had an

almost unlimited jumping capacity. However, now at the end of my life, I can only leap 90 *yojanas*. Long ago when Lord Vāmana covered the entire universe, I circumambulated Him as He took His three strides. Unfortunately, I am no longer capable of jumping to Laṅkā to rescue Sītā."

Finally, Aṅgada said, "I can probably jump 100 *yojanas*, but I doubt I could do so a second time to make the return journey."

Jāmbavān replied, "I am sure that with your prowess you could leap 1,000 *yojanas*. However, you are the leader of this expedition, and it would not be proper for you to accomplish the task yourself. Therefore, my dear prince, you must order someone else to do it."

Aṅgada replied, "It does not matter who is in charge. If someone does not go to Laṅkā, be it myself or someone else, then our only alternative is to fast until death. Therefore, Jāmbavān, please devise some means whereby we can cross the ocean and save ourselves from Sugrīva's wrath."

Jāmbavān then said, "Do not worry, for I shall now appeal to someone who will certainly be able to perform this difficult feat. O Hanumān, you are equal to Garuḍa, the carrier of Lord Viṣṇu. Why have you not spoken up?

Please listen as I now describe the glories of the best of all monkeys. Once, one of the foremost Apsarās, named Puñjikasthalī, was cursed by a *ṛṣi*, and thus took birth as Añjanā, the daughter of the monkey king, Kuñjara. Añjanā grew up to be unparalleled in beauty, and could change her form at will.

"Once, after having married the monkey chief, Kesari, Añjanā took the form of a human being and began wandering through the mountains. Upon seeing the beautiful Añjanā, Vāyu became captivated, and removed her dress by means of the wind. When Vāyu saw Añjanā's rounded and closely united thighs, her swelling breasts and other feminine attractions, he became overwhelmed with sexual desire and embraced her by force. Unable to see her assailant, Añjanā cried out, 'Who is violating

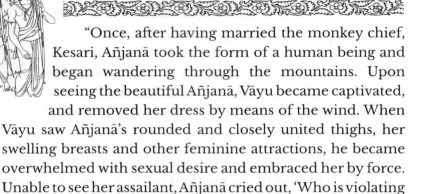

my vow to accept only one husband?' Vāyu, replied, 'I am the god of air, Vāyu. I have not physically spoiled your chastity, because I have entered you mentally. By my grace you will give birth to a powerful son who is equal to myself in ranging at will.'

"Añjanā became pleased by Vāyu's words, and soon thereafter, she gave birth to Hanumān within a mountain cave. The next morning, when baby Hanumān saw the rising sun, he thought it to be a shiny fruit. Desiring to catch it, he leapt more than 3,000 *yojanas* into the sky, but was thrown back to earth by the sun's brilliance. Unscathed, Hanumān jumped again. This time, however, Indra became angered by the monkey's audacity, and hurled his thunderbolt. Thus, the king of heaven's weapon dashed Hanumān against a mountainside, fracturing the left side of his chin. Indeed, it is because of this incident that Hanumān received his name, for Hanumān means, 'One having a broken chin.'

"Vāyu became furious at Indra's aggression against his son, and began withholding the air from the three worlds. This plunged the demigods into great anxiety. With Lord Brahmā at their head, they rushed to Vāyu's abode, hoping to pacify him. Just to satisfy the wind god, Lord Brahmā blessed Hanumān to become invincible in battle. Indra was pleased and surprised to see that the baby monkey had not been killed by his thunderbolt. Therefore, he awarded Hanumān the benediction of being able to die at will."

Jāmbavān concluded, "I consider Hanumān alone to be capable of executing our mission. Of course, in the past, this little jump would have been nothing for me. As Lord Trivikrama expanded His three steps to take away Bali's

kingdom, I soared around the world 21 times to circumambulate Him. When the demigods and demons wanted to produce nectar, it was I who single-handedly collected all the herbs that were thrown into the ocean of milk. However, I have grown very old. It is now time for Hanumān to exhibit his prowess."

Hanumān became greatly encouraged upon hearing these words of glorification. Then, to the joy of all the monkeys present, Hanumān began expanding himself into a gigantic form, while telling his own glories: "I am able to go around Mount Meru 1,000 times without even pausing, and by splashing the waters of the ocean, I could inundate the entire world. I could circumambulate Garuḍa 1,000 times as he flies through the sky, and I can uproot the entire city of Laṅkā and carry it a great distance, if I so desire."

All the monkeys were thrilled to hear Hanumān boast of his prowess. However, to remind him of the gravity of the situation, they said, "We shall all stand here upon one foot until you return. Our very lives rest upon you, as well as all hopes for recovering Sītā."

Hanumān then informed the monkeys, "I will leap from the peak of mount Mahendra, since it is capable of sustaining the immense pressure I will exert on the earth for my leap." Then Hanumān departed, and within a minute he arrived at the mighty Mahendra Hill, which would serve as the support for his monumental leap.

Sundara-kāṇḍa

The virtuous Hanumān first offered his obeisances unto Sūrya, Indra, Vāyu and Brahmā at the foot of mount Mahendra. Then, after climbing to its peak, he expanded his body to gigantic proportions. By grabbing the mountain with his hands and feet, he inadvertently crushed many deer underfoot. Hanumān paused for several moments, and composed his mind in preparation for the great leap. Because of the weight of his huge body, the entire mountain began to shake. Large snakes vomited fire from their mouths and bit into the rocks, causing them to split into thousands

of flaming fragments. The Vidyādharas flew up in the sky to witness Hanumān's spectacular jump.

Hanumān crouched down, summoning all his energy, and as the mountain peak began to crumble, spurts of water gushed forth from the immense pressure. Gandharva couples that had been sporting in the heavenly region, along with numerous *ṛṣis* that resided there, quickly fled the mountain out of fear. Hanumān then declared to the monkeys, "Either I shall bring back Sītā, or I shall uproot the entire city of Laṅkā, along with Rāvaṇa."

Hanumān drew in his breath and tensed his muscles. Suddenly he sprang into the air like an arrow shot from the bow of Lord Rāma. Due to the force of Hanumān's jump, all the trees on the peak of Mount Mahendra were uprooted and thrown into the sky. Hanumān soared like a huge cloud and stretched out his tail. As Hanumān sailed through the heavens, the uprooted trees followed in his wake and plummeted into the ocean. Colored flowers from their branches fluttered down and scattered over the surface of the water, creating a beautiful sight.

The hurricane created by Hanumān's flight agitated the ocean, creating waves as tall as mountains that crashed against his breast. The shadow of Hanumān projected upon the surface of the water measured 80 by 240 miles, and the suction created as he passed through the air drew the surrounding clouds to him. Hanumān resembled the moon as he became hidden in the masses of clouds, and visible again as he emerged from them. Out of parental affection, Vāyu blew cooling breezes, keeping the sunshine from scorching him.

As Hanumān soared through the sky, all classes of beings applauded him. The ocean deity also desired to assist him, out of respect for Lord Rāma. He felt obliged to help, since Lord Rāma had descended in the Ikṣvāku dynasty, and Rāma's forefather, King Sagara, had extended the ocean's boundaries.

Previously, Indra had placed the great Maināka Mountain in the middle of the ocean to obstruct the demons from traveling to the earth from the nether regions. The ocean now ordered Maināka to rise up out of the water, hoping to assist Hanumān by providing him with a resting place. However, when Hanumān saw the great mountain peak emerging from the sea, he considered it to be an impediment and knocked it down with his chest.

Appreciating Hanumān's prowess, Maināka took a human form and stood on his own summit. He said, "O son of Vāyu, you may rest awhile on my peak and then continue your journey. Please accept this humble service, for I desire to worship your father by offering you this assistance. In the Satya-yuga all mountains had wings, and we flew through the sky like so many Garuḍas. However, the demigods and *ṛṣis* became fearful at the possibility of our falling to the ground and smashing everything. Finally, in a fit of anger, Indra took up his thunderbolt and proceeded to cut off the wings of many thousands of mountains. Indra likewise attacked me, but Vāyu came to my rescue by forcibly casting me into the ocean. Thus, my wings were spared. Now, to repay that favor to your father, I request you stop awhile and accept my hospitality."

Hanumān replied, "Please excuse me, for I cannot dare

stop. I promised the other monkeys that I would not tarry on my journey. My time is short."

Hanumān touched the top of Maināka Mountain as a token of respect and then soared upwards, continuing his flight. Being pleased, Indra came forward and told Maināka, "There is no more need for you to be afraid of my thunderbolt. You may keep your wings and travel as you wish."

Meanwhile, the celestial *ṛṣis*, demigods and Gandharvas approached Surasā, the mother of the Nāgas, requesting, "We would like to ascertain the real strength of Hanumān. Thus, we wish you to assume the form of a huge Rākṣasī and try to impede him. Either Hanumān will quickly defeat you, or he will give way to despondency."

Taking the form of a huge disfigured Rākṣasī as large as a mountain, Surasā suddenly emerged from the ocean, blocking Hanumān's path. She announced, "By the benediction of Lord Brahmā it has been ordained that I can eat whatever food comes before me. O best of the monkeys, by the will of Providence you have crossed my path. Now I invite you to enter my gaping mouth."

Hanumān replied, "I am trying to serve Lord Rāma by locating His kidnapped wife, Sītā, and You should assist me. However, if you are determined to devour me instead, then after finding Sītā and reporting back to Rāma, I shall return here and enter your mouth without fail."

Surasā retorted, "O impudent one, because of Lord Brahma's benediction, you will be forced to enter my mouth now." Then, Surasā opened her mouth 10 *yojanas* wide to block Hanumān's path. Then Hanumān expanded

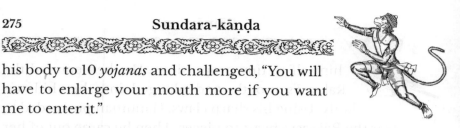

his body to 10 *yojanas* and challenged, "You will have to enlarge your mouth more if you want me to enter it."

Surasā then expanded her mouth to 20 *yojanas*, and the infuriated Hanumān expanded to 30 *yojanas*. Surasā countered by making her mouth 40 *yojanas*, and in response, Hanumān expanded himself to 50 *yojanas*. Surasā then expanded her mouth to 60 *yojanas* and Hanumān enlarged himself to 70. She then expanded herself to 80 *yojanas*, and Hanumān grew to 90. Countering this, Surasā expanded her mouth to a gaping 100 *yojanas* wide. Then, in the twinkling of an eye, Hanumān shrank to the size of a thumb, and quickly darted in and out of her mouth, saying, "O daughter of Dakṣa, the condition of your benediction has now been fulfilled, and I shall continue on my journey."

Surasā was delighted with Hanumān's clever victory. She then appeared before him in her original form, saying, "Well done! O foremost of monkeys, go now and accomplish your mission. May you soon unite Sītā and Lord Rāma."

Hanumān continued on his way, soaring through the sky. Suddenly, a Rākṣasī woman named Simhikā grabbed onto his shadow. Unaware of what had happened, Hanumān first thought he was losing his strength. However, upon looking around, he saw a huge ghastly creature emerging from the sea.

As Simhikā rushed toward Hanumān, her mouth opened wide, Hanumān began to expand his body. However, the sharp-witted Hanumān realized that the onrushing Rākṣasī's mouth was still large enough to swallow him. Thus, reversing his previous strategy, Hanumān suddenly shrank

himself to tiny proportions. He then entered the Rākṣasī's mouth, and plunged into her hideous body. Using his sharp claws, Hanumān proceeded to tear the Rākṣasī's heart to pieces. Then he came out of her body and resumed his expanded size. As Simhikā fell down dead into the water, the Siddhas, Cāraṇas and Vidyādharas glorified Hanumān for his victory.

Soon thereafter, the beaches and forests on the distant shore of Laṅkā came into view. Thinking the Rākṣasas would spot him, Hanumān resumed his normal size and landed on a crag of Trikūṭa, the main mountain on the island of Laṅkā.

Even after his jump of 100 *yojanas*, Hanumān did not feel even slightly tired. Gazing upward, he beheld the wonderful city of Laṅkā, perched atop the Trikūṭa Mountain, surrounded by moats filled with lotus flowers. The city was encircled by a high golden wall that was heavily guarded by fierce Rākṣasas.

As Hanumān approached the northern gate of Laṅkā, he saw towering white palaces and broad avenues adorned with golden arches, all crowded with innumerable fierce, ugly Rākṣasas, armed with all manner of weapons and able to change their forms at will.

Hanumān thought to himself, "This city appears to be unconquerable, even by the demigods, what to speak of an army of monkeys. How can Rāma hope to vanquish the Rākṣasas, since only myself, Sugrīva, Nīla and Aṅgada can cross the ocean to come here? Regardless, my first duty is to find out if Sītā is still alive. I must carefully consider how I can meet her, for incompetent messengers sometimes spoil even the best plans. The guards appear to be extremely

vigilant. Therefore, I cannot try to enter in my natural form. It appears that not even the wind could enter Laṅkā undetected. I must assume some inconspicuous guise and enter the city at night."

Hanumān eagerly waited for the sun to set, and when it finally grew dark, he became as small as a cat, and entered Laṅkā by jumping over the high wall. Hanumān saw that the city was beyond his imagination, full of seven and eight story palaces that were lavishly adorned with gold and jewels. The entire city was filled with magnificent houses with windows of diamond-studded lattice. Inside were beautiful women, and the sounds of laughter and sweet music could be heard. Throughout the city, Rākṣasa *brāhmaṇas* chanted Vedic hymns, praying for Rāvaṇa's protection.

The moon then rose above the horizon, thus helping Hanumān by spreading its silvery illumination. At that time Laṅkā personified, in the form of a hideous Rākṣasī woman, came before Hanumān challenging, "How have you entered this city unchecked? What is a monkey like you doing in the kingdom of the Rākṣasas?"

Hanumān responded, "I will only answer your question after you tell me who you are."

The Rākṣasī then angrily replied, "I am the presiding deity of Laṅkā. I carefully guard this city on behalf of Rāvaṇa. Because you have entered here without permission, you shall meet your death today by my hands."

Hanumān said, "I have come here to take a tour of the city, for I desire to see all the magnificent gardens and palaces."

Laṅkā defiantly replied, "This city is inhabited only by Rākṣasas. No stray monkeys are allowed to roam the streets. If you want to view the opulence of Laṅkā, you will have to kill me first."

To this, Hanumān declared, "I will look at the city as much as I like and depart the same way I entered."

The enraged Laṅkā shouted, "You will not!" and struck Hanumān with the palm of her left hand. Hanumān roared loudly with indignation and struck Laṅkā with his left fist, although not violently, because she was a woman. Laṅkā fell to the ground, moaning in pain, begging, "Please spare me, for a true hero will never strike a woman. Once, long ago, Lord Brahmā told me, 'When you are overpowered by a monkey, the destruction of your city and all the Rākṣasas is imminent.' I therefore admit defeat, for I can understand that Rāvaṇa's death is at hand. O monkey, you have my permission to enter Laṅkā."

Hanumān quickly traversed the entire city, jumping from one rooftop to the next. He detected many spies in various disguises. He also saw an army of 100,000 Rākṣasas protecting Rāvaṇa's palace, which was completely encircled by thick walls made of gold.

As Hanumān searched for Sītā throughout Laṅkā, he beheld great palaces with jewel-inlaid doors. The walls within were dust-free and as clear as crystal. The floors were laid out in fascinating designs. Filigree stairways inlaid with gold and silver led to balconies, and above them were magnificent domes and ceilings. Musical instruments played as the wives of the Rākṣasas came and reclined in the arms of their amorous husbands.

As he entered one residence after another, Hanumān saw lovers caressing each other, while other women applied sandalwood paste to their bodies. Here, someone slept, there, someone laughed, while others engaged in the affairs of lovemaking. Someone was sprawled out naked, having been left aside by her husband, and someone else, decorated with flowers and ornaments, was just welcoming her lover.

In this way, Hanumān observed thousands of beautiful women with moon-like faces, their lotus petal eyes casting sidelong glances that beguiled the hearts of their loved ones. However, as there was no trace of Sītā, Hanumān became somewhat disheartened.

Hanumān decided to search throughout the palaces belonging to Rāvaṇa's relatives and consorts. From a distance, these residences appeared to be like enormous clusters of monsoon clouds, illuminated by streaks of lightning.

After searching through many wonderfully opulent homes, Hanumān entered the palace of Rāvaṇa, which was filled with beautiful women and the sound of tinkling ornaments. Indeed, Hanumān felt as though he were being carried across the sky in a celestial chariot pulled by white swans. The interior of Rāvaṇa's palace was a ravishing paradise, with wish-fulfilling trees surrounded by jewel-like flowers.

While roaming about, Hanumān saw many pleasure rooms, their floors wet from wine and liquor. There were rooms filled with all varieties of weapons and rooms filled with treasure. However, to Hanumān's disappointment, Sītā was nowhere to be seen. But he had not yet searched

Rāvaṇa's personal quarters, which alone were four miles wide and eight miles long.

As Hanumān wandered throughout Rāvaṇa's vast domain, he considered how to enter the apartments. Finally, he came to the room where the Puṣpaka chariot was being kept. This chariot was originally built by Viśvakarmā for Lord Brahmā, and could traverse the sky simply by following the mental indication of the driver.

The Puṣpaka chariot hovered above the floor and was adorned with birds made from jewels that flapped their wings mechanically, and with snakes made of silver and gold. Inside were artificial elephants with shapely trunks that showered scented water upon a carved statue of the goddess of fortune, Lakṣmī, who stood elegantly within a pool of water, a lotus flower in each of her four lovely hands. The Puṣpaka chariot appeared like a large floating hill, and was fitted with stairways of gold, white crystal floors, and balconies made from sapphires.

To get a good look at Rāvaṇa's inner apartments, Hanumān jumped up onto the Puṣpaka chariot. From that vantage point he could see a great hall with a crystal floor that was inlaid with pearls, diamonds and gold, and covered by a great carpet having the geography of the earth, with all its mountains and seas, as its design. Stairways made of gems led to the upper levels, and everything was softly illuminated by golden lamps whose light reflected upon countless valuable jewels. Everything about this spectacular hall was gratifying to the five senses. Thus, Hanumān began to wonder, "Where am I? Is this heaven? This could well be the supreme realm of Lord Brahmā."

Upon entering the inner quarters, Hanumān saw thousands of beautiful, colorfully dressed women sprawled upon the expansive carpet. With half of the night gone, they were fast asleep under the influence of intoxicating wines and the exhaustion from their amorous revels. The women's jeweled bracelets, belts and ankle bells were now silent, although sparkling, and thus appeared like lotus-lakes, serene with silent swans and sleeping bees.

Hanumān gazed upon the ladies, who lay with eyes closed and lips tightly shut, like fragrant lotuses that close their petals upon the arrival of evening. In their stupor, the ladies' hair had become disheveled and their jewels scattered. While dancing and drinking, their ankle bracelets had been misplaced, their marks of *tilaka* erased, and their necklaces broken. Their belts were loosened, their dresses wrinkled, and their garlands torn and trampled. They appeared like flowering creepers that had been crushed by elephants.

Some of the ladies slept, using their bracelet-adorned arms as pillows, while others reposed on the breasts of their co-wives. Still others rested their heads upon another's lap, stomach or buttocks. Still others, captured in love's intoxication, relaxed with arms inter-clasped, embracing each other as they slept.

Seeing this scene, Hanumān wondered, "Whose limbs are those? Whose garlands? Whose clothes? Whose ornaments?" Indeed, the consorts of Rāvaṇa were so intimately united in sleep that it was difficult to know who was who—but not whom they served.

Under the influence of lust, innumerable daughters of kings, *brāhmaṇas*, Daityas and Gandharvas had become the wives of Rāvaṇa. Rāvaṇa had kidnapped some of them after defeating their relatives, but all had accepted him willingly under the infatuation of desire. None were low born, ugly, crude or stupid, and none were neglected by Rāvaṇa, lord of Laṅkā.

In their midst, Hanumān saw Rāvaṇa, lying asleep upon an elegant silken couch placed atop a crystal dais and covered with a white canopy that was decorated with flowers. Rāvaṇa was seen to have one head and two arms, for it was only in battle that he assumed his gigantic form with ten heads and twenty arms. Hanumān also noticed the numerous wounds upon Rāvaṇa's body, coming from such illustrious weapons as King Indra's thunderbolt, Airāvata's tusk and Lord Viṣṇu's *cakra*.

Rāvaṇa's dark-complexioned body was smeared with sandalwood paste. His earrings flashed like fire as he lay exhausted from a night of feasting, drinking and erotic enjoyment. Hanumān stared at Rāvaṇa respectfully, recoiling slightly in awe of his powerful, majestic appearance. Then Hanumān again turned his attention to Rāvaṇa's consorts, who surrounded him like so many glittering stars encircling the full moon. Several were sleeping in the arms of their beloved lord, while others caressed the musical instruments they had played earlier in the evening. Like a lotus clinging to a floating tree branch in mid-stream, one slender-waisted beauty embraced her *vīṇā*. Another held a drum in her lap as if it were her infant child. Another full-breasted lady hugged her tambourine tightly, as though it was her lover that had returned from a long absence.

Lying a bit apart from the rest of the women, on a lavishly decorated couch, was the fair complexioned Mandodarī,

Rāvaṇa's favorite queen. When Hanumān saw how young, beautiful and dignified she appeared, he thought, "This must be Sītā."

Feeling overjoyed at his discovery, Hanumān rejoiced like a monkey by slapping his arms, jumping for joy, kissing his tail and climbing up and down the palace pillars. However, after a moment's consideration, Hanumān concluded, "This cannot be Sītā. It must be someone else. Sītā would not be able to even eat or sleep in separation from Rāma. Nor would she decorate herself nicely or accept the association of another male, even if he were the king of heaven. Indeed, in comparison to Rāma, what are the demigods, what to speak of a wicked Rākṣasa like Rāvaṇa?"

Thereafter, Hanumān continued his search, wandering from room to room throughout the rest of Rāvaṇa's palace. He saw thousands of moon-faced women, sleeping amidst vessels containing huge quantities of meat and wine, along with drinking glasses that were scattered about. Hanumān had to observe all these women very closely while searching for Sītā, and thus began to have misgivings. Hanumān thought to himself, "Perhaps I have violated religious principles by gazing upon the wives of others, sleeping in a state of undress. What will be my destination?"

However, after some consideration, Hanumān concluded, "It is the motive that determines if an act is virtuous or sinful. While gazing upon these women, I have remained pure in mind, for my only concern is to find Sītā. Since I am looking for a woman, where else can I search, except among women? I am only doing this in the service of Lord Rāma. Therefore, my looking upon others' wives cannot be sinful."

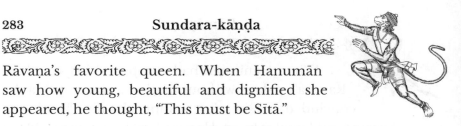

When Hanumān had completed his search of Rāvaṇa's palace without finding a trace of Sītā, he concluded that she must no longer be alive. Hanumān became saddened at heart. He wondered what he would tell the other monkeys, who were anxiously awaiting his return. However, Hanumān fought his depression by reminding himself that unwavering determination is the only cause for success. Still hoping for the best, he continued to search the places that remained uncovered.

But after scouring Laṅkā again and again, Hanumān became completely disheartened. Although Sampāti had assured him that Sītā was in Laṅkā, Hanumān could not find her anywhere. He began to speculate about what might have happened: "Perhaps Sītā died out of fear while being carried to Laṅkā by Rāvaṇa. Perhaps he dropped her out of fear of Rāma. Sītā might have wriggled free and fallen into the ocean; or perhaps Rāvaṇa devoured her when she refused to become his consort."

Hanumān's thoughts then turned to the disastrous results that would ensue if he were to return to Rāma and report his failure. "Without Sītā, Rāma will surely give up His life, and Lakṣmaṇa will follow suit. When Bharata and Śatrughna hear that Rāma and Lakṣmaṇa have died, They will also end Their lives. With all four sons gone, the three mothers will certainly wither away and die. Because of their failure, Sugrīva, Aṅgada and the other monkeys will give up their lives out of shame. Therefore, I must not return to Kiṣkindhyā. Either I will commit suicide or live out the rest of my life as a recluse."

As Hanumān struggled to emerge from these gloomy thoughts, he considered, "Maybe I should kill Rāvaṇa, or

drag him back to Rāma so that he can be offered as a human sacrifice to Lord Śiva."

Seated upon one of Laṅkā's high defense walls, Hanumān suddenly spied a large grove of *aśoka* trees on the outskirts of town that he had not yet explored. Hanumān resolved to continue his search. He first offered his obeisances to Rāma, Lakṣmaṇa and the principal demigods. Then he leapt from the defensive wall into the *aśoka* grove. Hanumān roamed about within the grove for some time, and then climbed a tall tree to gain a better view.

From the treetop Hanumān could see a mountain stream cascading down into a nearby lotus pond. Surrounded by flowering trees, this idyllic garden seemed the perfect place for Sītā. Hanumān decided to remain stationed in the treetop in the hope that Sītā would come there to take her morning bath and perform her devotional duties.

Gazing in another direction, Hanumān sighted a lofty temple, supported by 1,000 pillars and situated within a nearby garden. In front of the temple sat a woman dressed in a single, dirty, worn-out, fine yellow cloth. She appeared emaciated from fasting, and because of her anguish, she sighed heavily, again and again. Although her face was wet with tears, displaying her anxiety and exhaustion, she nonetheless shone with a divine radiance. Looking like a smoke-covered fire, she was surrounded by many Rākṣasīs.

Hanumān recognized her to be the woman he saw earlier being carried away by Rāvaṇa. Likewise, he detected that the ornaments she wore matched the description of those given by Rāma. Hanumān gazed at the woman's full-moon face, her graceful eyebrows, her full breasts, her bright red

lips, her slender waist, her lotus petal eyes, her delicate, symmetrical limbs, and concluded that she must be Sītā. Although as lovely as the goddess of love, she sat upon the ground like an ascetic practicing penances. Appearing most glorious, she suffered acute anguish, and thus appeared like a sacred text misinterpreted, like wealth squandered, like faith shattered, like hope frustrated, like ideals impeded, like intellect corrupted or like fame blackened.

Hanumān thought, "This is the woman whom Rāma loves and for whom He suffers, sometimes feeling pity, sometimes tenderness and sometimes grief—pity for the dear one whom He failed to protect, tenderness for the woman who is solely dependent upon Him, and grief at suddenly losing His beloved wife. Sītā's grace and beauty resemble that of Rāma. She is certainly worth the trouble of jumping over to Laṅkā and killing all the Rākṣasas. Indeed, if Sītā were placed on one side of a scale and the sovereignty of the three worlds on the other side, the latter would not measure even a fraction of her worth. It is painful to see how she suffers at the hands of Rāvaṇa. Still, I know that because of remaining absorbed in thoughts of Rāma, she cannot perceive her external suffering."

The moon rose to help Hanumān observe Sītā and the dangerous Rākṣasīs guarding her. Some of these Rākṣasīs had only one eye or ear, one had ears all over her body, and another had a nose in the middle of her forehead. Some were bald and some were dwarves, some were hunchbacks, and some had lips that hung down to their chins. Some had heads that resembled boars, deer, camels, tigers or horses. Others had only a single hand or foot. Other Rākṣasīs had

heads that were sunk into their bodies, like Kabandha, and most had meat and blood smeared over their bodies.

Hanumān wept tears of joy in finding Sītā. Remaining concealed atop the *aśoka* tree, he watched her as the night passed away.

Rāvaṇa was awakened before dawn by the singing of the bards, who praised his glories to the accompaniment of musical instruments. As he arose, Rāvaṇa began to think of Sītā, for he was irresistibly drawn to her. Unable to suppress his sensual longing for the princess of Videha, Rāvaṇa set out for the *aśoka* grove, accompanied by 100 beautiful women

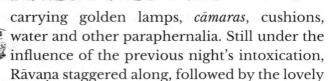

carrying golden lamps, *cāmaras*, cushions, water and other paraphernalia. Still under the influence of the previous night's intoxication, Rāvaṇa staggered along, followed by the lovely ladies, who appeared to be like flashes of lightning behind a cloud. When Hanumān saw Rāvaṇa approach, he concealed himself behind a cluster of leafy branches. When Sītā saw Rāvaṇa coming, she covered her body as best she could. Then, trembling violently, she sat down and wept. As Sītā sat upon the bare ground, she swayed back and forth, like a frail boat tossing upon a stormy ocean. In her wretched condition, Sītā appeared to be like an understanding that had become dim, hope that had been frustrated, an order flouted, or a sacred altar that had been desecrated. She was like a full moon in eclipse, an army that had been routed, or a stream dried up from drought. She was like a pond whose lotuses had been uprooted, an extinguished flame, or birds fleeing from fright.

Sītā's body had become emaciated and her mind depressed from her fasting and grief. Rāvaṇa came before Sītā and began speaking in the hope of seducing her: "O most fair and beautiful lady, why do you cover your shapely breasts and thin waist? O large-eyed beauty, I am afflicted with love for you, so please give up your shyness. Favor me, my beloved, and fulfill my unbearable longing to have you. It has always been the custom of Rākṣasas to carry away or rape the wives of others. However, I shall not touch you as long as you do not voluntarily agree to have me in return.

"O lovely goddess, why are you lying upon the bare ground? Why do you wear dirty clothes and fast for no reason? Why do you tie your hair in a single braid and

constantly sit brooding? Such behavior does not suit a ravishing princess like you. Become my queen and enjoy royal opulence beyond compare within the three worlds. You will have only the best garlands, sandalwood paste, perfumes and ornaments. You shall eat the finest foods, drink the most ambrosial beverages, lie upon the most luxurious couches, and revel with music, singing and dancing.

"O most lovely lady, youth quickly passes. Therefore, your stubbornness is folly. You have the loveliest face, fairer than the moon, and your bodily features are the perfection of artistic workmanship. Become my beloved, and in return I shall do anything for your pleasure. If you like, I shall conquer the entire earth and present it as a gift to your father, King Janaka. Who can dare to defy me? O Sītā, after seeing you, I have become so enamored that I can no longer find pleasure in any of my wives, not even Mandodarī. Why do you insist upon remaining faithful to Rāma, a mere human being, a straw in the street in comparison to me? I doubt whether Rāma still lives. Even if He does, you may rest assured you will never see Him again."

Sītā placed a straw between herself and Rāvaṇa as a symbol of her unwillingness to contact him directly. She gently replied, "You should withdraw your mind from me and remain contented with the consorts you already possess. You will never be able to possess me, just as a sinful man fails to achieve perfection. I was born in a noble family and married according to religious principles. I will never act contrary to the tenets of righteousness. There is no hope of your gaining my favor."

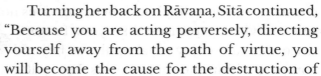

Turning her back on Rāvaṇa, Sītā continued, "Because you are acting perversely, directing yourself away from the path of virtue, you will become the cause for the destruction of your entire kingdom. Why not follow the example of good men, who protect their wives and the wives of others? The fool who is dissatisfied with his own wife, and seeks pleasure with the wives of others, is doomed. Why do you ignore the advice of the wise and reject that which is good? Why are you determined to cause the destruction of all the Rākṣasas? Do you not know that everyone rejoices at the destruction of wicked persons?

"I will never be tempted by your offers of insignificant opulence and royal comforts. I am as inseparable from Rāma as sunlight is from the sun. The only way that you can save yourself from Rāma's wrath is to voluntarily deliver me back to Him. You should try to make friendship with Him, for He is very merciful to those who take shelter of Him. Otherwise, it will not be long before Rāma and Lakṣmaṇa come here and suck out your life breath with Their arrows. You shall never escape Rāma's vengeance, even though you may be capable of saving yourself from Indra's thunderbolt. It is only a matter of time before Rāma finds you out and kills you for your wickedness."

Rāvaṇa retorted, "Generally, the more courteously a man treats a woman, the more agreeably she responds to him. In your case, however, the opposite holds true. I should kill you for your harsh words! You are fortunate, however, because my love for you controls my anger, like a charioteer that curbs unruly steeds. Love acts strangely, for the more

a beloved mistreats her lover, the more he showers her with affection. It is for this reason alone that I do not kill you, although death and dishonor are what you deserve. Already, ten months of your one year grace period have passed. Thus, I shall wait only two more months. Then, if you still refuse to reciprocate my love, I shall have you chopped to pieces by my cooks and served for my breakfast!"

Several of Rāvaṇa's consorts that had been forcibly abducted by him were also present there, and upon hearing his threats, they felt sympathetic toward Sītā. As Rāvaṇa prepared to depart, they briefly comforted Sītā, their compassionate words giving Sītā some small reassurance. Thus feeling encouraged, Sītā again rebuked Rāvaṇa, saying, "You cannot have a single well-wisher within your kingdom, for no one has tried to deter you from this ignoble act which is meant for your destruction. Rāma is like a mighty elephant, and you are a tiny rabbit. You can speak boldly only while Rāma is out of sight. I could reduce you to ashes myself by utilizing my mystic power, but I refrain from doing so because I have not received such an order from Rāma. You are a fool, for it is impossible to kidnap the wife of Lord Rāma. You have only been able to do so because this is the device Providence has chosen to have me as the instrumental cause of your death."

Struck by these sharp words, Rāvaṇa hissed like a serpent and gazed at Sītā with angry, bloodshot eyes. "I will kill you this very day," Rāvaṇa bellowed. Then, addressing the Rākṣasīs who guarded Sītā, he said, "You must make Sītā submit to me by any means possible, whether conciliation, gifts, or force."

Rāvaṇa turned menacingly toward Sītā, and it appeared he might suddenly become violent. However, Mandodarī, who had come with Rāvaṇa's youngest consort, Dhanyamālinī, embraced her husband, saying, "Come back to your palace and enjoy with us. Forget about this pale, emaciated Sītā. When a man desires to enjoy a woman who does not love him, he only suffers. However, when the woman loves him in return, he enjoys extreme delight."

Rāvaṇa was thus dissuaded from further abusing Sītā. Laughing conceitedly, he returned to his palace. The hideous Rākṣasī guards then approached Sītā and began to threaten her in harsh, angry voices. One Rākṣasī said, "You should give up your false pride and accept Rāvaṇa, for he is a very exalted personality. You should know that one of Lord Brahmā's mentally conceived sons was Pulastya, whose mentally conceived son was Viśravā Ṛṣi, whose son is Rāvaṇa. Do not hesitate to accept the king of the Rākṣasas, thinking him unworthy of you. If you remain adamant, it will certainly result in your destruction."

Another Rākṣasī said, "You are a fool for refusing to become Rāvaṇa's queen. Don't you know that at his command the trees scatter flowers and the clouds release torrents of rain? The sun does not shine and the wind refuses to blow if they displease Rāvaṇa. O sweet smiling goddess, listen to our advice, or else face a horrible death."

Sītā, however, calmly replied, "You can devour me if you like. I shall never submit to Rāvaṇa."

Finding Sītā unbending, the Rākṣasīs picked up spears, axes and knives, threatening Sītā as they circled around her.

One shouted, "You are young, soft and tender. I shall devour your heart, liver and spleen this very moment if you do not submit to Rāvaṇa." Others exclaimed, "I shall eat up your rosy red cheeks! I will savor your succulent thighs! I will drink your hot blood!"

Then another Rākṣasī interrupted, "I hate squabbling. Let's chop her up and divide her into equal morsels. Order wine to be brought. Let us feast upon her flesh and dance before the goddess Bhadrakālī."

Sītā could no longer bear their ghastly remarks and burst into tears. Trembling violently with fear, she cried out, "O Rāma! O Lakṣmaṇa!"

Sītā lamented, "Why doesn't Rāma come here to save me? Perhaps He doesn't know where I am. Maybe He has already died from feelings of separation and is now residing in heaven. Perhaps Rāvaṇa was somehow able to kill Him by means of some sinister trick. O, when will Rāma come to take me back to Ayodhyā, after destroying all these Rākṣasas? Why am I so unfortunate that I cannot give up my life at once? If only I could die, for death would surely be better than this unbearable misery."

While the Rākṣasīs were attempting to intimidate Sītā, one elderly woman named Trijaṭā suddenly awoke from a deep slumber. Trijaṭā approached the other Rākṣasīs, and prudently spoke as follows: "You wretches, how can you dare torment Sītā like this? You shall never be able to devour her. I shall now tell you why—I have just had an incredibly vivid dream, wherein I saw Rāma come here to rescue Sītā, and slaying all the Rākṣasas."

When the other Rākṣasīs begged her to describe her dream in detail, Trijaṭā continued, "I saw Rāma and Lakṣmaṇa dressed all in white and wearing white garlands. They were soaring through the air in a white celestial chariot drawn by 1,000 white horses. Then the scene changed, and I saw Rāma seated upon a gigantic four-tusked elephant, dressed all in white. Sītā, too, was dressed in white and was standing upon a white mountain in the middle of the sea. When Rāma came nearby, Sītā mounted the elephant, and became reunited with her beloved husband. After this, I saw Rāma, Sītā and Lakṣmaṇa flying through the air toward the north in the Puṣpaka chariot.

I then saw Rāvaṇa in my dream with a shaved head, his body smeared with red sandalwood paste. He was riding in a chariot drawn by asses, drinking oil, and laughing as though mentally deranged. As the chariot rode off, I saw Rāvaṇa disappear into a gloomy hell filled with filthy things that emitted a foul odor. I saw Kumbhakarṇa and the sons of Rāvaṇa in the same way, but not Vibhīṣaṇa. Vibhīṣaṇa was mounted upon a four-tusked elephant, covered by a white canopy, and was heralded by conchshells and kettledrums. Finally, I saw the whole of Laṅkā crumble and fall into the sea. I have concluded that very soon Rāma will come and recover Sītā after slaying the Rākṣasas. You must now give up tormenting Sītā and beg for her forgiveness."

Meanwhile, auspicious signs appeared in the irreproachable body of Sītā, like servants eager to wait upon a wealthy man. Her lotus-like left eye began to twitch and her left arm gently throbbed. Sītā's graceful left thigh also quivered as if Rāma Himself were standing before her.

Noticing all this, Trijaṭā declared, "Because of these auspicious signs, I can understand that Sītā will soon receive some very good news."

Hearing this, Sītā became elated, and said, "If all that you have described comes true, then I will make certain you are afforded all protection from the wrath of my husband."

However, Sītā soon lapsed into her usual hopeless mood as she gazed at the Rākṣasīs around her. She thought, "What if Rāvaṇa kills me before Rāma is able to come to save me? In this miserable situation, I cannot bear the torment."

Desiring to end her life, Sītā took the string binding her hair and knotted it tightly around her neck. Then she began tying the other end to the branch of an *aśoka* tree. However, just at that moment, Sītā again experienced many auspicious signs, and her mood brightened.

All the while, Hanumān had remained hidden, listening to Sītā and the Rākṣasīs. He began considering the situation. "I must go to comfort Sītā, for her intelligence has become covered due to her intense grief. I must somehow allay her fears and give her hope before returning to Rāma. Indeed, at any time she may decide to give up her life out of despair. Still, how can I talk with her in the midst of these Rākṣasīs? Never mind. Somehow I must do it. Rāma will surely ask me if I have any message from Sītā. If I reply that I have none, He may decide to burn me to ashes with His anger. Therefore, I think both Sītā and Rāma need to be consoled with news of each other.

"I will go to meet Sītā while her guards are inattentive. If I speak to her in Sanskrit, she will surely have faith in my

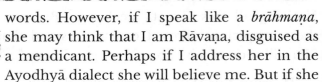

words. However, if I speak like a *brāhmaṇa*, she may think that I am Rāvaṇa, disguised as a mendicant. Perhaps if I address her in the Ayodhyā dialect she will believe me. But if she hears a monkey speaking like a human, she will still think I am Rāvaṇa. How perplexing this is, especially since Rāvaṇa can assume any form he likes. I must be very careful, for if she screams, her cries will alert the guards. If the guards see me, they will also become afraid because of my gigantic size. Thus, they will call for the help of Rāvaṇa's soldiers. Then I could be taken captive. Even if I were able to defeat all the Rākṣasas, I would probably be too tired to jump back to the mainland. I must consider how to approach Sītā very carefully, for a thoughtless messenger can ruin even the most perfect plan."

After pondering his dilemma in great detail, Hanumān firmly concluded, "I will first sing Rāma's praises to gain Sītā's confidence; then I shall deliver Rāma's message to her."

From within the branches of the great *aśoka* tree,Hanumān began to recite:

Descendant of Ikṣvāku
King Daśaratha was His name
Righteous and heroic
He ruled Ayodhyā of fame.

He received four mighty sons
Rāma the loved of his heart
Full of infinite potencies
Viṣṇu in a human part.

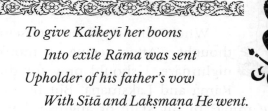

To give Kaikeyī her boons
Into exile Rāma was sent
Upholder of his father's vow
With Sītā and Lakṣmaṇa He went.

When Rāma killed the Rākṣasas
Who filled the ṛṣis with fear
Rāvaṇa kidnapped Sītā
With the help of Mārīca the deer.

Then in His search for Sītā
Rāma made Sugrīva a friend
To search the southern quarter
I, Hanumān, did He send.

After crossing many mountains
I jumped the ocean vast
And thus I have succeeded
In finding you at last.

Rāma will come to save you
His dearly beloved wife
Now give me a little message
To save your husband's life.

As Hanumān fell silent, Sītā began looking up into the tree to find the speaker. When she sighted Hanumān, Sītā thought she must be dreaming. "It is inauspicious to see a monkey in dreams," she murmured to herself. Overwrought from anguish, Sītā wept bitterly, and then suddenly fainted.

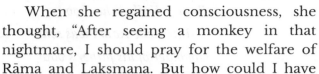

When she regained consciousness, she thought, "After seeing a monkey in that nightmare, I should pray for the welfare of Rāma and Lakṣmaṇa. But how could I have been dreaming? In my state of anguish, being separated from Rāma, I cannot sleep even for a moment. It must have been not a dream, but a hallucination. The monkey I saw could not have been real, for wherever I look, I see only Rāma. My ears only hear Rāma's voice, and I can think only of Rāma and nothing else. I cannot believe the monkey was illusory, for he appeared so real. O, Lords Brahmā, Indra, Sūrya and Vāyu, please let the monkey really exist and let his words of Rāma bring me auspiciousness."

Hanumān came down from his hiding place in the tree. Standing before Sītā with folded hands, he inquired, "Who are you? You appear to be a goddess, and I think you must be the consort of Rāma."

Sītā was delighted to hear Rāma's name, and in reply to Hanumān's questions, she practically narrated the entire story of her life. In conclusion, Sītā explained, "Rāvaṇa has given me only two more months to live. If Rāma does not come here before then, I shall give up my life."

Gaining confidence, Hanumān said, "I am an envoy from Rāma, and I can assure you He is quite well. Rāma has sent me here to locate you. He anxiously inquires about your welfare."

Sītā was delighted. With great happiness, they continued talking to each other. However, as they became engrossed in conversation, Hanumān gradually began inching his way closer to Sītā. Upon realizing this, Sītā was suddenly seized with the thought that he was actually Rāvaṇa, disguised as a monkey. Thus, she exclaimed, "O, how disgusting that I have been tricked into talking with you."

Sītā then sank to the ground. Exhausted from grief, she rebuked Hanumān, saying, "How abominable for you to come to me in a disguise." The next moment, however, Sītā considered, "I certainly feel delighted at heart to see this monkey. Perhaps my suspicions are false. Perhaps he really is a messenger from Rāma." Thus composing herself, Sītā again addressed Hanumān more favorably, "Please tell me more of Rāma. Your descriptions of Him are most pleasing to my ears and heart."

In truth, Sītā was absorbed in intense ecstasy in separation from Rāma. Thus, her talks were manifestations of transcendental madness. Like a deranged woman, Sītā again began speculating, "Maybe this monkey is a ghost. Perhaps I only imagine I see him because I have become mentally unbalanced, due to my agony. No! I should not even think like this! Why should I allow myself to become carried away by my disturbed mind? From his speech, it appears that this monkey came here in the service of Rāma. However, how can I believe that a mere monkey could jump over the ocean to Laṅkā? It must be Rāvaṇa who has come here in disguise."

Hanumān could understand Sītā's doubts, and to allay her fears, he continued to glorify Rāma and reassure her in various ways. Then, to test Hanumān, Sītā said, "Please tell me the story of how you met Rāma. Also, describe to me in full detail the bodily features of Rāma and His brother Lakṣmaṇa."

Hanumān then said, "O Princess of Videha, Rāma has eyes that resemble lotus petals. He has broad shoulders and mighty arms, and His neck is shaped like a conch. His eyes are coppery, and His voice deep like the sound of a kettledrum. He is solid in three places: His breast, wrist and fist. He is elevated in three places: His chest, the rim of His navel, and His abdomen. He is reddish in three places: His eyes, His nails and palms, and the soles of His feet. He is deep of voice, His navel is deep, and He walks swiftly. He has three folds of skin on the neck and belly. He is small in four places: neck, genitals, calves, and back. He walks with four different gaits: like a lion, like a tiger, like an elephant, and like a bull. Ten places on His body are like a lotus: His complexion, mouth, eyes, tongue, lips, palate, breast, nails, hands and feet. He is fine in four places: His bodily hair, skin, finger joints, and perception. Indeed, He has all these features and many more.

"The beauty of Lakṣmaṇa is also immeasurable. Lakṣmaṇa's complexion is golden, whereas Lord Rāma's is dark greenish-blue. I met the two brothers at the Ṛṣyamūka Mountain. When Rāma saw the jewels you dropped in the midst of the monkeys while being carried away by Rāvaṇa, He became overwhelmed with joy and tears fell from His eyes. To establish an alliance of friendship with Sugrīva, Rāma killed Vāli. To repay this favor, Sugrīva initiated a great search for you all over the world by dispatching millions of monkeys. Now, by good fortune, I have located you in this remote place.

"I am the son of the mighty monkey, Kesari. My father originally resided at the Malaya Hills, and later moved to

Gokarṇa Mountain. When Sambasadna was oppressing the celestial *ṛṣis*, Kesari killed the great demon at their request. Thereafter, I was begot by the wind god, Vāyu, through the womb of Kesari's consort."

After hearing Hanumān's description of Rāma, Sītā became convinced that he was indeed a messenger sent by her husband. She began shedding tears of joy. Hanumān then took the opportunity to give Rāma's ring to Sītā. Recognizing it, and seeing the name of her beloved on the inside band, Sītā's face blossomed with joy, as if she were experiencing the arrival of Rāma Himself. She said, "O Hanumān, I am eternally indebted to you for this gift. You are so magnanimous to have come here for my sake. Now, please tell me more about Rāma."

With folded hands, Hanumān replied, "It is only because Rāma does not know where you are that He has not come here to rescue you. Without you, Rāma does not know a moment's peace of mind. Truly, as soon as I return and inform Rāma of your presence here, He will immediately come and kill Rāvaṇa."

Sītā then urged, "You must stress to Rāma the urgency of the matter, for after two months, Rāvaṇa will kill me. Rāvaṇa's younger half-brother, Vibhīṣana, has repeatedly pleaded with Rāvaṇa to return me to Rāma. Likewise, Vibhīṣaṇa's eldest daughter has told me how a wise old minister named Avindhya forewarned Rāvaṇa of the imminent destruction of the Rākṣasas at the hands of Rāma. But Rāvaṇa refuses to listen to this advice."

Hanumān suggested, "If you like, I can immediately deliver you to Rāma by carrying you to Kiṣkindhyā on my

back. I am sure that the Rākṣasas could not keep up with me as I fly across the ocean."

Sītā was thrilled to hear this prospect, but still, she replied, "Your proposal seems quite like what a monkey would present. How can someone so small even think of carrying me across the ocean?"

Hanumān was a little offended by this remark, and so he thought, "How little she thinks of me!"

Then, to demonstrate his prowess, Hanumān revealed his gigantic form, boasting, "If you like, I can uproot the entire city of Laṅkā—then, along with Rāvaṇa, I will carry it back to Rāma! So please give up your doubts about me."

Sītā admitted, "You are certainly strong enough to carry me across the ocean. However, I do not think it such a good idea. What if I become faint as you dash across the sky and fall into the shark and crocodile infested water? Moreover, when the Rākṣasas rally and attack you, you will be fully engaged in fighting with them. What will happen to me? Even if you somehow manage to kill all the Rākṣasas, this would only serve to diminish the glory of Rāma.

"O Hanumān, since I am completely devoted to my husband, I do not want to touch the body of anyone else but Rāma. When Rāvaṇa kidnapped me, I was helpless and had no choice. However, Rāma must now come here Himself to rescue me after killing the wicked Rāvaṇa. This act alone would be worthy of enhancing His glorious reputation."

Hanumān replied, "I appreciate your statements, which are just befitting the chaste and righteous wife of Rāma. I will now leave, but first, please give me some token that I can give to Rāma to help me convince Him that I have actually met you."

With tear filled eyes, Sītā replied in a faint voice, "O Hanumān, to convince Rāma that you have met me, you may relate to Him the following incident: 'One day while we were residing at Citrakūṭa, after playing in the water, Rāma, still dripping wet, sat down on my lap. At that time a crow came and began pecking at me, as though eager to eat my flesh. I picked up a lump of dirt to throw to scare it away, but the determined crow remained on the scene, hiding nearby. Becoming angered, I accidentally pulled the string that held my slip, causing it to fall down. Seeing this, Rāma laughed heartily, taking advantage of my flustered countenance. In the meantime, the crow returned, and again pecked at me. I took shelter of Rāma by sitting on His lap, and He comforted me, wiping the tears from my eyes.

"Feeling exhausted, I soon fell asleep in Rāma's arms, and soon He too dozed off. Taking advantage of this opportunity, the crow suddenly swooped down and clawed at my breasts. This awakened Rāma, who felt drops of my blood falling on Him.

"Seeing the cuts on my breasts, Rāma became enraged, and asked me to identify the culprit. Then, before I could answer, He saw the crow sitting at a distance, his claws dripping with blood. In great anger, Rāma took a blade of *kuśa* grass from His mat and surcharged it with the power of a *brahmāstra*. As the straw burst into flames, Rāma hurled it at the crow. Then, as the bird flew up into the sky, the *kuśa*-grass weapon followed it.

"This crow was, however, the son of Indra, and while being chased by the *brahmāstra*, he tried to obtain shelter all over the universe. But even his father was powerless to help him. Finally the crow came and surrendered to Rāma. Out of compassion, Rāma forgave the pale, exhausted bird, but He said, "This *brahmāstra* cannot be ineffectual. Therefore, it must be directed somewhere."

"Saying this, Rāma directed the weapon to destroy the crow's right eye. Thereafter, Indra's son departed, after offering his obeisances."

Sītā became overwhelmed with sorrow while relating her pastime with Rāma. Then, with tear-stained eyes, she said, "O Hanumān, formerly Rāma used the *brahmāstra* against an insignificant crow. Why does He not attack Rāvaṇa now? Does Rāma no longer have any affection for me? In some former life I must have committed an abominable sin to cause Rāma to disregard me now."

Hoping to encourage the despondent Sītā, Hanumān reassured her, "Rāma is feeling great separation from you and is merged in the ocean of sorrow. Now, please give me some object that I can show to Rāma."

Sītā sighed and said, "At least I now have some real hope of being rescued. Somehow you must urge Rāma to come quickly, for if I must pass another month away from Him, I will surely die from grief."

Sītā produced a bright jewel from her cloth that she formerly used to ornament her head. Giving it to Hanumān, Sītā said, "When Rāma sees this jewel, He will remember

three persons, since it was given to me by my mother as a dowry gift in the presence of Rāma and His father. O Hanumān, please return quickly, and urge Rāma to quickly terminate my unbearable suffering."

Hanumān then circumambulated Sītā and was about to depart, when, in a voice choked with tears, Sītā said, "Please convince Rāma to hasten to my rescue."

Hanumān replied, "Do not worry. Soon you shall see Rāma, Lakṣmaṇa and all the heroic monkeys, as they come here to slay Rāvaṇa and the Rākṣasas."

Sītā pleaded, "Please stay for just one more day. By your association I have gained some small relief from my intolerable miseries. O, why do I even bother to raise my hopes? How will the monkeys be able to cross the vast ocean? I do not think that even Rāma and Lakṣmaṇa have the capacity, but only Garuḍa, Vāyu or yourself. Hanumān, I know you could rescue me single-handed. However, I request that you somehow enable Rāma to kill all the Rākṣasas and save me, for that will eternally enhance His glorious reputation."

Hanumān replied, "All the monkeys in Sugrīva's army are equal or superior to me. Surely they will all easily reach Laṅkā. It is only inferior persons like myself that are sent on errands. Please give up all your doubts for good. If need be, I will cross over the ocean, carrying Rāma and Lakṣmaṇa on my back."

Sītā then replied, "O Hanumān, I again urge you to see that my rescue is hastened. I do not know how much

longer I shall be able to survive under these conditions. I will give you one more message for Rāma: Remind Him of the time He painted my cheeks with a red mineral to replace the decorations that had worn off."

As Hanumān prepared to depart, Sītā repeatedly implored him to hasten her rescue. Hanumān then considered, "My mission would not be complete without ascertaining the true strength of the Rākṣasas. Therefore, I shall destroy this *aśoka* grove, the pleasure garden of Rāvaṇa, just to provoke his anger. When the king of the Rākṣasas sends his army to attack me, I will destroy it and then return to Rāma."

Thereafter, Hanumān started knocking down and uprooting *aśoka* trees. He stirred up the ponds and crushed the hilltops. Then, after practically destroying the entire garden, he made his stand at the entrance.

Upon hearing the frightened screams of the birds and animals, along with other sounds created by Hanumān's rampage, the Rākṣasī guards awoke with a start. Seeing Hanumān's huge form standing at the garden entrance, their hearts filled with terror. The Rākṣasīs surrounded Sītā and asked, "Who is this creature? What were you and he conversing about?"

Sītā denied knowing who Hanumān was, saying, "He must be a ferocious Rākṣasa. Since you are all Rākṣasas, it is *you* that should know him, not I. I too, am terrified by his huge, frightening appearance."

While some of the Rākṣasīs remained guarding Sītā, others went and reported the matter to Rāvaṇa. Reverently

bowing to their king, the Rākṣasīs said, "A huge, powerful monkey has come here. After talking to Sītā, he devastated the entire *aśoka* grove, except for the small area where Sītā stays. When we asked Sītā about him, however, she claimed not to know him." Rāvaṇa immediately became enraged and dispatched 80,000 fierce Rākṣasas to go and capture Hanumān.

When the army came before him brandishing their weapons, Hanumān further expanded his form and began lashing his tail violently, making a sound so loud that it reverberated throughout Laṅkā. Hanumān then challenged, "I am a servant of Lord Rāma. If I like, I can kill a thousand Rāvaṇas."

As Hanumān roared menacingly, the Rākṣasas were struck with fear. Regardless, they began attacking him from all sides. Hanumān grabbed an iron bar lying at the gate, and while flying through the air, he slaughtered the whole Rākṣasa army. The few survivors hurried back to Rāvaṇa to inform him of the massacre. Upon hearing the news, Rāvaṇa's eyes rolled with rage. He then ordered the extremely powerful son of Prahasta, named Jambumali, to go and fight Hanumān.

Meanwhile, Hanumān began to destroy the immense temple of the Rākṣasa's guardian deity, located in the *aśoka* grove. As he climbed up the edifice, which was as big as a large hill, Hanumān tore it to pieces with his claws, making crashing sounds that reverberated throughout Laṅkā. Hanumān then shouted, "May there be victory for Rāma and Lakṣmaṇa! My name is Hanumān, and I

will now destroy Laṅkā within the sight of the Rākṣasas."

Although the sound of Hanumān's voice struck terror into their hearts, the one hundred guards of the sanctuary took up their weapons and surrounded him. The enraged Hanumān then broke off one of the temple columns, and assuming a terrible aspect, he whirled the column around so that fire was generated as it struck the other pillars. Thus, as Hanumān destroyed the guards with the blazing pillar, the entire edifice became engulfed in flames. Again and again, Hanumān shouted, "Let there be victory for Rāma, Lakṣmaṇa and the monkeys!"

Jambumali then arrived on the scene, riding upon a chariot drawn by donkeys, while the twanging of his bow filled the entire sky with its awesome vibration. Without wasting time, Jambumali struck Hanumān in the mouth with one arrow and his arms with ten more. As blood covered his entire face, the infuriated Hanumān grabbed a huge rock and hurled it at Jambumali with great force. Jambumali, however, broke it to pieces with ten arrows. Hanumān then uprooted a large tree and began to whirl it around. Jambumali easily broke the tree into pieces with four arrows, even before it left Hanumān's hands. The Rākṣasa then pierced Hanumān's arms with five arrows, and his chest with ten more shafts and a dart. Hanumān remained undaunted. The great monkey warrior then picked up an iron bar and twirled it forcefully, smashing it against Jambumali's chest. The iron bar hit the Rākṣasa so violently that his head, legs, chariot and donkeys could no longer be distinguished from one another.

Hearing of Jambumali's death, Rāvaṇa became further enraged, and commanded the seven sons of his chief

minister to attack Hanumān with a large army. Thereafter, when the Rākṣasas approached the *aśoka* grove upon their chariots, they saw Hanumān stationed at the garden's arched gate. The Rākṣasas immediately began showering their arrows so heavily that Hanumān was momentarily obscured from view. Hanumān, however, leaped into the sky, thus avoiding their onslaught. Then he charged, roaring loudly. Within moments, Hanumān struck down innumerable Rākṣasas with his hands and feet, while he tore others to pieces with his nails. Others were crushed by the impact of Hanumān's chest and thighs, while still others simply fell to the ground, stunned with fear from Hanumān's roar. When all seven of the chief minister's sons were slain, the remaining warriors panicked and fled. Hanumān returned to the archway, awaiting further combat.

Rāvaṇa then sent five of his leading generals along with a large army, saying, "I want you to capture this Hanumān, for he could not be a mere monkey. He must be a superpowerful being."

Thereafter, the Rākṣasa army assailed Hanumān from all sides. The general named Durdhara released five arrows that pierced Hanumān in the forehead. This merely infuriated Hanumān, who swelled immensely in size. Then, leaping into the sky, he fell upon Durdhara's chariot like lightning striking a mountain. From the impact of Hanumān's gigantic body, the chariot was smashed to pieces, and Durdhara and the horses were crushed to death.

Enraged at the destruction of their comrade, two other generals named Virūpākṣa and Yupakṣa suddenly sprang into the air and struck Hanumān's chest with their clubs.

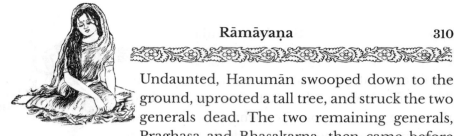

Undaunted, Hanumān swooped down to the ground, uprooted a tall tree, and struck the two generals dead. The two remaining generals, Praghasa and Bhasakarna, then came before Hanumān and pierced him with a spear and dart, causing his body to become covered with blood. The enraged Hanumān then quickly tore off a mountain peak with all its animals and trees, and pounded the two Rākṣasas into mere pulp.

With the five generals out of the way, Hanumān effortlessly destroyed the rest of the army. Hanumān killed the horses by wielding other dead horses, and crushed elephants with other elephants. He struck dead the soldiers with other slain warriors, and smashed chariots by wielding other broken chariots. After covering the ground with many mutilated, dead bodies, Hanumān once more stationed himself at the archway.

Upon hearing of this massacre, Rāvaṇa simply glanced at his son, Akṣa, who was seated close by. Desirous of battle, the prince, understanding his father's indication, eagerly leapt from his seat in the assembly. He then mounted his mystical chariot, which could travel through the air and was drawn by eight horses. As he approached the *aśoka* grove, Akṣa began showering all his arrows on Hanumān. As he came to close quarters, a fierce duel ensued, which made the earth begin to quake, the sun become dim, and the wind cease to blow.

When Akṣa managed to pierce Hanumān's head with three arrows, Hanumān began to expand his body, while the Rākṣasa warrior continued to shower arrows on him. The young Akṣa was childishly proud of his strength, and came fearlessly before Hanumān like an elephant approaching a well covered by grass.

After being struck by Akṣa's arrows, Hanumān assumed an awesome feature and sprang into the air. Akṣa closely followed him, while constantly releasing his arrows. However, Hanumān successfully dodged them while coursing through the sky.

When an arrow suddenly pierced his chest, Hanumān mentally praised the skill of his enemy, thinking, "Although a young boy, this Rākṣasa is fighting very heroically, and I really do not wish to kill him. However, as the battle progresses, his prowess only increases. If I do not kill him, I may become defeated. Therefore, it behooves me to kill him immediately, just as a spreading fire should be extinguished at once."

Increasing his speed, Hanumān killed all of Akṣa's horses with a slap of his hand, causing the disabled chariot to fall to the ground, smashed to pieces. Akṣa took up his bow and sword, jumped from the ruined chariot, and ascended into the sky like a *ṛṣi* on his way to heaven. Agile Hanumān, however, caught Akṣa by the legs. Then, spinning him around thousands of times, he dashed the son of Rāvaṇa violently to the ground. With all his limbs broken and his chest crushed, Akṣa gave up his life while vomiting blood.

Having witnessed Hanumān's victory, the *ṛṣis* stationed in the sky gazed upon him with wonder, while Rāvaṇa's heart filled with terror. As Hanumān again stationed himself at the archway, awaiting the next onslaught of Rākṣasas, the infuriated Rāvaṇa checked his anger and summoned Indrajit, his eldest son. Rāvaṇa said to him, "In warfare, you are unparalleled and equal only to me. You have conquered the king of heaven along with all the demigods and have

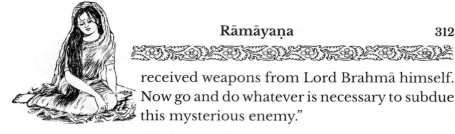

received weapons from Lord Brahmā himself. Now go and do whatever is necessary to subdue this mysterious enemy."

Hanumān felt great joy when he heard the twang of Indrajit's bow, as the Rākṣasa came before him riding his chariot. As Indrajit showered his arrows, Hanumān roared loudly, and expanded himself, then rose up into the sky to avoid the onslaught. In the fighting that ensued, Indrajit could not find any opportunity to pierce Hanumān with his arrows, nor could Hanumān strike Indrajit. Upon seeing the futility of his weapons, Indrajit considered Hanumān incapable of being killed. He began to think of how to capture him instead. Then Indrajit employed a special *brahmāstra* that immediately bound up Hanumān, making him fall to the ground, practically bereft of consciousness.

Hanumān could understand that he was being bound up by the power of Lord Brahmā in the form of a weapon. At the same time, he could remember receiving a benediction from Lord Brahmā that such a weapon would lose its effectiveness after a short while. Therefore, Hanumān thought, "I cannot free myself just now, but still I have nothing to fear. Rather than considering this a setback, I should take it as a good opportunity to see Rāvaṇa firsthand. Even though I have been taken captive, I am certain that from the benediction of Lord Brahmā, I will soon free myself."

Some of the Rākṣasa warriors then came and tied Hanumān with strong ropes. As they bound him, they abused him with harsh words. However, as soon as Hanumān was tied up by their ropes, the effects of the *brahmāstra* became nullified, because that weapon's power could not be used in conjunction with another means of bondage (in this case, the

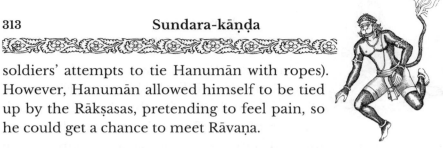

soldiers' attempts to tie Hanumān with ropes). However, Hanumān allowed himself to be tied up by the Rākṣasas, pretending to feel pain, so he could get a chance to meet Rāvaṇa.

Indrajit could understand that Hanumān was feigning bondage, being freed from the effects of the *brahmāstra*. Thus he thought, "The capture of Hanumān has been rendered useless by these thoughtless Rākṣasas. Moreover, now that the *brahmāstra* has been nullified, it cannot be evoked again against the same adversary."

While Indrajit pondered over this predicament, the Rākṣasas dragged Hanumān into the presence of Rāvaṇa, while excitedly saying among themselves, "Who is this monkey-like creature? We should kill him at once. Eat him up! Let's roast him!"

Hanumān was face to face with Rāvaṇa. Rāvaṇa ordered his ministers to interrogate Hanumān. In reply to their questions, Hanumān said, "I am a messenger from Sugrīva, the king of the monkeys, who sends you his best wishes. The noble minded Sugrīva hopes that you are conducting yourself according to the principles of religion, and that your kingdom is therefore prospering."

Inwardly, Hanumān was enraged at being captured, and at the thought of how Rāvaṇa had kidnapped Sītā further inflamed his anger. However, as he gazed upon the king of the Rākṣasas seated upon his crystal throne, Hanumān thought, "With Rāvaṇa's charm, presence of mind, courage, splendor and auspicious bodily symptoms, he would have surpassed even Indra in glory, had he not become adverse to righteousness."

Likewise, Rāvaṇa was enraged, yet felt apprehensive while looking at Hanumān. Rāvaṇa wondered, "Is this Nandī, the bull carrier of Lord Śiva, who previously cursed me when I mocked him? Or is this Bāna, the king of the Asuras, disguised as a monkey?"

Prahasta, the foremost of Rāvaṇa's ministers, then assured Hanumān, "If you simply tell us the real reason why you have come here, we will let you go free."

Hanumān replied, "As a curious monkey, I have simply come here with the desire of meeting Rāvaṇa. I knew that an insignificant person like me would have a difficult time gaining the king's audience. Therefore, I destroyed the pleasure garden with the hope that I would be captured and brought to the royal assembly. I didn't intend to harm anyone, but when the Rākṣasa warriors attacked me, I was forced to kill them in self-defense.

"Long ago I received a benediction from Lord Brahmā that I could not be bound by any weapon or ropes. Thus, you should know that I have purposefully allowed myself to be captured—the power of Indrajit's *brahmāstra* has already been nullified.

"Now, please listen as I disclose the real reason for my coming here. My name is Hanumān, and I have been sent as an envoy of Lord Rāma, the son of Mahārāja Daśaratha. For a long time I have been searching for Rāma's abducted wife, Sītā, and it was my good fortune to find her here. O king of the Rākṣasas, please know for certain that no one is immune to the arrows of Rāma and Lakṣmaṇa. Not even the self-born Brahmā, Lord Śiva or Indra dare to face Rāma on the battlefield.

"O Rāvaṇa, you are the knower of religious principles. One who is actually wise would never court disaster by giving up the path of virtue. Please take my advice and give Sītā back to Rāma before it is too late. Previously, you gained immunity from death at the hands of the demigods and demons by virtue of your severe austerities. Likewise, you should now realize that your unrighteous act of abducting Sītā will bring about disaster for you. Even I could annihilate all of Laṅkā, what to speak of Rāma, who can dissolve and recreate the entire cosmic manifestation."

Hanumān's speech simply made Rāvaṇa more furious. As his reddish eyes rolled in anger, he screamed, "Kill this monkey at once!"

However, in a gentle voice, Vibhīṣaṇa advised, "My dear elder brother, it is not proper to put messengers to death. You are certainly a great scholar. However, all your knowledge will be void if you become swayed by uncontrolled anger."

Rāvaṇa, however, did not appreciate this unwanted advice. He angrily replied, "There is no sin incurred for killing an evil-doer. Let Hanumān die."

Vibhīṣaṇa then argued, "In the scriptures there is no injunction that a messenger can be killed. Indeed, it is unheard of. The only punishments that can be administered are mutilation of the limbs, flogging, shaving of the head and branding. My dear Rāvaṇa, great heroes like yourself never fall prey to the influence of uncontrolled anger. I suggest that you try to kill the enemy who sent Hanumān, and not Hanumān himself. Why don't you send your army to fight with Rāma and Lakṣmaṇa, for it is They who seek revenge."

By the influence of his pious brother, Rāvaṇa finally relented, saying, "Monkeys always prize their tails very highly. Therefore, set fire to his tail and parade Hanumān through the streets of Laṅkā. Then the people can see what kind of hero he is. Afterwards he can be released to return to his relatives with a burnt tail and suffer great humiliation."

Being so commanded, the Rākṣasas then wrapped cotton rags around Hanumān's tail and soaked the cloth in oil. As the rags were set ablaze, Hanumān expanded himself in a fit of rage and began beating the Rākṣasas by lashing his tail about. The Rākṣasas, however, took hold of Hanumān and tied him more tightly. Indeed, Hanumān allowed this, for he wanted to take a tour of Laṅkā to better inspect its fortifications.

The Rākṣasas rudely dragged Hanumān through the city streets, announcing to the people that they had captured a spy. As all the women, children and elders curiously came out to see the prisoner, the Rākṣasī guards informed Sītā of Hanumān's plight. Hearing this, Sītā became greatly distressed, and meditated upon Agni, praying, "If I have earned any pious credit by my devotion and austerities, then let them be utilized so that the fire feels cool to Hanumān."

Just then, the sacrificial fire maintained by Sītā began to burn mildly. Thereafter, the fire on Hanumān's tail burned coolly, as Vāyu, blew ice-winds. Hanumān wondered, "Why am I not being burnt, although the flames are blazing brightly? Indeed, it feels as if the Rākṣasas have wrapped ice around my tail! Surely this is due to the mercy of either Rāma or Sītā!"

Then Hanumān considered, "It is not befitting a great warrior and servant of Lord Rāma to be bound up and made a laughing-stock by these Rākṣasas! I've had enough of this humiliation!" In the twinkling of an eye, Hanumān slipped from his bonds by suddenly shrinking in size. Then, jumping into the air with a shout, Hanumān instantly assumed his gigantic form and picked up an iron bar lying at the city gates. In a moment Hanumān killed the guards and then considered, "What else can I do to torment Rāvaṇa and the Rākṣasas before returning to Rāma? Since my tail is ablaze, why not use it to engulf Laṅkā in a great conflagration?"

His mind made up, Hanumān jumped onto the roof of the Prime Minister's palace, setting it afire. Then, jumping from rooftop to rooftop, he ignited a great fire that spread all over Laṅkā, avoiding only the palace of the pious Vibhīṣaṇa.

Hanumān also went within many palaces, including Rāvaṇa's. Because of the raging wind, the fires soon blazed out of control, causing the upper stories of the palaces to crumble and crash to the ground. The intense heat melted the gold and silver, which then mixed with pearls and other jewels and flowed out into the streets like lava.

A great uproar was then heard among the Rākṣasas as they tried to save themselves and their possessions. Anguished cries and loud wails reached a pitiful climax as multitudes of Rākṣasas, horses and elephants were burnt. Igniting the fat from the burning bodies, the fire began blazing higher and higher—so much so that it appeared that the time of universal destruction had come. In a state of panic, the inhabitants of Laṅkā exclaimed, "Is this Agni himself ravaging our city in the form of a monkey? Or is it Indra, Brahmā, Time personified, or the unlimited energy of Lord Viṣṇu, coming here to destroy us all?"

After going around the entire city, Hanumān paused to gaze upon the fire, feeling great satisfaction. Then Hanumān went to the ocean and extinguished the fire on his tail and contemplated his return to Rāma. As he again turned to witness the fire consuming Laṅkā, Hanumān suddenly became filled with a terrible apprehension as he heard the screams of the dying Rākṣasas. "What a fool I have been to set fire to Laṅkā!" Hanumān thought. "What if Sītā has also

been burned?! Just see the result of uncontrolled anger. It is the most sinful trait of the living entity, for it causes him to act indiscriminately. Indeed, what is there that an enraged man will not do or say? A person under the sway of anger can murder his own guru or parents, and insult the great souls. Only one who has learned to control his anger deserves to be called a human being.

"If I have caused the death of Sītā, then I have killed my master as well, and shall have to give up my life as atonement. To hell with the foolish nature of monkeys, which produces actions born of passion and anger. Passionate acts always give uncertain results. In this case, I may have brought about mass destruction. If Sītā has died, Rāma and Lakṣmaṇa will no longer be able to live. Then, one after the other, Bharata, Śatrughna, Sugrīva and many others will give up their lives. Without the shelter of these exalted persons, all other living entities will gradually become disinterested in life. Thus, it may be that I have unwittingly become the cause for the destruction of the entire world!"

As Hanumān lamented in this way, he suddenly observed several auspicious omens, and concluded that, "The virtuous Sītā could not have been harmed. Indeed, by the mercy of Rāma, even I was not burnt by the fire, what to speak of His beloved consort. The purity of her character alone is sufficient to protect her. The strength of her austerities, her devotion to truth, and her dedication to Lord Rāma are more powerful than fire itself."

All along, the Siddhas, Cāraṇas and other celestial beings had been praising Hanumān for his heroic exploits. Now,

to reassure Hanumān, they informed him that Sītā was safe. Overjoyed and relieved, Hanumān rushed to where Sītā was staying. Upon seeing her, he shed tears of happiness. Sītā again pleaded, "Dear Hanumān, please remain here for just one day. I gain great relief from my burning grief by your association. Indeed, your return is uncertain, as is my survival, because of my intense unhappiness. I don't see how Rāma, Lakṣmaṇa and the monkeys will ever be able to

cross the ocean. Regardless, you must urge them to come quickly and rescue me, for I do not feel I can remain alive under these conditions."

Hanumān tried to comfort Sītā, and he assured her of Rāma's ability to rescue her. Having made up his mind to depart, Hanumān ascended the Arśita Mountain. In his eagerness to see Rāma after completing his mission, Hanumān began crushing the peaks of the mountain with his feet. Then, as Hanumān expanded his size, the mountain began to crumble. The Gandharvas and animals residing there began fleeing in fear. Indeed, as Hanumān took his mighty leap, the 30 *yojana* high mountain sank down until it was level with the earth.

Sailing through the sky, Hanumān again touched Maināka Mountain in a gesture of respect. Finally, as he approached Mahendra Mountain, Hanumān began roaring jubilantly, while waving his tail, anxious to meet his monkey friends.

When they heard Hanumān's roar, the monkeys waiting on the shore became eager to catch a glimpse of their hero. Jāmbavān told the others, "Judging from his exuberance, Hanumān has been successful in his mission."

The monkeys began excitedly springing from tree to tree, mountain peak to mountain peak, waving their cloths. As Hanumān finally came into view, they stood up with folded hands to watch him descend upon Mahendra Mountain. The monkeys gathered around Hanumān, shouting with delight, and presented him with fruits and roots. Hanumān first offered his respects to the elders, including Jāmbavān, and then to prince Aṅgada. He answered their eager

inquiries, and informed them that he had found Sītā. Hearing that Sītā was still alive, the monkeys became overjoyed, and embraced Hanumān again and again.

Thereafter, Aṅgada praised Hanumān for his great heroism and devotion to Lord Rāma, and sat down with Hanumān to talk. Jāmbavān then approached and requested Hanumān to narrate the entire story of his jump to Laṅkā and subsequent discovery of Sītā. As the monkeys eagerly crowded around, Hanumān mentally offered his respects to Sītā and related the details of his journey to Lanka, how he found Sītā, and his desecration of the city. He concluded by saying, "Because of her constantly being tormented by fierce Rākṣasīs, the gentle Sītā suffers unbearable anguish. Although Rāvaṇa offers her everything in his possession, Sītā scorns him, for she knows no one but Rāma as her Lord. Although constant absorption in Rāma keeps her alive, Sītā will certainly wither away and die if she is not rescued soon.

"So let us attack Laṅkā at once and bring Sītā back to Rāma at Kiṣkindhyā. I know that I am able to defeat all the Rākṣasas single-handed, as is Aṅgada. Think of how pleased Rāma would be if we not only found Sītā, but rescued her, too! Indeed, I could easily have brought Sītā back here with me, but because I did not have your permission, I restrained myself."

Aṅgada then said, "Once, out of respect for the Aśvinīkumāras, Lord Brahmā blessed their sons Mainda and Dvivida that they would be incapable of being slain in battle. Because of this, these proud monkeys were able to defeat the entire army of the demigods, and forcibly drank their nectar. I think they could easily conquer Rāvaṇa. Indeed,

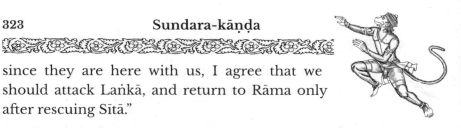

since they are here with us, I agree that we should attack Laṅkā, and return to Rāma only after rescuing Sītā."

Jāmbavān said, "O prince, your plan lacks wisdom. You have forgot that we were only ordered to find Sītā and not to fight for her recovery. Even if we were successful, I think that Rāma would be displeased, for He vowed before all the monkeys that He would kill Rāvaṇa and win back Sītā."

Aṅgada, Hanumān and the other monkeys accepted Jāmbavān's advice. Without further delay, they departed for Kiṣkindhyā. Along the way, the monkeys came to Madhuvana, a heavenly forest owned by Sugrīva. Being eager to drink honey, they requested Aṅgada to stop for a while.

In that forest, the monkeys began to partake of roots, fruits and honey to their full satisfaction. Within a short time, they all became intoxicated. While laughing, dancing and singing, they sported in a most boisterous manner, turning the nice garden into a shambles. At this, the superintendent of the grove, named Dadhimukha, became very angry. When he came and told the monkeys to stop, they insulted him with harsh words. Then, trying to save the garden, Dadhimukha began chastising some of the monkeys, pacifying others, and even striking some with his hands. Unfortunately, this infuriated the intoxicated monkeys. They jumped on Dadhimukha and began kicking, biting and scratching him. Indeed, Hanumān encouraged the monkeys, saying, "Enjoy yourselves as you please. I will check anyone who tries to stop you." Aṅgada echoed this sentiment, and thus the monkeys fearlessly thrashed the guards and stripped the garden of all its edibles.

Eventually Dadhimukha was set free, and the monkeys continued their drunken activities. Some of the monkeys lay down lazily, while others became insulting and boisterous. All the guards then approached Dadhimukha, submitting their complaints about the monkeys' behavior. The superintendent assured them he would put a stop to their rampage. Dadhimukha uprooted a huge tree, and the guards followed him by picking up huge boulders. As the guards approached, Hanumān and the other monkeys prepared to encounter them. Under the influence of intoxication, Aṅgada grabbed Dadhimukha, who happened to be his grand uncle, and after throwing him to the ground, began beating him mercilessly.

Finally, when Dadhimukha was let go, he took the guards with him to meet Sugrīva, thinking the king would surely kill the monkeys for their misconduct. When Dadhimukha thus arrived at Kiṣkindhyā and touched Sugrīva's feet with his head, the king could see that he was highly agitated. Dadhimukha then described the misbehavior of Aṅgada and his followers.

At this time, Rāma and Lakṣmaṇa came by to see what was

the matter, and Sugrīva explained, "Aṅgada and his party are now at Madhuvana. From the description of their raucous behavior it appears they have been successful in their mission. I am sure that Hanumān has found Sītā. Otherwise, the monkeys would never dare act with such abandon."

Hearing this, Rāma and Lakṣmaṇa became enlivened. Likewise, Sugrīva was overjoyed, and told Dadhimukha, "Indirectly your complaint conveys good news to me. Therefore, the mischief by the monkeys should be tolerated. Please return now to Madhuvana and tell Aṅgada and the others that I want to see them immediately."

Taking this order upon his head, Dadhimukha sprang into the air. When he arrived at Madhuvana, he saw that the monkeys had become sober, and were passing the honey from their bodies as urine. Dadhimukha then approached Aṅgada with sweet words, saying, "Please forgive me for trying to forbid you and your followers from enjoying the gardens. O prince, your uncle was exceedingly pleased to learn of your arrival, and wants you to return to Kiṣkindhyā at once."

Turning to his followers, Aṅgada said, "I suggest we return to Kiṣkindhyā without delay. Still, even though I am the prince, I do not consider myself superior to any of you. On the contrary, I feel completely dependent on all of you. I shall do whatever you recommend. I await your order."

Fully satisfied by his statement, the monkeys replied, "O prince, your humility is just befitting an exalted personality. It indicates your eligibility to receive further good fortune. Let us not waste another moment, for Sugrīva and Rāma await our arrival."

Thereafter, all the monkeys leaped towards Kiṣkindhyā, like so many stones shot from a catapult. Seeing the monkeys approach in the distance, Sugrīva went to the grief-stricken Rāma, saying, "Aṅgada has come! I knew he would not dare return to Kiṣkindhyā without achieving success. And unless he had located Sītā, he would never devastate the Madhuvana garden given to my father, Ṛkṣarāja, by my grandfather, Lord Brahmā, if he had failed in his mission."

Before long, Aṅgada's party arrived back in the presence of Rāma. Hanumān excitedly declared, "Sītā is safe. She has remained fixed in her vows of chastity, never once accepting Rāvaṇa's advances." Rāma looked upon Hanumān with eyes laden with love and respect.

All the monkeys offered their obeisances to Sugrīva, Rāma and Lakṣmaṇa. Unable to contain themselves, they each repeated everything Hanumān had told them about Sītā. When the monkeys finally fell silent, Rāma said, "Describe to Me the exact location of Rāvaṇa's abode, and tell Me more of Sītā. How does she really feel about Me now?"

All the monkeys then pushed Hanumān forward so he could give an authoritative answer. Bowing to the south, Hanumān related the events leading to his discovery of Sītā. Then he delivered to Rāma the jewel from Sītā's head and said, "The devotion of King Janaka's daughter is completely fixed upon You. In separation from You, she can hardly maintain her life." Hanumān then related Sītā's messages: How Indra's son in the form of a crow had scratched her breasts, how Rāma had decorated her face with red oxide, and how, due to being tortured by the Rākṣasīs, she would

surely give up her life if He did not come to rescue her within one month.

As He listened to Hanumān, Rāma pressed Sītā's jewel to His heart, and both He and Lakṣmaṇa shed incessant tears. Rāma said, "This jewel was presented to Sītā by her father at the time of our marriage. Long ago, King Indra gave the jewel to Mahārāja Janaka after becoming pleased with the king's sacrificial performances. Oh Hanumān, I have become practically unconscious from intense grief. Therefore, please repeat the messages given by Sītā, for they act just like cool water sprinkled upon my head.

In reply, Hanumān narrated, "After Sītā finished telling me the story of how You chastised Indra's son, Jayanta, she said, 'Although Rāma is unlimitedly powerful and unconquerable, He does not come here to rescue me. I can only conclude that this misfortune is the result of some terrible sin I committed in a past life.'"

Hanumān continued, "I offered to carry Sītā back to You, but she refused, for she was unwilling to touch another male. Again and again, she said, 'You must convince Rāma to come here quickly to rescue me. My grief is practically unbearable, and I do not know how much longer I can go on living. Oh Hanumān, how will Rāma, Lakṣmaṇa and the monkeys ever be able to cross over the ocean to Laṅkā? I know you are able to kill Rāvaṇa and deliver me to Rāma. However, it is my desire that Rāma Himself come here to rescue me, so His spotless reputation will be further enhanced. I do not wish to be returned to Rāma the way I was brought to Laṅkā—carried by another.'"

Hanumān concluded, "I assured Sītā that the other monkeys were superior to me, and could easily jump over the ocean to Laṅkā. I also told her that if necessary, I could carry You and Lakṣmaṇa on my back. In this way I pacified Sītā a little. However, considering her precarious condition, I urge You to quickly devise some means whereby we can all attack Laṅkā without further delay."

Yuddha-kāṇḍa

Rāma was extremely pleased with Hanumān's extraordinary accomplishment. He praised Hanumān, saying, "Except for Garuḍa, no one else could do what you did. Of all servants, the best is he who accomplishes more than the duty entrusted by his master. A mediocre servant is he who never attempts to do more that what his master orders, even though he may be capable of doing more. Finally, the worst servant, among the lowest of men, is he who does not carry out the order of the master, even though qualified.

"Dear Hanumān, you have not only found Sītā, but also comforted her with your words. You surveyed the entire city of Laṅkā, tested the strength of the great Rākṣasa warriors, and struck fear into the heart of Rāvaṇa. Indeed, your service has saved My very life. Thus, it greatly pains Me that I cannot reward you properly. Since I am living in exile without proper means, all I can offer in exchange for your service is My embrace." Saying this, Rāma affectionately pressed Hanumān to His heart.

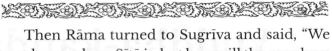

Then Rāma turned to Sugrīva and said, "We now know where Sītā is, but how will the monkeys ever be able to cross the ocean? It suddenly appears to Me that all our hopes and hard labor have been rendered useless." Falling silent, Rāma became engrossed in thought.

Sugrīva replied, "O my Lord, You should cast off Your grief, just as an ungrateful person can easily give up kindness. For one who lacks enthusiasm, all activities become the cause of misery. For one whose mind is bewildered by grief, all endeavors end in failure. I take great delight in the prospect of fighting with the Rākṣasas. I am convinced that the monkeys are equal to the task. Perhaps we could somehow build a bridge across the ocean. If the monkeys could only get to Laṅkā, I am sure they will emerge victorious."

Looking to Hanumān, Rāma said, "Utilizing My mystic power, I can easily cross the ocean, or dry it up if I so desire. Therefore, please describe to Me in detail the fortifications of Laṅkā and any other relevant information gathered in your foray."

Hanumān eagerly replied, "Laṅkā has four types of defenses. Their first defense is natural. The city is situated atop a high mountain, encircled by a river and surrounded by dense forests. Then, there are fortifications. High golden walls surround Laṅkā, with four massive gates facing the four directions, each equipped with gigantic catapults. Surrounding the walls are wide moats filled with fierce alligators. Four draw bridges, which lead to the four gates, span these moats. When I set fire to Laṅkā I broke all the drawbridges and tore down many sections of the wall.

My dear Lord Rāma, may I suggest that only the greatest warriors, such as Aṅgada, Dvivida, Mainda, Jāmbavān, Panasa, Nīla and myself jump over to Laṅkā. We can defeat Rāvaṇa without any need to worry about transporting the entire army of monkeys across the ocean."

Rāma replied, "It is My vow that I shall personally go to destroy Laṅkā."

Turning to Sugrīva, Rāma said, "The sun is now at the meridian and the auspicious time called Abhijit has arrived. This is the opportune time to begin a military campaign. Likewise, there is trembling in my right eyelid, indicating victory. Therefore, quickly assemble the monkeys so that we can begin our march to Laṅkā immediately."

Lakṣmaṇa and Sugrīva applauded Rāma's initiative, and within moments, hordes of monkeys emerged from the caves and the wooded mountain slopes. Rāma then ordered Nīla, "I want you to march in front of the army. Take some of the monkeys with you and have them spread out in all directions, just in case enemy warriors are waiting to ambush us. Leave all weak monkeys behind, for the conquest we face is formidable."

Rāma then arranged the army so He was riding upon Hanumān's back in the center of the formation, with Lakṣmaṇa riding upon Aṅgada. Thus, as Sugrīva passed Rāma's orders through the ranks, the army set out to the south.

The powerful monkeys marched on with great bravado, roaring like lions and leaping up and down. Sometimes they

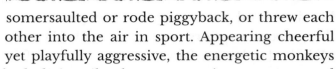

somersaulted or rode piggyback, or threw each other into the air in sport. Appearing cheerful yet playfully aggressive, the energetic monkeys lashed their tails about, uprooting creepers and dislodging stones as they clambered up and down the hills.

Traveling along, Lakṣmaṇa said to Rāma, "Look at the auspicious symptoms around us! There is a cool and fragrant breeze blowing behind us, and the forest animals are making noises that indicate their satisfaction. Indeed, the land itself appears to be in a peaceful condition, while overhead, the sun is shining especially bright."

The army traveled on, day and night, eager to fight for Sītā's recovery. While traveling, the monkeys bathed and sported in the mountain lakes, ate fruits and roots, and drank honey from the forests. Finally Rāma arrived at Mount Mahendra, and climbed to its peak. From there He could see the vast ocean, stretching to the horizon. When Rāma rejoined the monkeys at the bottom, the army continued on. Before long they arrived at the seashore. Rāma told Sugrīva, "We are now confronted with the problem of crossing over the ocean. How can we possibly cross? Let the monkeys set up their camp while we devise some means for reaching Laṅkā."

As they busied themselves pitching camp, the monkey hordes appeared like a great brown sea, agitated with tossing brown waves. The monkey leader gazed with wonder at the vast ocean, which is the refuge of demons, going all the way down to the lowest planetary system. With wide open eyes, the army stared at the fathomless sea, infested with aquatic monsters like the one-hundred *yojana* long Timi fish, and the Timiṅgilas, which can swallow the Timis in a single gulp. The monkey heroes beheld the impassable expanse of wave

heaving, wind whipped water, with Laṅkā on the other side. While sitting at leisure, Rāma said to Lakṣmaṇa, "It is said that grief disappears with the passage of time. However, My anguish in separation from Sītā only increases with the passing of each day. O Lakṣmaṇa, My most painful thought is of how Sītā's allotted time is steadily slipping away. My heart burns with longing for the time when I shall kill Rāvaṇa and rescue her. Only then will I be able to cast off My grief for good, just as a person throws away his old, worn out garment." As Rāma vented His anguish before Lakṣmaṇa, the sun gradually set.

After witnessing Hanumān's devastating prowess, Rāvaṇa called a meeting with all the leading Rākṣasas. The Rākṣasa king said, "Impenetrable Laṅkā has been ravaged. My palaces are in ruins and many of the best Rākṣasa warriors are dead. According to authoritative opinion, the root cause of victory is good counsel. That is why I have called you all here. There are three classes of men in this world: Before acting, the wise person takes counsel of superiors and friends who have a common interest. Then, according to their advice, he exerts himself to his fullest capacity, while ultimately depending upon Providence. The mediocre person thinks over a matter himself, considering things in the light of his own understanding, and then acts accordingly. The vilest of men are those who entirely give up faith in God and perform their actions whimsically, without a sense of duty. Being unable to properly judge what is beneficial and what is harmful, such persons go ahead blindly, saying, 'I shall do it no matter what!'

"Similarly, there are three types of advice. Good advice is given after an objective study of the problem, and in alignment with religious principles. Mediocre advice is given after a heated discussion of the problem, and places more emphasis upon self-interest than religious principles. Bad advice is that which is given out of false pride or flattery, and which does not properly take into consideration the ultimate consequences.

"I am convinced that very soon Rāma will come to attack Laṅkā with an army of monkeys. His prowess was demonstrated at Janasthāna. Thus, I have no doubt He will be able to cross the ocean without difficulty. My dear Rākṣasas, all of you are very intelligent. I want your advice about what must be done for our welfare."

Ignorant of Rāma's strength, and eager to please their master, the Rākṣasas replied, "O king, why should you be afraid? You are powerful enough to defeat all your enemies single-handed. Just remember how you defeated Kuvera, taking Laṅkā away from him. Remember how Maya Dānava fearfully handed over his daughter, Mandodarī, to you. Why should you even bother to worry? You can rest peacefully, while your son Indrajit annihilates Rāma and all the monkeys before they even cross the ocean. Previously, after defeating all the demigods, Indrajit arrested Indra, the king of heaven, keeping him captive at Laṅkā. Only at Lord Brahmā's request was Indra allowed to go free and resume his heavenly post."

Rāvaṇa's commander-in-chief, Prahasta, then said, "We have conquered the demigods, Dānavas, Gandharvas, and Piśācas. Why should we be afraid of these mere mortals?

Hanumān was only able to exert his prowess because we were unwary, considering him to be a mere monkey."

Another Rākṣasa named Durmukha stoodup and declared, "I will not allow this insult to go unavenged. Wherever they may be—inheaven, on earth, or within the sea—I shall rid the world of every single monkey!"

Brandishing a club stained with flesh and blood, the Rākṣasa Vajradaṁṣṭra shouted, "Who cares for fighting with a bunch of monkeys? It is Rāma and Lakṣmaṇa whom I shall crush to death. O king, just give me the order!"

Kumbhakarṇa's powerful son, Nikumbha, then bellowed, "Let all of you remain here with our master. I shall go and vanquish Rāma and all the monkeys single-handed!"

Another Rākṣasa named Vajrahanu, as large as a hill, boasted, "O king, remain here and conduct your business as usual. Drink wine and make merry while I attend to Rāma, Lakṣmaṇa and their army of monkeys."

Indeed, many of the Rākṣasa heroes boasted of their prowess, assuring Rāvaṇa that they could conquer the enemy single-handed. Brandishing their weapons, the agitated Rākṣasas were poised for combat when Vibhīṣaṇa politely restrained them. When they were seated, the pious Vibhīṣaṇa said, "My dear elder brother, the wise have advised that violence should be resorted to only after the other three tactics of conciliation, gifts and dissension have failed. Even then, violence only succeeds against those who are evil, unwary, under siege by another enemy, or doomed by fate. Rāma is supremely powerful and virtuous and eager for revenge. How can you hope to defeat Him? Sītā's abduction is the root cause of our present crisis. You should return her to Rāma before His arrows destroy Laṅkā and all its inhabitants."

After hearing Vibhīṣaṇa's advice, Rāvaṇa dismissed the assembly and retired to his quarters. The next morning, Vibhīṣaṇa came before Rāvaṇa as the Rākṣasa king sat on his throne, listening to the *brāhmaṇas* offer prayers for his

welfare. Seating himself nearby, Vibhīṣaṇa said, "My dear elder brother, ever since you brought Sītā to Laṅkā, many inauspicious omens have manifested. The sacrificial fire now gives off sparks and smoke, and snakes are frequently found inside the kitchen and sacrificial arenas. The offerings made in sacrifice are sometimes full of ants, and swarms of crows perch atop the palaces. Vultures continuously hover over the city, and she-jackals can be heard crying out ominously every morning and evening. This is all because of your sinful act of kidnapping Sītā. O Rāvaṇa, the only atonement for you is to return her to Rāma at once. I speak to you honestly, whereas your other ministers simply flatter you, because they are afraid of incurring your displeasure."

Because Rāvaṇa was overwhelmed by his desire to enjoy Sītā, he became angry upon hearing his brother's sagacious advice. Nearly shouting, Rāvaṇa declared, "I do not fear Rāma or anyone else. I shall never agree to return Sītā under any circumstance. My dear younger brother, you may take your leave and go about your business."

In the months since kidnapping Sītā, Rāvaṇa had grown emaciated due to his unfulfilled passion for Sītā. Even his relatives had begun to disrespect him because of his abominable acts.

Knowing war to be imminent, the king of the Rākṣasas wanted to consult further with his ministers. Thus, the next day he ordered them to convene again. Thereafter, when Rāvaṇa arrived at the assembly hall riding upon his chariot, everyone offered their respects by bowing their heads to the ground, as thousands of trumpets heralded his arrival. Rāvaṇa said to his commander, "Prahasta, you must

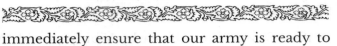

immediately ensure that our army is ready to defend the city, both from within and without."

As Prahasta left to oversee the army's preparations, Rāvaṇa addressed the assembly: "My dear Rākṣasas, I am pleased to announce that after sleeping for six months, Kumbhakarṇa has awakened and is gracing us with his presence today. Please listen attentively, for I want you all to fully understand my position. As you know, I have become obsessed with the lovely-limbed Sītā. Indeed, I have become the slave of my passion for her."

Then, hoping to put himself in a better light, Rāvaṇa began weaving a deceitful tale, saying, "Sītā has agreed to become my consort, but only after the expiration of one year. That is the exact time I have allotted for Rāma to come to her rescue. For this reason I have remained patient, but it now appears that Rāma, Lakṣmaṇa and a vast army of monkeys are preparing to attack Laṅkā. In truth, I do not feel that two mere human beings and a band of monkeys can pose much of a threat. However, since one monkey, Hanumān, was able to inflict so much damage upon us, I must admit that victory is uncertain. That is why I have called for all of you. I want you to advise me how I can kill Rāma, thus keeping the lovely Sītā for myself."

Kumbhakarṇa then stood up and sharply replied, "O foolish king, you should have consulted us when you planned to kidnap Sītā, instead of acting impulsively. That would have saved you from repenting later on. Regardless, you may give up your great anxiety, for I shall counteract your blunder by killing Rāma and Lakṣmaṇa and devouring all the monkeys."

Mahapārśva then spoke up, "O king, why should one not taste the honey procured with great endeavor within the snake infested forest? You can forcibly enjoy Sītā to your heart's content. Who can stop you? No one is as powerful as you are. You are free to do as you like without fear."

Rāvaṇa replied, "There is something in my past that I have always kept a secret. Since you have inquired, I will now disclose to you an incident that happened long ago. Once, I happened to see an Apsarā of incomparable beauty named Puñjikasthalī, who was on her way to offer her respects to the universal grandsire, Lord Brahmā. The sight of the Apsarā inflamed me with desire and I forcibly seized and raped her. After gratifying myself I released her, and she fled, naked, to the shelter of Lord Brahmā. The grandsire became enraged when he learned what I had done, and cursed me, saying, 'O wicked king of the Rākṣasas, your head will split into 100 pieces if you ever try to rape another woman again.'

"My dear Mahapārśva, it is in fear of this curse that I do not drag Sītā to my bed by force. However, I am not afraid of Rāma, for I know I am the most powerful created being in the universe. Rāma is obviously ignorant of my prowess. Therefore, since He desires to attack me, I shall make short work of Him."

Vibhīṣaṇa said, "My dear Rāvaṇa, can't you see that Sītā is just like a poisonous snake that you have willingly placed around your neck? Use your good intelligence and return Sītā to Rāma, before she becomes the cause of Laṅkā's destruction and the annihilation of all the Rākṣasas. I can assure you that there is no Rākṣasa warrior who will be able to stand before Rāma on the battlefield and live to tell about it."

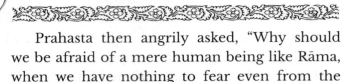

Prahasta then angrily asked, "Why should we be afraid of a mere human being like Rāma, when we have nothing to fear even from the greatest demigods and demons?"

As Rāvaṇa's well-wisher, Vibhīṣaṇa replied, "Rāma possesses unlimited and inconceivable potency on a level with Lord Viṣṇu Himself. Therefore, Prahasta, you will do your king a great service if you dissuade him from fighting with Rāma. Instead, you are now performing the greatest disservice by encouraging Rāvaṇa to fight."

Turning to Rāvaṇa, Vibhīṣaṇa said, "I am only thinking of your welfare when I say that you should return Sītā to Rāma. The minister who measures the relative strength of the king and his enemy, and then gives advice accordingly, is the true well-wisher."

Unable to tolerate his uncle's words any longer, Indrajit hotly interrupted, "Vibhīṣaṇa, you are simply a coward and a eunuch. Your advice has no place in this assembly, for it is devoid of courage and heroism. Previously I dragged Indra and his carrier Airāvata to the ground, causing all the demigods to flee in fear. It will be easy for me to kill two ordinary humans like Rāma and Lakṣmaṇa."

Vibhīṣaṇa harshly replied, "You are but a mere boy. Because your intelligence is not yet developed, you cannot decide what is to be done and what is to be avoided. You are actually Rāvaṇa's enemy and not his son, because you are dull headed, indiscriminate, uncultured and wicked. Sītā should be given back to Rāma along with generous gifts, so that the Rākṣasas may continue to live peacefully."

Rāvaṇa also got tired of hearing Vibhīṣaṇa's contrary advice. To chastise his youngest half-brother, he said, "It is better to live with an enemy or a poisonous snake than one who claims to be a friend but is actually a traitor—especially if that person is one's own brother! It appears that one's own relatives rejoice the most at their family member's misfortune. Once, when some elephants saw hunters approaching with snares in their hands, they recited the following two verses:

Fire and weapons
We do not fear
The dangerous are the
So-called near and dear.

They are the ones
Who take special pains
To make sure that
We are all put in chains.

"From cows we derive milk, in *brāhmaṇas* we find austerity, in women we see fickleness and from relatives we are put into danger. Vibhīṣaṇa, you are envious of me. That is why you cannot tolerate the honor I receive. If anyone else had spoken as you did, I would have killed him at once. You, O wretched half-brother, are a disgrace to our noble family!"

Enraged by Rāvaṇa's rebuke, Vibhīṣaṇa rose up with club in hand, along with four of his followers, and declared, "O king, although you are my superior, I can no longer tolerate your words, for you have chosen to follow the path of irreligion. Flatterers who only utter palatable words are easy to find. However, persons who actually speak for one's benefit,

even though the truth may be unpalatable, are very rare. O Rāvaṇa, I have only given you advice with the hope of saving you from meeting death at the hands of Rāma. You have rejected my advice, however, and are free to do so. Thus, I wish you well, O brother, but I shall no longer remain here with you."

Vibhīṣaṇa and his followers departed, and within one hour reached Rāma's camp. When the monkeys saw Vibhīṣaṇa hovering overhead, like a peak of Mount Meru illuminated with lightning, Sugrīva told Hanumān, "Take care! This Rākṣasa must have come here to kill us!" All the monkeys began picking up rocks and uprooting trees, awaiting Sugrīva's instructions.

Vibhīṣaṇa announced, "O king of the monkeys, I am the youngest half-brother of Rāvaṇa. As former minister to Rāvaṇa, I advised him repeatedly to return Sītā to Rāma. After being rebuked by Rāvaṇa with harsh words, I have left my home, wife and children to take shelter at the lotus feet of Rāma. Please go and tell Him of my intentions."

Sugrīva went to Rāma and said, "One of the enemy Rākṣasas has arrived. Although he says he has deserted Rāvaṇa, he cannot be trusted. Indeed, one can never place any trust in a Rākṣasa. He must be a spy. If we believe in him, then when we least expect it, he may do us great injury. I suggest that he be killed immediately."

Rāma, however, went to the other monkeys, headed by Hanumān, and asked their opinions. The monkeys replied, "Dear Lord Rāma, You are the knower of everything. Therefore, we can understand that You are inquiring from us just to honor us."

Aṅgada then suggested, "If the presence of this Rākṣasa can give us an advantage, he should be accepted with great caution. However, if he poses too much of a threat, he should be turned away."

Saraba advised, "We should assign someone to constantly watch over him. If, after being thoroughly tested, he is found to be our ally, he should be welcomed."

Jāmbavān warned, "This Rākṣasa should be regarded with great caution and suspicion." Likewise, Mainda advised, "He should be thoroughly interrogated before any decision is made."

The ever-wise Hanumān, gifted in the art of speech, then said, "We do not have time to test Vibhīṣaṇa. In my opinion he has come here in all sincerity, hoping to take shelter of Lord Rāma. He has understood that Rāvaṇa is wicked and that Rāma is the supreme emblem of purity and righteousness. His peaceful demeanor and considerate speech indicate the honesty of his purpose, for a deceitful person cannot remain so composed. It is not possible for anyone to fully conceal his inner intentions. The facial expression always gives some clue into one's thoughts. I think Vibhīṣaṇa should be accepted as our ally without reservation."

Although Rāma was pleased by Hanumān's statement, Sugrīva said, "Since Vibhīṣaṇa has deserted his half-brother at a time of adversity, it should be understood that there is no one he would not betray."

Rāma then replied, "I believe that Vibhīṣaṇa has genuinely rejected Rāvaṇa. Such dissension often occurs in royal families. Let us welcome him as our ally."

Still unconvinced, Sugrīva meekly protested, "He may have been sent by Rāvaṇa. Therefore, to be safe we should immediately capture and kill him. If we accept him, he may turn on us at any moment."

Rāma smiled and said, "Do you truly think this Rākṣasa could hurt Me? With the mere tip of My finger I could kill all the Rākṣasas and demons. Please listen as I tell you the following story: 'Once there was a hunter who caught a

pigeon in his snare. Afterward he took rest under a nearby tree. The wife of the captured pigeon was residing in that tree, and upon seeing that the hunter had come to her house, she offered him ample hospitality. Indeed, since she had nothing else to feed the hunter, the bird offered him her own flesh to fulfill her obligation to receive a guest.'"

Rāma continued, "O Sugrīva, since a mere bird acted in this way, what can be said of a man like Myself? There are many places in the scriptures where it is stated that when an enemy arrives with folded hands he must be protected by all means. The great sage Kaṇḍu has commented that it is only out of fear or folly that one would act otherwise, thus incurring sin. Moreover, as the Supreme Personality of Godhead, it is My eternal principle that if any living being takes shelter of Me, even once, saying, ' I am Yours,' then I award that person freedom from all fear. Even if Rāvaṇa were to come here to surrender unto Me, I would give him all protection."

Sugrīva's heart became filled with love upon hearing Rāma's sublime statement. With tears in his eyes, he admitted, "O Rāma, Your words and deeds are always just befitting Your supreme position. I too, feel that Vibhīṣaṇa is sincere. Therefore, let friendship be made without delay."

After being assured of safety, Vibhīṣaṇa descended to the earth and fell down flat at the lotus feet of Lord Rāma. In a mood of full surrender, he explained, "I am the youngest half-brother of Rāvaṇa and my name is Vibhīṣaṇa. Although I instructed the Rākṣasa king for his benefit, he rebuked me harshly. Therefore I have abandoned my home, family and

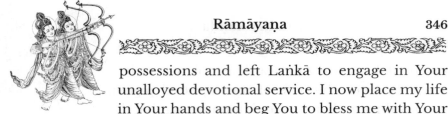

possessions and left Laṅkā to engage in Your unalloyed devotional service. I now place my life in Your hands and beg You to bless me with Your causeless mercy."

While lovingly gazing upon Vibhīṣaṇa, as if drinking him in with His eyes, Rāma requested him to describe the strengths and weaknesses of the enemy. In reply, Vibhīṣaṇa said, "Because of receiving benedictions from Lord Brahmā, Rāvaṇa has become immune to death at the hands of demigods, Gandharvas, Daityas, Dānavas and Nāgas. Indeed, he cannot be killed by any creature except human beings, whom he considers to be too insignificant. Rāvaṇa's younger brother, Kumbhakarṇa, is as huge as a great mountain and as powerful as Indra. The commander-in-chief of the Rākṣasas is Prahasta, who once vanquished the Yakṣa hero, Manibhadra, at Mount Kailāsa. Likewise, there is Rāvaṇa's son, Indrajit, who is equal to his father in all respects. He wears impenetrable armor, and after propitiating the god of fire, he is able to make himself invisible on the battlefield. There are millions of other Rākṣasas, headed by Mahodara, Mahapārśva and Akampana. All of them are very fierce and can change their forms at will."

Rāma then said, "O Vibhīṣaṇa, I am well aware of Rāvaṇa's prowess. I give you My word that after killing him and all the other Rākṣasa warriors, I shall install you upon the royal throne at Laṅkā."

In turn, Vibhīṣaṇa assured Rāma that he would help Him to conquer Laṅkā. Rāma was very satisfied with His devotee. After warmly embracing Vibhīṣaṇa, He ordered Lakṣmaṇa to bring some water from the sea so He could immediately perform the installation ceremony.

Upon seeing the extraordinary mercy of Lord Rāma upon the Rākṣasa, the monkeys became ecstatic and shouted with joy. Hanumān and Sugrīva said, "We feel confident about combating the Rākṣasas, but we are perplexed about how to cross over the unfathomable ocean. Perhaps you can advise us in this matter."

Vibhīṣaṇa replied, "I suggest that Rāma call upon Varuṇa, the presiding deity of the ocean. Previously, His forefather, Sagara, excavated Varuṇa's waters and extended his domain. Because of this past service, the ocean will certainly help Rāma accomplish His mission."

Sugrīva then relayed Vibhīṣaṇa's idea to Rāma and Lakṣmaṇa. Rāma thought it to be a good idea, but nonetheless replied to Sugrīva, "I shall do whatever you and Lakṣmaṇa decide." Sugrīva and Lakṣmaṇa readily agreed with Vibhīṣaṇa. Thereafter, Rāma sat down upon a *kuśa* mat, His face turned toward the sea.

Meanwhile, a spy named Śārdūla sighted the monkeys, and reported to Rāvaṇa how the army had set up camp, covering an area of eighty miles in all directions. The perturbed Rākṣasa king then ordered his envoy Śuka to approach Sugrīva and deliver the following message: "I have never done any harm to you. Therefore, why are you preparing to attack Laṅkā? Since the kidnapping of Sītā has nothing to do with you, it would be better for you to return to Kiṣkindhyā and go on living peacefully there."

Taking the form of a bird, Śuka flew to Sugrīva and began to deliver Rāvaṇa's message while in the sky. However, as Śuka was speaking, some monkeys jumped into the air and

captured him. Thus, while dragging him to the ground, the monkeys cut off Śuka's wings and savagely beat him. In great distress, Śuka cried out, "O Rāma, those who adhere to righteousness never indulge in killing an envoy."

Rāma intervened, and after being let go, Śuka once more rose into the sky, asking Sugrīva if he had any message for Rāvaṇa. Sugrīva replied, "You may tell your master this: 'O Rāvaṇa, you are just like the stool of your dynasty, for you wish to enjoy the wife of another. Therefore, as a consequence, when my army swarms over the sea to Laṅkā, Rāma will kill you and all your relations.'"

Aṅgada then said, "This bird does not appear to be an envoy, but a spy who will convey information about our strength to the enemy. Therefore, he should be arrested at once."

Taking this as an order, the monkeys again sprang into the air. Capturing Śuka again, they bound him with ropes. Śuka again appealed to Rāma, and He mercifully assured him he would be set free once they reached Laṅkā.

Thereafter Rāma solicited Varuṇa, the presiding deity of the ocean, with folded hands. Rāma was determined to reach Laṅkā by any means, and was prepared to kill the ocean god if he refused to cooperate. When three days and nights passed without any response from the ocean deity, Rāma became greatly irritated. Addressing Lakṣmaṇa, He said, "I can now practically see that in this material world the good qualities of patience, forgiveness and politeness are useless when dealing with persons bereft of all virtue. In this material world such rascals give more respect to persons

who are impudent, aggressive, harsh in speech, and who run about advertising themselves. Because of My mildness and forbearance, the ocean considers Me to be impotent. Thus, he will not deign to come before Me. Lakṣmaṇa, give Me My bow, and I will teach this ocean a lesson. Watch as I dry up the water. Then the monkeys can march to Laṅkā on foot without difficulty!"

His anger blazing like fire, Rāma strung His mighty bow and twanged it powerfully, causing the entire earth to tremble. Rāma shot His arrows deep into the water, agitating the entire ocean, causing high, tossing waves, and terrifying the entities living within, including the Nāgas and Rākṣasas. Then, as He invoked His supremely powerful *brahmāstra*, Lakṣmaṇa put His head on Rāma's bow and said, "My dear brother, please restrain Your anger and do not release any more arrows. Surely there must be a more noble means for drying up the ocean and facilitating the monkeys to cross over to Laṅkā."

Even the great *brahmarṣi*s, from their vantage point in the sky, were terrified to see Rāma's uncommon exhibition of anger. Ignoring Lakṣmaṇa's plea, Rāma picked up the *brahmāstra* arrow and threatened the ocean, "I will now dry up all your water so all that remains is a desert of sand. O god of the sea, since you are too proud to render service unto Me, I shall utilize My own prowess so that the monkeys can cross to Laṅkā on foot!"

As Rāma drew His bow taut, heaven and earth began to tremble, and darkness enveloped the sky. Celestial winds raged furiously, uprooting gigantic trees and tearing off mountain peaks. Lightning streaked across the sky, as did hundreds of meteors, while thunder reverberated in all directions. The ocean overflowed its limit by eighty miles, filling all beings with terror. Still, Rāma remained unmoved, fixed in His determination.

Suddenly the ocean god rose up from the water and appeared before Rāma, surrounded by many serpents with flaming hoods. As giant alligators, tortoises and fish were thrown up by the billowing waves, the ocean's presiding deity stepped onto the shore, followed by the presiding goddesses of such rivers as the Gaṅgā and Sindhu. Decorated with a

garland of red flowers and golden ornaments, dressed in bright red cloth, and encircled by clouds and wind, the ocean personified approached Rāma with folded hands, saying, "O all-pervading Supreme Person, we are dull-minded and did not understand who You are, but now we understand that You are the Supreme Person, the master of the entire universe, the unchanging and original Personality of Godhead. The demigods are infatuated with the mode of goodness, the Prajāpatis with the mode of passion, and the lord of ghosts with the mode of ignorance, but You are the master of all these qualities.

"O gentle descendent of the Raghu dynasty, the earth, water, fire, air and ether are all eternally imbued with their natural characteristics. As a great reservoir of water, I am by nature unfathomable and impossible to cross. I cannot be otherwise. O Rāma, it is for You alone that I will make a special concession, enabling You to cross my waters. My Lord, You may use my water as You like. Indeed, You may cross it and go to the abode of Rāvaṇa, who is the great source of disturbance and crying for the three worlds. He is the son of Viśravā, but is condemned like urine. Please go kill him and thus regain Your wife, Sītā. O great hero, although my water presents no impediment to Your going to Laṅkā, please construct a bridge over it to spread Your transcendental fame. Upon seeing this wonderfully uncommon deed of Your Lordship, all the great heroes and kings in the future will glorify You. If You construct a bridge, I shall make it float by bearing its weight with my energy. Thus, Your vast army of monkeys can attack Laṅkā and You can recover Your dear wife, Sītā."

Standing with the *brahmāstra* arrow drawn back to its full length, Rāma said, "Please tell Me where I can release this arrow, for having fixed it upon My bowstring, I am unwilling to withdraw it."

The ocean personified replied, "To the north is a holy place known as Drumakulyā, where a fierce tribe of sinful thieves called Ābhīras now live. Because they drink ocean water there, I have become repulsed by their sinful touch. O My Lord, I would be very pleased if You would let Your powerful arrow fall there."

Rāma released His arrow as requested, making it fall at Drumakulyā. The arrow pierced through the earth, and brought all the water from Rasātala gushing up through the crevice, causing the entire subterranean region to dry up. The place where the arrow fell then became known as Marukantara, and Rāma gave it the following benediction: "This land will become verdant with fruits, honey and all varieties of herbs; it will be excellent for raising cows, and those who reside here will have few diseases."

The ocean personified then said, "My dear Rāma, here is Nala, the son of the celestial engineer and architect, Viśvakarmā. This powerful monkey is Your great devotee. Indeed, he is as talented as his father. He can oversee the construction of Your bridge, as I allow it to float upon my waters."

The presiding deity of the ocean disappeared. Nala then came before Rāma, and after offering his obeisances, he said, "Forbearance, conciliation and gifts are wasted upon persons who are ungrateful. I know that Varuṇa has granted You passage only out of fear of punishment, and

not from a sense of gratitude. My Lord, long ago my father Viśvakarmā awarded my mother the benediction that she would have a son equal to him in all respects. For this reason, I possess all of Viśvakarmā's architectural and engineering skills. I am quite capable of building the bridge. Although I have these talents, no one knew of them before, because

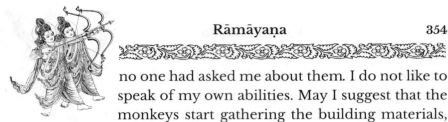

no one had asked me about them. I do not like to speak of my own abilities. May I suggest that the monkeys start gathering the building materials, so that work can begin at once."

Under Rāma's direction, millions of monkeys began the construction, and some entered the forests in search of materials. After tearing up great rocks, trees and entire mountains, they brought them to the shore through the use of mechanical contrivances. Then, as the huge stones and trees were thrown into the ocean, the water splashed high into the sky, creating a magnificent scene, as the rocks miraculously floated. The monkeys tied them together with heavy ropes and vines, making sure they were properly placed. While the construction was going on, Vibhīṣaṇa and his ministers kept guard at the shore.

Hanumān also carried large boulders and threw them into the sea. While doing so, he happened to see a squirrel kicking dust into the ocean in an attempt to assist the Supreme Lord. "Move out of the way or you'll get hurt," Hanumān told the squirrel. "We are carrying huge boulders. What will your little dust accomplish?"

As soon as Hanumān said this, Lord Rāma appeared and rebuked him, saying, "Why are you saying this? Both the squirrel and you are serving Me. Although you are lifting mountain peaks, and he is moving small grains of sand, you are both doing your best. I therefore consider your service and his service of equal value."

In this way, the bridge was constructed. It was one hundred *yojanas* long and ten *yojanas* wide. The surface was made smooth by placing the trunks of trees against one

another. It was then covered over with tops of branches, full of blossoming flowers.[7]

The demigods and great *ṛṣis* assembled in the sky to behold the wonderful bridge spanning the deep shimmering ocean. Sugrīva then requested Rāma and Lakṣmaṇa to mount the backs of Hanumān and Aṅgada. Soon thereafter, the entire army, consisting of billions of monkeys, began to march.

---

7. Śrīla Prabhupāda comments: "One feature of the Supreme Personality of Godhead Lord Rāmacandra is omnipotence. The Lord can act without regard to material impediments or inconveniences, but to prove that He is the Supreme Personality of Godhead and was not merely advertised as Godhead or elected by popular vote, He constructed a wonderful bridge over the ocean. Nowadays it has become fashionable to create some artificial God who performs no uncommon activities; a little magic will bewilder a foolish person into selecting an artificial God because he does not understand how powerful God is. Lord Rāmacandra, however, constructed a bridge over the water with stone by making the stone float. This is proof of God's uncommonly wonderful power. Why should someone be accepted as God without displaying extraordinary potency by doing something never to be done by any common man? We accept Lord Rāmacandra as the Supreme Personality of Godhead because He constructed this bridge, and we accept Lord Kṛṣṇa as the Supreme Personality of Godhead because He lifted Govardhana Hill when He was only seven years old. We should not accept any rascal as God or an incarnation of God, for God displays special features in His various activities. The activities of the Lord are not common; they are all transcendentally wonderful and not able to be performed by any other living being. The symptoms of the Lord's activities are all mentioned in the scriptures, and after one understands them one can accept the Lord as He is.

Upon reaching Suvela Mountain at the far shore of Laṅkā island, the monkeys became thrilled. As Sugrīva set up camp, all the great demigods and *ṛṣis* came and individually bathed the king and the monkeys with water from the sacred rivers, blessing the king to obtain victory.

Rāma then embraced Lakṣmaṇa saying, "Make certain that the army stays on constant alert, for I perceive evil omens foreboding the destruction of many great heroes among the monkeys, bears and Rākṣasas. Indeed, just see how the fierce winds stir up clouds of dust. There are tremors in the earth and dark clouds are raining blood. The evening twilight is heavily tinged with red, and the animals cry out pitifully. O Lakṣmaṇa, I think we should immediately begin our march on the city of Laṅkā."

Thus, at Rāma's desire, the army of monkeys departed. As they drew near Laṅkā the Rākṣasas could hear their loud roaring. While looking at the golden city, magnificently perched atop Trikūṭa Mountain, Rāma thought only of Sītā imprisoned within. Rāma then ordered the commanders to arrange the army in a human shaped formation, with Himself and Lakṣmaṇa at the head. As they approached

Laṅkā, the monkeys took up great trees and mountain peaks, while Rāma sent orders to Rāvaṇa to release Sītā or to prepare for death.

The monkey chiefs released the Rākṣasa messenger in the form of a bird, who immediately went to Rāvaṇa. When the Rākṣasa king saw how Śuka's wings had been cut off, he laughingly inquired, "Who has done this?"

Śuka replied, "I delivered your message to Sugrīva, but the monkeys captured me and severely beat me. Then they cut off my wings. It was only due to the mercy of the virtuous Rāma that I was released. O king, the army of monkeys has already arrived here to rescue Sītā. You must return her to Rāma or immediately attack the hordes of monkeys, before they swarm over the boundary walls."

Rāvaṇa angrily replied, "I will never give up Sītā! I will kill Rāma and all His monkey soldiers! However, I am quite amazed that these monkeys could build a bridge across the ocean. I want you and Sāraṇa to disguise yourselves as monkeys and secretly enter the enemy's ranks to estimate their strength."

Śuka and Sāraṇa obediently went to the monkeys' camp, but because of the vastness of the monkey army, now spread throughout the forests, mountains and along the shore, the two spies could not even begin to estimate the number of soldiers. As they moved along, however, Vibhīṣaṇa identified them as disguised Rākṣasas and captured them, taking them to Rāma.

Afraid for their lives, Śuka and Sāraṇa stood before Rāma with folded hands pleading, "We have not come here of our

own accord. We were sent by Rāvaṇa to ascertain the strength of Your army."

At this, Rāma simply laughed and replied, "If you have accomplished your mission then you can return to Rāvaṇa at once. However, if you have not yet completed your observations, then you can continue your tour without fear, guided by Vibhīṣaṇa. In return for our hospitality, I only request you to deliver this message to Rāvaṇa: 'Accompanied by My army of monkeys, I will destroy Laṅkā and kill all the Rākṣasas."

Out of gratitude, Śuka and Sāraṇa offered obeisances unto Rāma, saying, "May You be victorious!"

They then returned to Rāvaṇa and explained, "We were captured by Vibhīṣaṇa, but then mercifully released by magnanimous Rāma. Due to the army's vastness, it was impossible for us to estimate the extent of it. However, we can assure you that Rāma, Lakṣmaṇa, Sugrīva and Vibhīṣaṇa can uproot Laṅkā and carry it away if they so choose, even without the help of the other monkeys. Indeed, we are convinced that Rāma could destroy Laṅkā and all the Rākṣasas single-handed. We advise you to return Sītā to Rāma and establish an alliance with Him."

Rāvaṇa replied, "I will never give back Sītā, even if all the demigods and demons combine together to attack me. You only speak such rubbish because you are afraid of being tormented by a few monkeys. What have *I* got to fear?"

Rāvaṇa climbed to the roof of his palace, accompanied by his two spies, hoping to gain a good view of the enemy. Rāvaṇa then asked Sāraṇa to point out the chief monkeys. Sāraṇa showed his master all the great heroes, including,

Hanumān, Sugrīva, Aṅgada, Nala, Mainda, Dvivida, Śveta, Panasa, Vinatā, Gavaya, and finally Dhūmra, the commander in chief of the bears, and his younger brother, Jāmbavān. Sāraṇa also described their physical characteristics and praised their incomparable prowess.

The monkey army was so expansive that in order to describe the extent of it, Sāraṇa first had to explain the Vedic system of counting. He explained that 100,000 is one lakh; 100 lakhs equals one crore; one lakh of crores is called a *ṣaṅku*, and one lakh of *ṣaṅkus* is called a *maha-ṣaṅku*; one lakh of *maha-ṣaṅkus* is called a *vrinda*, and one lakh of *vrindas* is called a *padmā*, with one lakh of *padmās* equaling a *maha-padmā*; one lakh of *maha-padmās* is called a *kharva*, and one lakh of *kharvas* is a *maha-kharva*; one lakh of *maha-kharvas* is called a *samudra*, and one lakh of *samudras* is an *ogha*; one lakh of *oghas* is called a *mahaugha*. Sāraṇa then explained that Rāma's army of monkeys consisted of at least 100 crores of *mahaughas* of soldiers.

Seeing Rāma, Lakṣmaṇa and the other monkey heroes, Rāvaṇa became enraged. As Śuka and Sāraṇa hung their heads, Rāvaṇa chastised them severely. Trying to restrain his anger, he said, "You are supposed to be my ministers, yet you are ignorant of politics and are praising the enemy. Your speech is most unpalatable. I must be fortunate indeed to have retained my sovereignty for so long, guided by such ignorant fools as you. How can you speak so foolishly? Have you no fear of death? It is only the memory of your past service that keeps me from killing you this instant!"

Śuka and Sāraṇa became ashamed to hear Rāvaṇa chastise them in this way. Hoping to pacify their master,

they shouted, "O king, may victory be yours!" and then departed.

Rāvaṇa ordered Mahodara to bring more spies forward. Soon afterward, Śārdūla and others arrived, pronouncing benedictions for Rāvaṇa's victory. Rāvaṇa ordered the spies to ascertain the enemy's plans. Then the spies circumambulated Rāvaṇa and slipped out to where Rāma and the monkey soldiers were camped.

Although the spies were disguised as monkeys, Vibhīṣaṇa easily detected them as Rākṣasas and arrested them. Then the monkeys surrounded them and beat them severely. However, when their plight came to Rāma's attention, He mercifully ordered that they too be set free.

Returning to Laṅkā in a stupefied condition, Śārdūla and his men came before Rāvaṇa and reported, "The enemy army of monkeys is now encamped near the Suvela Mountain. They are incapable of being spied upon. Just moments after our arrival we were captured by Vibhīṣaṇa and then beaten by the monkeys. It is only by the grace of Rāma that we were released and able to return with our lives. O king, it appears that Rāma is capable of destroying not only Laṅkā, but the entire cosmic manifestation as well. You must either return Sītā or immediately be prepared to fight with Rāma's army before they reach Laṅkā's boundary walls."

Rāvaṇa considered Śārdūla's words for half a moment and then declared, "I shall never return Sītā under any circumstance!"

Rāvaṇa asked for advice from his assembled ministers. Finally, he retired to his private rooms and called for

Vidyujjiha, a Rākṣasa expert in conjuring tricks. Rāvaṇa told him, "I want you to create an illusory head of Rāma and a perfect imitation of His bow and arrows. I am going now to the *aśoka* grove to see Sītā. You should follow me and remain hidden. When I call for you, bring your magical creations."

Rāvaṇa went to the *aśoka* grove, eager to see Sītā. He came before the anguished daughter of King Janaka and announced, "Rāma has been slain by my commander-in-chief. You should give up your stubbornness and become my beloved queen. I will tell you just how it happened: After Rāma crossed the ocean, night set in, and being exhausted, Rāma, Lakṣmaṇa and the monkey warriors fell asleep on Laṅkā's shore. In the darkness, the great Rākṣasa heroes went there and began slaughtering them all. Prahasta cut off Rāma's head as He soundly slept, and Lakṣmaṇa, Hanumān and the other monkey chiefs were killed as the others fled in fear. O noble lady, I have brought Rāma's severed head here just to convince you that I am telling the truth."

Rāvaṇa then ordered the Rākṣasī guards to call for Vidyujjihva. The magician thus appeared, bearing an illusory head of Rāma, along with His bow and arrows. Rāvaṇa then told Sītā, "Look! This is the bloodied head of your husband!"

Then, turning to Vidyujjihva, Rāvaṇa said, "Show Sītā Rāma's severed head! Let her see the remains of her mortal husband!"

Vidyujjihva placed the illusory head at Sītā's feet and hastily departed. Rāvaṇa then took Rāma's illusory bow and arrows and threw them toward Sītā, saying, "Submit to me now, for you have no other hope!"

The illusory severed head had features exactly resembling Rāma's. When Sītā saw it, she cried out mournfully, "O Kaikeyi, this is the result of your evil plans. Now your cherished goal is fulfilled. You must be very happy!"

Crying convulsively, Sītā fell to the ground like a plantain tree uprooted by a strong wind. Soon she recovered and sat

down beside the illusory head, lamenting, "O Rāma! Without You I have become a widow. My life has come to an end! What greater calamity could befall a woman than the death of her husband before her own demise? Alas! I am most despicable, for it is I who have caused the death of my husband. It is for my sake alone that He crossed the ocean, only to die without even a fight! Little did Rāma know that when He married me, He wedded His own death as well. Surely, in a previous life I obstructed the marriage of another girl. Thus, I now suffer in this life! O Rāma! Have You departed for the next world without me?"

Sītā then said to Rāvaṇa, "Please take me to where the body of Rāma is lying. Then, as I place my body upon His, you may kill me so that I may attain the same destination as my husband."

Just at that moment a messenger arrived, informing Rāvaṇa that Prahasta urgently required his presence in a meeting of his ministers. Rāvaṇa departed, and as soon as he was gone, the illusory head and bow vanished from Sītā's sight.

Entering the assembly, Rāvaṇa immediately ordered the Rākṣasas to mobilize for battle. Without further discussion, they began preparations for war.

Meanwhile Vibhīṣaṇa's wife, Saramā, came to console Sītā. Saramā had already befriended her at Rāvaṇa's urging, for he did not wish Sītā to die prematurely from grief.

Saramā said, "I was hiding behind a nearby bush and could hear everything Rāvaṇa said. I can assure you that

Rāma is not dead. The head you saw was created by a Rākṣasa conjurer's trick. In truth, Rāma has arrived at Laṅkā with Lakṣmaṇa and the army of monkeys. They are now preparing to attack Rāvaṇa. That is why Rāvaṇa just left here in such an agitated state. He knows that he is unable to defeat Rāma and the monkey heroes under His protection. Even from here I can hear the Rākṣasas making preparations. Soon there will be a great war between the two armies. Do not worry, Sītā, for Rāma will defeat Rāvaṇa without a doubt. If you would like to give Rāma a message, I can deliver it for you."

Sītā was greatly relieved to hear Saramā's assurance. She requested her, "O Saramā, please try to learn what Rāvaṇa's plans are. Is he going to fight with Rāma, or will he return me to Rāma?"

Saramā went out, and while remaining hidden, overheard Rāvaṇa's conversation with his ministers. She returned to Sītā and reported, "As I listened, many of Rāvaṇa's elder ministers advised Rāvaṇa to return you to Rāma, describing the unlimited prowess of Rāma and Lakṣmaṇa. Even Rāvaṇa's mother urged him to make peace with Rāma.

"Rāvaṇa, however, remained adamant. Therefore, I can understand that he will only give you up at the time of death. Even as the meeting was going on, Rāvaṇa could hear the sound of conchshells, drums and other noises from the monkeys. Then Mālyavān, Rāvaṇa's maternal grandfather, said, 'A wise king never fights with an enemy who has superior strength. Therefore, I advise you to return Sītā to Rāma and establish peaceful relations with Him. Otherwise, O Rāvaṇa, you may rest assured that virtue, having taken the form of the enemy, will conquer over your evil self.

"'Because you have persecuted the great *ṛṣis*, the power of their austerity is now aimed at you for your destruction. Furthermore, the benedictions you received from Lord Brahmā did not give you immunity from death at the hands of human beings or monkeys. You should carefully consider the dangerous position you are now in.

"'My dear grandson, you should heed my advice, for many inauspicious signs have already become visible, indicating the destruction of Laṅkā. Clouds are pouring down showers of hot blood. Our horses and elephants have tears in their eyes, and carnivorous animals freely enter the gardens of Laṅkā, crying out ominously. In their dreams, the citizens see black women with yellow teeth plundering their houses, and standing before them, laughing at them. Dogs are eating the sacrificial offerings, and different species of animals are seen mating with each other. Time personified, appearing in a huge black form with a shaved head, is seen peering into all the houses of Laṅkā every morning and evening.

"'O Rāvaṇa, I consider Rāma to be Lord Viṣṇu Himself, appearing in the form of a human being. You must immediately go and surrender to Him, and rid yourself from this impending calamity.'"

Saramā continued, "Rāvaṇa could not accept this good advice. Instead he angrily replied, 'You are a rascal, taking the side of the enemy. You seem very eager to glorify the prowess of Rāma, but what do you think of me? You must be praising the enemy because you are envious of me or because you have been won over to the other side. Perhaps you are afraid of Him. I can assure you that you will soon witness the death of Rāma by my own hands.'

"Mālyavān remained silent for a time. Then after offering his respects to the king, he retired to his quarters. Rāvaṇa then made arrangements for Laṅkā's defense. He posted Prahasta at the eastern gate, Mahapārśva and Mahodara at the southern gate, Indrajit at the western gate, Śuka and Sāraṇa and himself at the northern gate, and Virūpākṣa in the city's center. Then the king dismissed his ministers and retired to the interior of his palace."

As Rāma and the monkey army approached Laṅkā, they discussed how they could best besiege the city. Vibhīṣaṇa said, "Along with my ministers, Anala, Panasa, Sampāti and Pramati, I took the form of a bird and surveyed the military arrangements of Rāvaṇa. We now know how their defenses are laid out. My dear Rāma, I am confident that just as Rāvaṇa defeated Kuvera by invading Laṅkā with 60 lakhs of Rākṣasas, You too will gain victory, with the help of these hordes of monkeys."

Rāma then ordered, "Nīla will lead the attack on Prahasta at the eastern gate. Aṅgada and his soldiers will fight against Mahapārśva and Mahodara at the southern gate. Hanumān will lead the attack against Indrajit at the western gate, and Lakṣmaṇa and I will contend with Rāvaṇa at the northern gate. Sugrīva, Jāmbavān and Vibhīṣaṇa will stay in the center of our army to provide assistance wherever needed. I want only seven of us to fight in the form of human beings—Myself, Lakṣmaṇa, and Vibhīṣaṇa and his four ministers. All others should retain their monkey forms, for that will allow us to remain distinguished from the enemy warriors."

The sun was already setting when Rāma, Lakṣmaṇa and the monkey leaders climbed to the peak of Suvela Mountain

to spend the night. From the mountain top they had a good view of Laṅkā, even though darkness had already set in. The city's innumerable twinkling lights made it appear as if it were suspended from the sky. The leaders of Rāma's army could also see that the Rākṣasa warriors were prepared for the upcoming fight.

The next morning, everyone was amazed to see the heavenly city, complete with its array of flowering gardens, filled with celestial trees and singing birds. Laṅkā was beautifully situated on a leveled peak of the Trikūṭa Mountain, measuring one hundred *yojanas* by one hundred *yojanas*. The walled city had an area of twenty by twenty *yojanas*, and in the center stood the magnificent palace of Rāvaṇa, supported by 1,000 pillars.

While gazing at the city, and feeling great appreciation for its magnificence, Rāma sighted Rāvaṇa perched atop the northern gate, with a canopy held over his head, being fanned by his servants.

Sugrīva ordered numerous monkeys ahead, jumping from mountain top to mountain top, to occupy the outer gardens of Laṅkā. Suddenly, he too, sighted Rāvaṇa. Thus, Sugrīva impetuously leapt from the peak of Mount Suvela to where the Rākṣasa king was sitting atop the northern gate. Gazing at Rāvaṇa with great disdain, Sugrīva announced, "I am a servant of Lord Rāma, and I shall kill you this very day!"

Sugrīva pounced on Rāvaṇa, knocking his crown off in the process. The surprised Rākṣasa king then grabbed Sugrīva, and while uttering similar threats, threw Sugrīva to the ground. Sugrīva, however, bounced up immediately

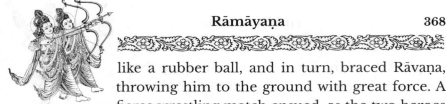

like a rubber ball, and in turn, braced Rāvaṇa, throwing him to the ground with great force. A fierce wrestling match ensued, as the two heroes scratched each other with their nails, covering them both with blood and perspiration.

After striking each other with their fists and arms and wrestling for a long time, Sugrīva and Rāvaṇa both fell down from the gate onto the ground in the area between the boundary wall and the moat. Then, jumping to their feet, the two kings continued fighting, exhibiting all their knowledge in the art of wrestling. At last, when Rāvaṇa realized he could not defeat Sugrīva with mere physical strength, he called upon his mystic powers. Understanding this, Sugrīva decided to abandon the fight. He bounded into the air and immediately returned to where Rāma was staying.

Sugrīva was now feeling blissful at having performed such a heroic feat, and his followers responded by jumping excitedly. Embracing Sugrīva in love, Rāma, mildly chastised him, saying, "You have acted foolishly, for you dared to do something without My sanction. Besides this, a king should never take such risks, because the death of the ruler is a great calamity for the entire nation. O Sugrīva, if Rāvaṇa had killed you then I certainly would have slain him in retaliation. Then, after installing Vibhiṣaṇa upon the throne at Laṅkā and Bharata on the throne at Ayodhyā, I would have given up My own life for having allowed you to be killed in My presence."

Sugrīva replied, "After seeing that rascal Rāvaṇa, the abductor of Sītā, I could not bear to simply ignore him!"

Rāma said, "Regardless, you courageously displayed your heroism, and all the monkey soldiers have been inspired by your fearless example."

Turning to Lakṣmaṇa, Rāma said, "By observing various omens, I can understand that there will soon be great destruction, a slaughter of the leading monkeys, bears and Rākṣasas. Let us attack Laṅkā immediately!"

Rāma climbed down from Suvela Mountain to review His army. He then began His march to Laṅkā, bow in hand, while the monkeys following Him uprooted trees and mountain peaks. Soon afterward they arrived at the city walls, and Rāma encamped His army outside the northern gate. Similarly, Nīla took up his position outside the eastern gate, Aṅgada at the southern gate, and Hanumān outside the western gate. Sugrīva positioned his army in between the northern and western gates. Thus, the monkeys completely surrounded the walled city, awaiting the encounter.

The Rākṣasa warriors were astonished to see a seemingly unlimited number of monkeys surrounding their city. With weapons in hand, the leaders fearfully rushed to Rāvaṇa's palace to inform Rāvaṇa how the monkeys were sieging the city. Rāvaṇa quickly went to a balcony to personally survey the situation. Seeing how the entire earth around Laṅkā had become brown, covered by multitudes of monkeys, the Rākṣasa king was struck with wonder. For a long time Rāvaṇa stood motionless, staring at Rāma, wondering what he should do next.

Rāma then ordered Aṅgada to deliver a message to Rāvaṇa. Leaping into the air, Aṅgada quickly came before Rāvaṇa, who was sitting atop the northern gate surrounded by his ministers. Staying a slight distance from Rāvaṇa, Aṅgada announced, "My name is Aṅgada, nephew of King Sugrīva, and heir apparent to the royal throne at Kiṣkindhyā.

I have come here as Rāma's envoy with this message: 'O king of the Rākṣasas, now that all of your pious credits have been exhausted, I am going to kill you in retaliation for your atrocities against the *ṛṣis*. If you do not surrender to Me at once, then I shall rid the entire world of Rākṣasas. Either submit to Me or come before Me so that I can purify you with the onslaught of My deadly arrows. If you are unwilling to return Sītā and bow down before Me, then I advise you to take a good look at Laṅkā, for it will be your last.'"

Inflamed with rage, Rāvaṇa ordered his ministers to kill Aṅgada. Aṅgada allowed four Rākṣasas to seize him, for he desired to show off his prowess. Then He suddenly jumped to the top Rāvaṇa's palace, carrying aloft the four Rākṣasas clutching at his arms. The force of Aṅgada's leap shook the Rākṣasas loose, and they plummeted to the ground at Rāvaṇa's feet. Aṅgada then violently kicked the roof of Rāvaṇa's palace, causing the top dome to crumble, while Rāvaṇa looked on helplessly. Having thus vexed the Rākṣasa king, Aṅgada let out a loud roar and returned to Rāma. Witnessing Aṅgada's prowess, Rāvaṇa foresaw his own destruction, and began sighing repeatedly.

Once again, Rāma thought of Sītā and thus commanded His army, "Make short work of the Rākṣasas!"

The monkeys shouted in unison, "All victory to Rāma and Lakṣmaṇa!" causing Laṅkā to resound with their vibration. The monkeys then began scaling the defensive walls, and breaking them down with trees and boulders. Rāvaṇa then ordered his troops to advance quickly, and in this way the fierce conflict began, amidst a terrible roaring sound.

The Rākṣasas struck the monkeys with their clubs and other weapons, and the monkeys countered by using trees, stones, and their claws and teeth. The monkeys did not have proper equipment with which to fight the soldiers of Rāvaṇa, for Rāvaṇa's soldiers were equipped with sophisticated weapons whereas the monkeys could only throw stones, mountain peaks and trees. It was only Lord Rāmacandra and Lakṣmaṇa who shot some arrows. But because the soldiers of Rāvaṇa were condemned by the curse of mother Sītā, the monkeys were able to kill them simply by throwing stones and trees.

Stationed atop Laṅkā's defensive walls, the Rākṣasas pierced numerous monkeys with their weapons, while other monkeys leapt up and dragged the Rākṣasas down to the ground, causing the earth to become a mire of flesh and blood. As Hanumān fought with Jambumali, Aṅgada with Indrajit, Nīla with Nikumbha and Sugrīva with Praghasa, rivers of blood created by the massacre carried away the slain warriors.

Indrajit struck Aṅgada with his mace, but the monkey prince deftly grabbed it out of the Rākṣasa's hands and smashed it against his chariot. Jambumali pierced Hanumān with a spear, but then the son of Vāyu jumped into the Rākṣasa's chariot and killed him with a violent slap. Nikumbha pierced Nīla with numerous arrows, but the monkey hero still managed to cut off the Rākṣasa's head, using a wheel from his broken chariot. Rāma, Sugrīva and Nala killed numerous other Rākṣasas, and the heroic army of monkeys inflicted heavy losses upon the enemy. During

the fierce battle, headless trunks of Rākṣasas and monkeys alike were seen darting here and there, adding to the ghastliness of the battle scene.

As night finally fell, the monkeys questioned those around them, asking, "Are you a monkey?" When someone was found to be an enemy, the monkeys attacked him with

deadly enthusiasm. Throughout the fighting, both sides suffered heavy losses.

Although the Rākṣasas were more visible because of their golden armor, it was their nature to become enlivened at night. Thus the hordes of Rākṣasas suddenly attacked Rāma in the darkness with great enthusiasm, their loud roaring creating a tumultuous sound. With the giant monkey Golaṅgula supporting Him on one side and Jāmbavān's brother Dhumra on the other, Rāma pierced Mahapārśva, Mahodara, Śuka, Sāraṇa and two other Rākṣasas with six golden arrows that brightly lit up the night. Then, as those six Rākṣasas fled for their lives, Aṅgada smashed Indrajit's chariot and killed his driver. Indrajit, who was also injured, abandoned his disabled chariot and vanished from view while the demigods and *ṛṣis* praised the monkey prince from their positions in the sky.

Remaining invisible in the sky, the enraged Indrajit showered down arrows that took the form of serpents. Because of a benediction from Lord Brahmā, the snake arrows immediately bound Rāma and Lakṣmaṇa very tightly. Unable to move because of Indrajit's serpent arrows, Rāma and Lakṣmaṇa dispatched ten of the foremost monkeys, headed by Aṅgada, Nīla and Hanumān, to search out Indrajit. However, as the monkeys sprang into the air, exploring in all directions, the invisible Indrajit pierced them with innumerable arrows. At the same time, he showered Rāma and Lakṣmaṇa with so many arrows that blood flowed profusely from wounds that completely covered Their bodies. Indrajit announced, "O Rāma and Lakṣmaṇa, even Indra cannot see me, what to speak of others. Now it will be my great pleasure to dispatch You both to the abode of

Yamarāja with my unceasing torrents of sharp arrows."

As Indrajit continued to assault Rāma and Lakṣmaṇa, They became covered with wounds. There was not a single space large enough to place a finger where the arrows had not pierced them. Finally, Rāma's bow fell from His hands, and He fell to the ground, covered in His own blood. Lakṣmaṇa, too, swooned away, giving up all hope of survival. Seeing this terrible sight, the monkeys became despondent, with tears in their eyes. As the leaders of the monkeys came to surround Rāma and Lakṣmaṇa, Indrajit proclaimed to his followers, "The two mighty brothers

have fallen victim to my magical snake arrows, imbued with the power of Lord Brahmā! Not even Indra and all the demigods could save Rāma and Lakṣmaṇa now!"

The enlivened Rākṣasas then shouted, "Rāma is dead! Indrajit has killed Him single-handed!" Convinced that Rāma and Lakṣmaṇa were now dead, Indrajit departed for the palace of Rāvaṇa, intoxicated by his apparent victory.

Sugrīva and Vibhīṣaṇa then came to the spot where Rāma and Lakṣmaṇa lay motionless. They were bathed in Their own blood, and barely breathed. Sugrīva was especially pained to see the two brothers completely enmeshed in the serpentine arrows that covered Them, and Vibhīṣaṇa took special care to comfort him. While washing the tears from Sugrīva's eyes, he said, "O king, I know that Rāma and Lakṣmaṇa can be revived. Rest assured, for They will not die. Please guard Rāma carefully while I rally the army and restore the monkeys to confidence."

As the foremost monkeys guarded Rāma and Lakṣmaṇa, Indrajit went to Rāvaṇa and proudly reported the news of his apparent victory. When Rāvaṇa heard that Rāma and Lakṣmaṇa were slain, he jumped to his feet and lovingly embraced his son, saying, "My dear boy, how did you accomplish this most difficult feat? Tell me everything!"

Indrajit replied, "While remaining invisible in the sky, I first bound up Rāma and Lakṣmaṇa with my serpentine arrows. Then I riddled them with countless sharp arrows. They are now lying lifeless on the ground, and the monkey warriors are giving up the fight out of hopelessness."

Considering Rāma and Lakṣmaṇa to be dead, Rāvaṇa gave up all fear and anxiety. After dismissing Indrajit, he called for the Rākṣasīs who guarded Sītā. Confident that Sītā would now submit to him, Rāvaṇa joyfully said, "Rāma and Lakṣmaṇa have been slain by my incomparable son, Indrajit. I want you to immediately convey this news to Sītā. Take her on the Puṣpaka chariot, so that she may see for herself how her husband is slain on the battlefield." After dismissing the Rākṣasīs, Rāvaṇa ordered the news of Indrajit's victory to be broadcast all over Laṅkā for the pleasure of the citizens.

When the Rākṣasīs informed Sītā of Rāma's death, she immediately fell to the ground. She was sobbing uncontrollably, completely overcome by shock and grief. The Rākṣasīs helped her onto the Puṣpaka chariot, along with their leader, Trijaṭā, and within a moment they rose up high into the air.

While flying over the battlefield, Sītā could see many slain monkeys and Rākṣasas. Then she suddenly beheld Rāma and Lakṣmaṇa lying on the ground, surrounded by grieving monkeys. As Sītā heard the Rākṣasas rejoicing, she gazed upon Rāma's arrow-riddled body, His bow lying beside Him, and was unable to contain her grief. Wailing loudly, Sītā began lamenting, "Formerly, learned *brāhmaṇas*, masters of astrology and palmistry, all assured me, 'O fortunate Princess, you will bear sons and never suffer for becoming a widow. In the future you will become the queen of an illustrious king who will perform many great sacrifices.' Now that Rāma is dead, I can understand that they are all cheaters and liars.

The *brāhmaṇas* assured me of my good fortune, describing my auspicious bodily features. They told me, 'O princess, you have fine dark hair, and your eyebrows are curved and separated. Your closely set teeth are even, and your rosy fingers and toes have no space between them. Your thighs are rounded, shapely and hairless, and your ample breasts touch each other. Your navel is deep, your skin is soft and your complexion is fair and brilliant. All of your toes touch the ground as you walk, and the soles of your feet are marked with the auspicious signs of the lotus flower, indicating an exalted, royal birth. Combined with your lotus petal eyes and gentle smile, all these symptoms indicate that the highest good fortune awaits you.'"

Sītā cried, "Of what use are these auspicious marks, now that my husband is dead? Without Rāma my good fortune had ended!"

Trijaṭā then approached Sītā, saying, "O princess, you may rest assured that Rāma and Lakṣmaṇa are not dead, for this celestial chariot will not carry a widow. Look below, for even though the monkeys are in a state of confusion, they continue to guard Rāma and Lakṣmaṇa. What would be the necessity of guarding Them if They were dead? Even from here I can see that luster remains in the faces of Rāma and Lakṣmaṇa. Therefore, Sītā, do not give way to unnecessary grief. It is certain that your husband is still alive."

Sītā was slightly encouraged by Trijaṭā's words, and was then escorted back to the *aśoka* grove. Regardless, while thinking of her husband's desperate condition, Sītā soon gave way to grief and despair.

In the midst of the grief-stricken monkeys, Rāma returned to consciousness. Upon seeing Lakṣmaṇa lying at His side, smeared with blood and without any sign of life, Rāma exclaimed with anguish, "Even if I succeed in recovering Sītā, the entire endeavor will be useless if Lakṣmaṇa dies! Even if it were possible to somehow find a consort to replace the daughter of Janaka, I could never find another friend such as Lakṣmaṇa. If Lakṣmaṇa dies, I too will give up My life, for I cannot bear to think of returning to Ayodhyā without Him. How could I ever face His mother after allowing Him to die on the battlefield in My presence?"

Turning to Sugrīva, Rāma said, "The monkey warriors should now retreat, for without Lakṣmaṇa and Myself to protect them, they will be highly vulnerable. O noble king of the monkeys, please accept My unlimited gratitude for the sincere friendship and valor that you and your army have displayed, risking your lives in My service." All the monkeys began to cry upon hearing Rāma's sweet words.

Vibhīṣaṇa then returned, having restored the monkey army's confidence. When Vibhīṣaṇa saw how Rāma and Lakṣmaṇa looked just like porcupines, lying upon a bed of arrows, he immediately broke down and cried. Sugrīva then embraced him, saying, "You should not doubt that Rāma and Lakṣmaṇa will soon recover and go on to defeat Rāvaṇa in battle."

Sugrīva then went to his father-in-law, Suṣeṇa, saying, "Please arrange for Rāma and Lakṣmaṇa to be taken to Kiṣkindhyā, where They can safely recover from Their wounds. Let all the monkeys accompany Them, while

I remain here alone. After defeating Rāvaṇa single-handed, I will return to Kiṣkindhyā with Sītā."

Suṣeṇa replied, "Long, long ago, when there was a great war between the demigods and the demons, the demons were able to kill many of the celestials with their mystic illusions. Bṛhaspati, however, revived all the slain demigods by using mantras and special medicinal herbs. I suggest that Panasa and Sampāti go to the ocean of milk, for they are familiar with these herbs, known as Sañjīvana-karaṇī and Viśalya. Created by Lord Brahmā himself, Sañjīvana-karaṇī can revive a person who is practically dead. Likewise, Viśalya instantly cures all wounds created by arrows. These herbs can be found on the Candra and Droṇa Mountains, which arose in the middle of the Milk Ocean as it was being churned to produce nectar. It is best for Hanumān to go, for he can make the journey in the shortest time."

As Suṣeṇa spoke, a fierce wind began to blow, bringing dense clouds and streaks of lightning. The sea became agitated with high, swelling waves, the mountains began to tremble, and tall trees were knocked down. Everyone looked around, wondering why this was happening, and saw that the disturbances were caused by the flight of a gigantic bird coming towards them.

It was Garuḍa, the eagle carrier of Lord Viṣṇu. Upon seeing him, the snake arrows binding Rāma and Lakṣmaṇa immediately fled. Garuḍa then came and wiped Rāma and Lakṣmaṇa's faces with his hands. By his touch alone, Their bodies began to shine, and became redoubled in strength. Garuḍa picked Rāma up and lovingly embraced Him.

In great happiness, Rāma said, "We are both eternally indebted to you. If you consider Us worthy, please reveal your identity to us."

The gigantic bird replied, "I am Your eternal servant, Garuḍa, the son of Vinatā. All the demigods, headed by Indra, could not have raised You from the bondage of Indrajit's snake-arrows. These snakes are the sons of Kadrū, and were converted into arrows by the mystic power Indrajit received from Lord Brahmā. I came here just to chase them away, for snakes are my natural food and they are always afraid of me. My dear Lord, You should be very careful while fighting with the Rākṣasas. They are very tricky, whereas heroes like Yourself are always straightforward. I now wish to take my leave. Before I depart, let me assure You that You shall be victorious and get back Your beloved Sītā."

Garuḍa then circumambulated Rāma, and after embracing Him again, soared into the sky. Seeing that Rāma and Lakṣmaṇa had recovered from Their wounds, the monkeys jumped for joy. In their ecstasy they beat drums, lashed their tails and roared like lions, thus creating a great tumult. Then, after taking up trees and great boulders, they again prepared to continue the fight.

Hearing the joyful roaring of the monkeys, Rāvaṇa suspected that Rāma and Lakṣmaṇa had revived. To make sure, he ordered his Rākṣasas to investigate the reason for the monkeys' bravado. After climbing onto the defensive walls, the Rākṣasas saw that Rāma and Lakṣmaṇa were alive and well. With great fear they rushed to give Rāvaṇa the news. His doubts thus confirmed, Rāvaṇa again became filled with anxiety, and his face turned pale. Swelling with rage, he

ordered the great Rākṣasa warrior, Dhūmrākṣa, to go immediately and attack Rāma.

After quickly mobilizing his army, Dhūmrākṣa mounted his donkey-drawn chariot. Laughing robustly and exhibiting great pride, he headed for the western gate, where Hanumān had taken his stand.

As Dhūmrākṣa rode through the streets of Laṅkā, a great vulture landed on the back of his chariot, while other

carnivorous birds perched upon his flagpole. Suddenly, someone threw a headless trunk in his path, and clouds began pouring down rain mixed with blood. Dhūmrākṣa became greatly perturbed at these ominous signs, and some Rākṣasa soldiers even fainted. Still, Dhūmrākṣa courageously approached the monkey warriors, who were all eager for combat.

A fierce battle ensued, and many Rākṣasas and monkeys were killed. The monkeys smashed the Rākṣasas with huge rocks and trees, and tore at them with their sharp teeth and nails. Finally, because of the monkeys' superior prowess, the Rākṣasa army panicked and fled.

At this, Dhūmrākṣa became filled with rage and began to ravage the monkey warriors so severely that they too, began fleeing in terror. Hanumān became enraged. He picked up a huge rock and hurled it at Dhūmrākṣa's chariot, smashing it to pieces. The Rākṣasa hero saved himself by jumping to the ground, while Hanumān continued on his rampage. Taking a mountain peak, Hanumān rushed at Dhūmrākṣa. The Rākṣasa also came forward to meet Hanumān, deftly smashing him on the head with his club. But Hanumān hardly minded the blow. He hurled the mountain peak at Dhūmrākṣa's head. The peak shattered the Rākṣasa's limbs, and he fell down dead.

Dhūmrākṣa's army fled back to the shelter of Laṅkā, causing the enraged Rāvaṇa to send Vajradaṁṣṭra into the fight. The great Rākṣasa hero led his army to the southern gate, where Aṅgada was stationed. On the way there he saw showers of meteors streaking across the sky, and ferocious she-jackals belched fire. Nevertheless, Vajradaṁṣṭra took

courage, and plunged into battle. Aṅgada responded especially fiercely. He smashed the Rākṣasa soldiers with an uprooted tree, and their entire army fled, with their general helplessly looking on.

The enraged Vajradaṁṣṭra retaliated by killing innumerable enemy soldiers with his arrows, causing the monkeys to take shelter of Aṅgada. As the son of Vāli set out to confront Vajradaṁṣṭra directly, the Rākṣasa hero released 100,000 arrows that bathed Aṅgada in his own blood.

Aṅgada struck back by hurling a huge tree, but Vajradaṁṣṭra easily cut it to pieces. Then, roaring loudly, Aṅgada threw a huge mountain crag, forcing Vajradaṁṣṭra to jump to safety, as his chariot was smashed. Taking advantage of this opportunity, Aṅgada quickly took up another huge mass of boulders, and smashed it upon Vajradaṁṣṭra's head. The Rākṣasa fell to the ground unconscious, vomiting blood and clutching his mace to his chest.

Vajradaṁṣṭra, however, soon regained consciousness. Coming before Aṅgada, he severely struck the monkey chief in the chest with his club. Then the two warriors started beating each other with their fists. As they gradually became exhausted, blood began to flow from their mouths. Then, after a brief lull, Aṅgada uprooted a tree, while Vajradaṁṣṭra took up his sword and shield. However, after fighting for some time, both heroes fell to their knees in exhaustion. Seizing this opportune moment, Aṅgada quickly summoned his strength. He snatched Vajradaṁṣṭra's sword and sliced off the Rākṣasa's head. Upon seeing their general slain, the remnants of the Rākṣasa army fearfully retreated to Laṅkā.

Rāvaṇa next called for the great Rākṣasa hero Akampana, saying, "You are well versed in the use of all weapons, and your eagerness for battle is second to none. Go now and exterminate the army of monkeys. Do away with Rāma and Lakṣmaṇa once and for all!"

As Akampana approached the battlefield, his left eye began to twitch convulsively, his voice became choked up, and his horses became depressed. Ignoring these evil omens, Akampana sallied forth with the foremost of Rākṣasa warriors, bearing their clubs, swords, *cakras*, spears, axes and bows.

In the gruesome encounter that followed, the dust raised by the opposing armies became so thick that friends could not be discerned from foes. Monkeys began slaying monkeys, and Rākṣasas killed other Rākṣasas. Mainda, Dvivida, Nala and Kumuda littered the battlefield with innumerable gore-smeared bodies of Rākṣasas, and the enraged Akampana responded by routing the monkey army with a deluge of arrows. Seeing the monkey ranks scattering like clouds in the wind, Hanumān approached Akampana, while others supported him from behind.

Akampana sent forth showers of arrows, but Hanumān simply laughed and tore off a huge crag from a mountain peak. He rushed at Akampana, whirling the huge mass of rock around with one hand and roaring. But the Rākṣasa general easily smashed the crag with his arrows. Hanumān flared with rage, and he uprooted a huge banyan tree and rushed toward Akampana.

Seeing Hanumān in such a fierce aspect, smashing their chariots and the trees that stood in his path, the Rākṣasa

soldiers began to flee. Akampana, however, stood fast. As Hanumān continued rushing forward, the Rākṣasa shot him with fourteen arrows. Still, Hanumān did not waver. Hanumān closed in and crashed the giant tree on his head, causing him to fall dead on the ground. While the leaderless Rākṣasas retreated to Laṅkā for safety, Rāma, Lakṣmaṇa and the monkey warriors surrounded Hanumān, blessing him with heartfelt praise.

It was still before noon when Rāvaṇa heard of Akampana's death. Hearing that yet another of his supposedly invincible generals had been killed by a band of monkeys, Rāvaṇa became greatly agitated. He called his ministers for a tour of the city's remaining fortifications. Rāvaṇa told his commander-in-chief, "O Prahasta, only you, myself, Kumbhakarṇa, Indrajit and Nikumbha are capable of defeating the monkeys. We are now hard pressed. I want you to be the next to attack the enemy."

Prahasta replied, "O king, previously I advised you to return Sītā to Rāma. However, now that war has been declared, please know that I am prepared to lay down my life on your behalf."

Prahasta quickly mobilized his army. Within an hour he mounted his chariot and departed for the fight. While approaching the battlefield, Prahasta observed carnivorous birds circling counter-clockwise above his head. Meteors streaked across the sky, while she-jackals shrieked ominously. A squawking vulture came and perched atop his flag staff, and cold, piercing winds blew as dark clouds showered blood upon him. His charioteer's whip repeatedly slipped from his hands, and his horses stumbled, although the path was level.

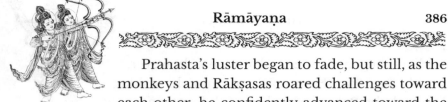

Prahasta's luster began to fade, but still, as the monkeys and Rākṣasas roared challenges toward each other, he confidently advanced toward the army of Sugrīva, like a moth rushing into a flame. When the fighting began, Prahasta's four main assistants—Narāntaka, Kumbhahanu, Mahānāda and Samunnata—created a great massacre in the ranks of the monkey army. Dvivida then killed Narāntaka by hurling a huge mountain peak. The monkey Durmukha smashed Samunnata to death with a gigantic tree. Likewise, Jāmbavān hurled a huge rock that crushed Mahānāda's chest, and Tāra eliminated Kumbhahanu with the help of a tall tree.

In reply, the greatly angry Prahasta released torrents of arrows, slaughtering thousands of monkeys and scattering those who remained alive. Nīla, the commander-in-chief of the monkeys, responded by exterminating innumerable Rākṣasa soldiers.

Soon thereafter, Nīla and Prahasta came face to face. Prahasta's arrows shot through Nīla's body and entered the earth. Still, as the Rākṣasa rushed toward him, Nīla uprooted a huge tree and struck a severe blow. Undaunted, Prahasta continued showering his arrows. When he was unable to dodge the arrows, Nīla simply accepted them with closed eyes, just as a bull might receive an autumn thundershower.

Taking up another tree, Nīla killed Prahasta's horses, and while roaring loudly, broke the Rākṣasa's bow. Picking up a club, Prahasta jumped down from his disabled chariot. The two warriors began fighting hand to hand, tooth to tooth. Prahasta struck Nīla on the forehead with his club, making a gash that bled profusely.

Without wavering, Nīla countered by striking Prahasta in the chest with a tree. Also oblivious to the blow, the Rākṣasa commander again rushed toward Nīla, who grabbed a giant rock. Then, as Prahasta came close, Nīla hurled the boulder upon his head, breaking it into pieces, and causing the Rākṣasa to immediately fall down dead. At this, the Rākṣasa army panicked and fled to Laṅkā, while Rāma and Lakṣmaṇa congratulated Nīla.

When Rāvaṇa learned of the death of his commander-in-chief, his heart became afflicted with unbearable grief. Addressing his ministers, the Rākṣasa king said, "I can no longer ignore my powerful enemies. I shall now go and personally enter the battlefield."

Rāvaṇa mounted his splendid chariot and came out of the city to fight, surrounded by his army of Rākṣasas. When Rāma saw the huge Rākṣasa army approaching, he questioned Vibhīṣaṇa about its leaders. Then, catching sight of Rāvaṇa, Rāma exclaimed, "Due to his extraordinary effulgence and prowess, it is difficult for Me to look upon the Rākṣasa king. However, it certainly is My good fortune that Rāvaṇa has come within My view, for now I can finally vent My long kept wrath!"

Before leaving the city, Rāvaṇa ordered a large army to stay back and guard Laṅkā. He warned them to remain alert, lest the monkeys take advantage of his absence. Coming from the city, Rāvaṇa divided the sea of monkeys in twain, while Rāma and Lakṣmaṇa took up Their bows in anticipation.

The fight began as Sugrīva picked up a mountain peak and suddenly darted forward, hurling the mass of rocks at

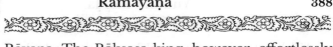

Rāvaṇa. The Rākṣasa king, however, effortlessly broke the rocks into fragments with his arrows and released another shaft that deeply pierced Sugrīva. When Sugrīva fell to the ground, moaning in pain, the Rākṣasas jumped up and down jubilantly. Six more monkey chiefs then picked up mountain peaks and rushed at Rāvaṇa. However, the Rākṣasa king again shattered the rocks to pieces with his arrows. Then, after making those monkey chiefs fall wounded to the ground, Rāvaṇa began slaughtering numerous enemy soldiers with showers of arrows. Feeling extremely hard pressed, the monkeys took shelter of Lord Rāma.

Rāma proceeded toward Rāvaṇa, but Lakṣmaṇa implored Him for permission to be the first to fight with the Rākṣasa king. When Rāma consented, Hanumān protected Him, checking the Rākṣasa king's arrows by hurling rocks.

Unable to contain himself, Hanumān suddenly darted toward Rāvaṇa. With his right arm raised above his head, Hanumān challenged, "The benediction you received from Lord Brahmā does not grant you immunity from death at the hands of monkeys. I will strike you dead with a single blow of my mighty fist!"

Rāvaṇa replied with his own challenge, "I invite you to hit me once freely, and then I will strike you dead!"

Hanumān retorted, "Why do you speak so foolishly? Do you not remember how easily I killed your son, Akṣa?"

At this, Rāvaṇa darted forward and slapped Hanumān on the chest, causing him to reel backward, losing his balance. When he recovered, the enraged Hanumān retaliated by violently striking Rāvaṇa with the palm of his hand. Rāvaṇa

staggered, and the demigods and *ṛṣis* observing the fight applauded Hanumān. Indeed, when Rāvaṇa recovered himself, he also praised Hanumān for being a worthy adversary.

Hanumān replied, "I can understand that my prowess is actually very insignificant, for you are still alive and well. If you think I am a worthy opponent, please feel free to strike me again."

The enraged Rāvaṇa pounded Hanumān in the chest with his clenched fist, causing the monkey hero to reel backwards dizzily. Then, leaving Hanumān aside, Rāvaṇa turned his attention to Nīla, and began shooting him with streams of arrows. Although hard pressed, Nīla picked up a mountain peak and hurled it at Rāvaṇa. As the Rākṣasa king proceeded to break the rocks to pieces with his arrows, Hanumān recovered, but he refrained from further fighting, since he was unwilling to attack someone engaged in fighting with another.

As Nīla picked up one mighty tree after another, Rāvaṇa chopped them all to pieces with his arrows, and continued to oppress his enemy. Finally, to avoid Rāvaṇa's arrows, Nīla shrank himself to a tiny size and jumped onto Rāvaṇa's flagstaff. Rāvaṇa flared with rage upon seeing this trick. As Nīla darted from Rāvaṇa's bow and back to the flagstaff, Rāma and Lakṣmaṇa became astonished. Rāvaṇa also appreciated this daring feat. Nevertheless, he evoked a powerful fire weapon that struck Nīla in the chest, knocking him down to his knees.

With Nīla out of the way, Rāvaṇa approached Lakṣmaṇa. After they exchanged harsh words, Rāvaṇa released seven

arrows, but Lakṣmaṇa easily cut them to pieces. Becoming excited, Rāvaṇa released a shower of arrows, but Lakṣmaṇa was able to neutralize them all with His own shafts. Lakṣmaṇa then took the offensive by releasing His arrows at the astonished Rāvaṇa, but the Rākṣasa king was able to cut them to pieces. Finally, Rāvaṇa released a *brahmāstra* arrow, which struck Lakṣmaṇa in the forehead. Lakṣmaṇa fell down in a swoon on the battlefield.

With great difficulty, Lakṣmaṇa recovered Himself. Then, taking up His bow, He renewed His attack. Lakṣmaṇa sliced Rāvaṇa's bow to pieces with His arrows, and then made the Rākṣasa king faint by puncturing him with three powerful shafts. Rāvaṇa lay upon the ground, his limbs bathed in blood. It was only with great effort that he regained consciousness and raised himself up.

Desiring to put an end to his adversary, Rāvaṇa took a lance that was awarded to him by Lord Brahmā, and hurled it violently at Lakṣmaṇa. Although Lakṣmaṇa tried His best to counteract it with His weapons, the powerful lance entered His chest. The impact was so great that Lakṣmaṇa fell to the ground. As Lakṣmaṇa fought to remain conscious, Rāvaṇa came to arrest Him. However, as the Rākṣasa king grabbed Him, Lakṣmaṇa remembered that He was a direct expansion of Lord Viṣṇu, and began to exhibit His unlimited prowess. Indeed, Rāvaṇa, who had the power to lift up the entire three worlds, could not pick up Lakṣmaṇa, even though exerting all his strength.

As Rāvaṇa mounted his chariot, Hanumān suddenly darted forward, striking Rāvaṇa a violent blow to the chest with his fist. Blood flowed from Rāvaṇa's ten mouths,

twenty ears and twenty eyes, and he fell down unconscious onto the floor of his chariot. All the monkeys shouted with joy. Hanumān then went to where Lakṣmaṇa lay injured. Out of affection for Hanumān, Lakṣmaṇa again made His body light so Hanumān could carry Him. The mystical lance, its mission completed, withdrew itself from Lakṣmaṇa's chest and returned to Rāvaṇa.

Meanwhile, Rāvaṇa regained consciousness and again took up his bow. Lakṣmaṇa also stood up, His wounds completely healed by the inconceivable potency of Lord Viṣṇu.

Because Rāvaṇa had struck down so many monkeys, Rāma decided that the time had come to personally approach him for combat. At Hanumān's request, Rāma mounted his shoulders and rushed toward the Rākṣasa king, challenging him to fight.

While feeling great enmity toward Rāma, Rāvaṇa began showering his arrows upon Hanumān. However, since Hanumān remained unaffected, Rāma was able to move next to Rāvaṇa's chariot and smash it to pieces. Then, taking up an effulgent arrow, Rāma gashed Rāvaṇa's chest, making him reel dizzily and drop his bow. Finally, after cutting off Rāvaṇa's flag, Rāma declared, "You have performed a heroic feat by killing unlimited monkeys on the battlefield. Therefore, you must be quite exhausted from fighting, and I will refrain from killing you. You may return to Laṅkā to rest. When you are recovered I will fight with you again."

Shamed and embarrassed, Rāvaṇa returned to Laṅkā with his head hung down, and Rāma and Lakṣmaṇa turned to extracting arrows from the monkeys' bodies. Upon witnessing Rāvaṇa's humiliation, the demigods and *ṛṣis* stationed in the sky rejoiced, confident that their mission would soon be accomplished.

Despondently sitting on his throne, Rāvaṇa explained to his ministers, "Long ago when I received benedictions from Lord Brahmā, he warned me to beware of human beings. After that, a king in the line of Ikṣvāku named Anaraṇya once cursed me, saying, 'In the future, someone will appear in my dynasty who will kill you and all your relatives.' Later, I was again cursed by Vedavatī after I accosted her. Indeed, I believe it is she who has become the daughter of King Janaka, just to bring about my death.

Moreover, when I once lifted Mount Kailāsa, Umā became frightened and cursed me, saying, 'O wicked Rākṣasa, a woman will one day become the cause of your death.' Then, I once laughed at Nandīśvara because of his monkey-like face. He too, angrily cursed me, saying, 'Your entire dynasty will be destroyed by an army of monkeys.' In addition, Rambhā, Lord Brahmā, Puñjikasthalī, and Nalakuvara all cursed me for raping innocent women. Now I can see that the seeds of my past sins are finally bearing fruit. O Rākṣasas, go quickly and awaken Kumbhakarṇa, for there is no one who can excel him on the battlefield. He fell asleep nine days ago, due to the curse of Lord Brahmā. Normally he sleeps for six months at a time without interruption. However, his unlimited prowess is of no use unless he comes to my assistance.

The Rākṣasas then went to Kumbhakarṇa's residence, but were perplexed as to how they could awaken him before

his natural time. Taking with them enormous quantities of food and other articles, including perfume and garlands, the Rākṣasas entered Kumbhakarṇa's cave-like subterranean abode, which measured one *yojana* in diameter.

As soon as they opened the door to Kumbhakarṇa's room, the Rākṣasas were thrown back by the hurricane-like winds coming from the Rākṣasa's nostrils. Finally, after much difficulty, they managed to enter the sleeping colossus' room, and began their attempts to awaken him.

The large room where Kumbhakarṇa slept was furnished with marble walls and jeweled floors. Lying atop an enormous bed, Kumbhakarṇa appeared effulgent because of his shining jeweled crown.

The Rākṣasas first set out huge vats of meat and blood before the sleeping giant. Then they smeared sandalwood paste and varieties of perfume on his huge body, which was covered with coarse, bristly hair. Although the Rākṣasas loudly praised his glories, Kumbhakarṇa continued to sleep soundly.

Next, the Rākṣasas began roaring loudly, blew on conchshells and beat drums close to Kumbhakarṇa's ears. They clapped their hands, screamed and wailed, banged on gongs and cymbals, and pushed on his arms and legs. Still, Kumbhakarṇa would not stir.

Then the Rākṣasas began to beat Kumbhakarṇa with big hammers and clubs, while others pounded on him with their fists. However, because of the fierce winds that

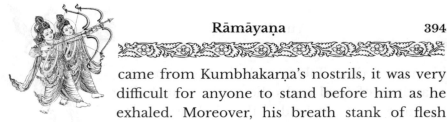

came from Kumbhakarṇa's nostrils, it was very difficult for anyone to stand before him as he exhaled. Moreover, his breath stank of flesh and blood. Indeed, his stinking mouth appeared like an entrance to hell. The 10,000 Rākṣasas surrounding Kumbhakarṇa moved back and forth like waves of the sea as he breathed in and out.

Next the Rākṣasas led in elephants, horses, camels and donkeys, and prodded the animals to walk over Kumbhakarṇa's body. Others beat his legs with big logs. But the colossal Rākṣasa would not awaken.

Frustrated and angry, the Rākṣasas began to pull out Kumbhakarṇa's hair, bite his ears and pour buckets of water into his ears. Still Kumbhakarṇa slept.

The Rākṣasas then beat him with clubs studded with nails, and made 1,000 elephants trample over his body. Then Kumbhakarṇa finally awakened, feeling as if someone had touched him lightly.

The hideous Rākṣasa drowsily stretched his arms, yawned and looked for something to eat. Although some Rākṣasas were still throwing mountain peaks upon his body, Kumbhakarṇa could not feel it. Yawning again and again, Kumbhakarṇa finally got up, looking like Time personified awakening for the final destruction of all beings. Kumbhakarṇa greedily ate all the meat and blood placed before him, and when the Rākṣasas saw that he was satiated, they approached him with folded hands. His eyes still clouded with sleep, Kumbhakarṇa glanced at them and angrily inquired, "Why have I been awakened in this untimely manner? A great danger must have befallen you

that only I can counteract. Otherwise, no one would dare come here to disturb me!"

The minister named Yupakṣa replied, "The city of Laṅkā has been besieged by an army of huge monkeys led by Rāma and Lakṣmaṇa. Many Rākṣasa heroes have already been killed. Indeed, when Rāvaṇa himself entered the fight, he was defeated and then released by Rāma."

Kumbhakarṇa said, "I will go at once and drink the blood of Rāma and Lakṣmaṇa. Then, having eliminated the cause of his fears, I will present myself before Rāvaṇa."

Mahodara, however, suggested, "It would be better for you to see Rāvaṇa first and receive his commands, for he is your elder brother and king."

Thereafter, the Rākṣasas went to Rāvaṇa and explained, "After great endeavor we finally succeeded in awakening Kumbhakarṇa. Do you want him to come here first, or proceed directly to the battlefield to fight with Rāma?"

Rāvaṇa replied, "Let him be brought to me first so I can properly honor him. Just make sure that you supply him with sufficient amounts of meat and wine so that he will arrive here in a good mood."

The Rākṣasas went back to Kumbhakarṇa, bringing with them mountains of food, and 200 buckets of wine. After cramming all the meat, blood and wine down his throat, Kumbhakarṇa became rejuvenated. He then ventured from his huge cave to meet with his elder brother.

When they saw the gigantic Rākṣasa emerging from the cave, the monkeys became struck with wonder and fear.

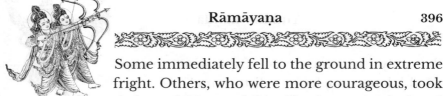

Some immediately fell to the ground in extreme fright. Others, who were more courageous, took shelter of Rāma, while still others panicked and fled in all directions.

Seeing the monkey army, Kumbhakarṇa expanded his already huge size just to frighten them. When Rāma saw Kumbhakarṇa, He exclaimed, "Who is this monster that towers above us like a second Mount Meru?"

Vibhīṣaṇa replied, "This is the son of the sage Viśravā named Kumbhakarṇa. He is the largest of all the Rākṣasas, and has defeated even the lord of death, Yamarāja. When Kumbhakarṇa took birth, he immediately began to devour thousands of living creatures. Because of this, the created beings took shelter of King Indra, who became enraged to learn what had happened.

"Indra launched an attack on Kumbhakarṇa. When Indra released his thunderbolt, the Rākṣasa was knocked unconscious. However, he soon regained his senses and tore out one of Airāvata's tusks and smashed it against Indra's chest, causing him severe pain.

"The defeated king of heaven then took shelter of Lord Brahmā. Indra told him, 'The son of Viśravā named Kumbhakarṇa is tormenting the *ṛṣis* and carrying away the wives of others. Moreover, he is devouring living beings at such a rate that it will not be long before we are all extinct.'

"Lord Brahmā entered meditation, and when he beheld Kumbhakarṇa with his mystic vision, he became alarmed. After pondering the situation, Lord Brahmā approached Kumbhakarṇa, saying, 'You have been created for the destruction of the world, but it is now time for universal

maintenance. Therefore, for the welfare of all living beings, you will remain continually buried in deep sleep from this day forward.'

Kumbhakarṇa soon became overpowered by Lord Brahmā's curse. Rāvaṇa then pleaded, 'O Brahmā, you have cut down a tree that is just about to bear fruit. O supreme teacher within the universe, it is not proper for you to curse your great-grandson like this. I know your words cannot prove futile, but you should at least allow Kumbhakarṇa some time for remaining awake.'

"'Lord Brahmā replied, 'I shall grant your wish. Kumbhakarṇa will sleep continuously for six months and then awaken for one day. At that time he can wander over the earth and devour whatever he likes, before falling into another slumber.'"

Vibhīṣaṇa concluded, "Rāvaṇa has awakened Kumbhakarṇa prematurely because of being hard pressed in battle. Just by seeing the monstrous Rākṣasa, our monkey soldiers have been thrown into confusion. I suggest that we tell the monkeys that Kumbhakarṇa is simply a large mechanical device. This will help them to overcome their fear."

As Kumbhakarṇa entered Rāvaṇa's palace, Rāma ordered Nīla to rally the monkeys and attack the city gates. Again, fierce fighting broke out between the monkeys and the Rākṣasas. At the same time Kumbhakarṇa, along with thousands of his followers, came before Rāvaṇa as he sat on the Puṣpaka chariot, feeling most disturbed.

Upon seeing Kumbhakarṇa, Rāvaṇa became enlivened. After seating him at his side, the Rākṣasa king embraced

his brother. Kumbhakarṇa inquired, "O Rāvaṇa, what service do you wish me to do for you?"

Rāvaṇa replied, "As you know, Rāma has attacked Laṅkā with a huge army of monkeys. Already, many prominent Rākṣasas have died at their hands. My dear brother, I am depending on you to kill Rāma and Lakṣmaṇa, for I can see no one else capable of doing so."

Kumbhakarṇa laughed heartily upon hearing Rāvaṇa's fearful plea, and said, "What was predicted by Vibhīṣaṇa and other intelligent ministers has now come to pass. My dear brother, you are a rascal for ignoring the good advice of sincere well-wishers. Vibhīṣaṇa and Mandodarī were correct when they advised you to return Sītā to Rāma. O king, it is still not too late for you to rectify your mistakes, although the decision is certainly yours alone."

Rāvaṇa became incensed upon hearing this unsolicited advice, but checked his anger. He replied, "It is futile for you to talk like this now, for the battle is in full motion. My dear brother, even if I did make a mistake in kidnapping Sītā, I now request you to nullify the error by manifesting your unparalleled prowess."

To pacify Rāvaṇa, Kumbhakarṇa sweetly replied, "O king, do not worry, for I promise to kill Rāma and Lakṣmaṇa, and all the monkeys, headed by Sugrīva and Hanumān. These so-called heroes have only been successful on the battlefield because I was not present. Now you will see how insignificant the enemy is in the face of my supreme might."

Desiring to please Rāvaṇa, Mahodara interrupted Kumbhakarṇa, saying, "You are an arrogant fool for daring to criticize your elder brother. He is the king and can do

whatever he likes. There was nothing wrong in Rāvaṇa's kidnapping Sītā. Indeed, many kings are naturally inclined to exhibit their prowess by performing such activities. O proud giant, let me assure you that you will not be able to defeat Rāma simply by dint of your strength, as you now claim."

Mahodara continued, "O king, I have devised a clever plan for winning over Sītā. Let Kumbhakarṇa, myself and other Rākṣasa heroes attack Rāma together. If we are able to kill Him, then victory will be ours. However, even if we cannot defeat Him, we can still return to Laṅkā, claiming that we have devoured Him. The false story of Rāma's death should then be broadcast all over the city to the accompaniment of beating drums and rewarding of our soldiers and servants. Thus, the rumor will soon reach Sītā. You should then go to her as she finds herself drowning in an ocean of grief. Tempt her with promises of royal comfort and luxury, trying your best to gain her confidence. Since she will feel that she is without any other protector, I am sure that she will submit to you. O king, if you fight with Rāma, you will surely lose your life on the battlefield. However, if you take my advice, you can win Sītā without ever encountering Rāma."

Kumbhakarṇa, replied harshly, "Mahodara, your words would only appeal to cowardly kings. I have already made up my mind to kill Rāma. My determination cannot go in vain. The rest of you have bungled the war, causing Laṅkā to be divested of its population. I shall now rectify the situation alone. I need no one to help me."

At this, Rāvaṇa laughed, saying, "What you say is true. Mahodara must truly be afraid of Rāma. O Kumbhakarṇa, no one can stand before you when you enter the battlefield,

consumed with rage. Now please go and fight, putting an end to our anxieties. But do not go alone. Surround yourself with an army of Rākṣasas so you can become even more invincible."

Rāvaṇa's spirits lifted as he considered the prowess of his younger brother. As Kumbhakarṇa picked up a deadly dart and prepared to depart, Rāvaṇa placed a golden necklace and garlands around his neck, and decorated him with other ornaments. Then Kumbhakarṇa put on a suit of impenetrable golden armor. After he circumambulated Rāvaṇa and bowed down before him, his elder brother embraced and blessed him.

As he approached the battlefield, Kumbhakarṇa expanded his body to 600 bow-lengths in height and 100 bow-lengths in width. Even though he was determined to kill Rāma and Lakṣmaṇa and devour the entire monkey army, he soon began to notice many fearful omens. Meteors streaked across the sky and she-jackals howled ominously. Kumbhakarṇa's left eye began to twitch and his left arm throbbed. Then a vulture alighted upon the spear Kumbhakarṇa carried. But under the sway of destiny, the puffed up Kumbhakarṇa did not heed these inauspicious warnings.

As Kumbhakarṇa stepped over the defensive wall and entered the battlefield, the monkeys panicked, running away in fear. However, Aṅgada managed to rally the army, and when the monkeys returned, they showered Kumbhakarṇa with countless trees and mountain peaks. Regardless, their missiles simply broke to pieces upon striking the gigantic Rākṣasa's body. In retaliation, Kumbhakarṇa began to slaughter multitudes of monkeys.

The monkeys again panicked. In the stampede that followed, some fell from the cliffs into the ocean, while others kept their eyes closed in fear. Aṅgada then rallied the army saying, "It is better to die gloriously in battle than to flee in hope of finding a life of ease. Such cowards have to pass the duration of their lives being ridiculed by their relatives. Indeed, such insults give more pain than death."

Still the monkeys and their commanders continued to flee, for they considered their lives to be very dear. Finally, when Aṅgada assured them that Rāma would kill the giant, they gradually returned to the battlefield.

Soon the monkeys rushed at Kumbhakarṇa, and the gigantic Rākṣasa struck down 8,700 of them, swinging his club on all sides. Then, taking as many as thirty monkeys at a time in his arms, Kumbhakarṇa stuffed them into his cavernous mouth.

Dvivida then threw a huge rock at Kumbhakarṇa. When the rock missed its mark, it landed among the Rākṣasa's army, smashing many of the soldiers. From the sky, Hanumān tried to shower mountain peaks upon Kumbhakarṇa, but the colossal Rākṣasa easily tore them to pieces with his hands. Then, when Kumbhakarṇa took up his spear and rushed at the monkeys, Hanumān stood in his path and hurled a great mountain peak at him. Kumbhakarṇa avoided the blow, however, and when he threw his spear in retaliation, it pierced Hanumān's chest, causing him to vomit blood and cry out in pain.

While the Rākṣasas rejoiced upon seeing Hanumān's plight, the monkeys fearfully scattered in all directions.

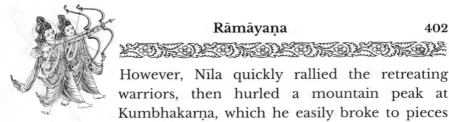

However, Nīla quickly rallied the retreating warriors, then hurled a mountain peak at Kumbhakarṇa, which he easily broke to pieces with his fist.

Ṛṣabha, Sarabha, Nīla, Gavakṣa and Gandhamāda then pounced upon Kumbhakarṇa all at once, but the giant Rākṣasa felt their powerful blows to be as severe as loving caresses. Kumbhakarṇa caught hold of Ṛṣabha, and after squeezing him in his hand, threw him down unconscious on the ground. The Rākṣasa then struck the other four monkey heroes, making them all fall down in a swoon. At this, the other monkeys became enraged, and thousands of them attacked Kumbhakarṇa at once, climbing all over his body as if it were a mountain. As the monkeys tried to bite him with their long, sharp teeth, Kumbhakarṇa grabbed them in his arms and stuffed them into his gaping mouth.

In this way, Kumbhakarṇa ranged over the battlefield, and devoured innumerable monkeys, although some managed to escape through his nostrils and ears after entering his mouth. As the monkey soldiers ran to the shelter of Rāma's lotus feet, Aṅgada suddenly rushed at Kumbhakarṇa, flinging a mountain peak at his head. This only served to enrage the giant Rākṣasa further, who then rushed at Aṅgada and hurled his spear. Aṅgada jumped to dodge the spear, and slapped Kumbhakarṇa in the chest, making him fall to the ground unconscious.

Kumbhakarṇa quickly got up however, and hit Aṅgada with the back of his hand, causing him to fall down in a daze. Kumbhakarṇa then picked up his spear and rushed at Sugrīva, who quickly took up a mountain peak to oppose

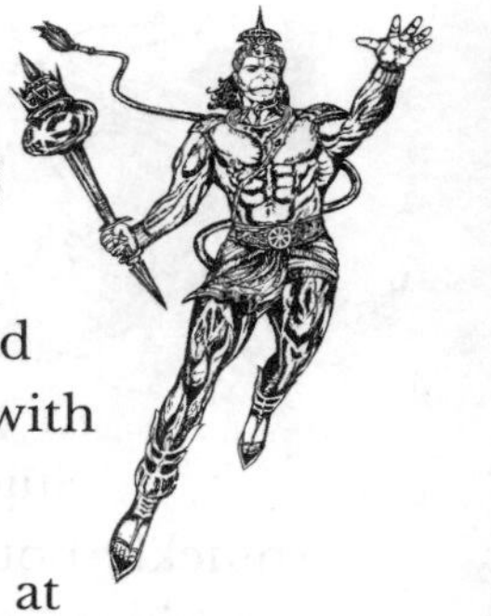

him. But when Sugrīva hurled the giant mass of rocks at Kumbhakarṇa's chest, it merely shattered into millions of pieces. The Rākṣasas shouted with joy, while the monkeys grew despondent.

Kumbhakarṇa violently hurled his spear at Sugrīva, roaring tumultuously. Hanumān, however, had been carefully watching the duel, and upon seeing Sugrīva's plight, suddenly leapt up and caught the spear in mid-air, breaking it in half over his knee.

The monkeys roared with delight upon seeing this extraordinary feat, leaving Kumbhakarṇa disheartened. Then, after breaking off a mountain peak with great agitation, Kumbhakarṇa hurled it impetuously at Sugrīva. When the monkey king fell unconscious from the blow, Kumbhakarṇa picked him up and tucked him under his arm, carrying him back to Laṅkā.

Seeing this, Hanumān thought, "If Sugrīva is taken prisoner, our cause is lost. Therefore, I shall expand myself to become as huge as a mountain and then kill Kumbhakarṇa."

The next moment, however, Hanumān reconsidered, "Surely Sugrīva will soon regain consciousness and somehow free himself. If it appears that the king has to be saved by someone else, he will become humiliated and disheartened."

Kumbhakarṇa entered Laṅkā with Sugrīva held captive, while the rejoicing citizens showered unbroken grains and scented water upon their victorious hero. These offerings, however, helped to revive Sugrīva. Thus, after getting his bearings, the monkey king began to fight back. Sugrīva first tore off Kumbhakarṇa's earlobes with his sharp nails.

Then he bit off the Rākṣasa's nose and split his sides open with the claws on his toes. Sharply pained, Kumbhakarṇa angrily threw down Sugrīva and began beating him. However, Sugrīva quickly bounded into the air and returned to Rāma's side within an instant.

Feeling famished, the enraged Kumbhakarṇa picked up a huge hammer and reentered the enemy ranks to devour the monkeys. Taking handfuls of monkeys and Rākṣasas alike, Kumbhakarṇa stuffed them into his mouth, and streams of blood and fat poured out from the corners. Although the panic-stricken monkeys tried to take shelter of Rāma, Kumbhakarṇa ran here and there, encircling hundreds at a time in his outstretched arms.

Lakṣmaṇa then came to attack Kumbhakarṇa with showers of arrows, but the Rākṣasa deflected them all. Seeing this, the enraged Lakṣmaṇa proceeded to cover his armor with more arrows. Kumbhakarṇa disdainfully said, "I wish to fight with Rāma, not His younger brother!" In response, Lakṣmaṇa pointed to Rāma. Kumbhakarṇa then passed Lakṣmaṇa by, heading toward Rāma.

When the giant rushed at Him, Rāma quickly released a Rudra weapon. As it disappeared into his chest, Kumbhakarṇa began to stagger, dropping his club and scattering his other weapons here and there. The unarmed Kumbhakarṇa then drove off with his fists the monkeys who hoped to take advantage of the setback. Then he seized a mountain peak and rushed toward Rāma. Rāma quickly tore the mass of rocks into small pieces with seven arrows, and the falling debris knocked down more than 200 monkeys.

Lakṣmaṇa then told Rāma, "Kumbhakarṇa is so intoxicated from drinking blood that he devours monkeys and Rākṣasas alike without discriminating between them. If thousands of monkeys were to suddenly climb over Kumbhakarṇa's body, thus weighing it down, this Rākṣasa could easily be defeated."

Then innumerable monkeys began to crawl all over Kumbhakarṇa's body. The giant tried shaking the monkeys loose from his body as he continued meandering about, looking for monkeys to devour. Rāma took this opportunity to rush forward. With His bowstring stretched to His ear, Rāma challenged, "O worst of the Rākṣasas, please stand before Me for a moment while my arrows dispatch you to the abode of Yamarāja!"

Looking up, Kumbhakarṇa was overjoyed to see Rāma before him. Laughing gleefully, he said, "What good fortune! Since You have so kindly given me this opportunity, I shall devour You at once!"

Rāma then showered torrents of arrows, but without being disturbed, Kumbhakarṇa picked up a terrible mace, hoping to slay his enemy without delay. In response, Rāma evoked a powerful Vāyu weapon, severing the giant's right arm, which held his gigantic club. Kumbhakarṇa screamed out in agony as his colossal arm fell to the ground, crushing an entire division of monkey soldiers. Mad with rage, Kumbhakarṇa tore up a huge tree with his left arm and rushed toward Rāma. However, by invoking a mighty Aindra weapon, Rāma severed the giant's remaining arm. As the huge arm tumbled to the ground, numerous monkeys and Rākṣasas were crushed.

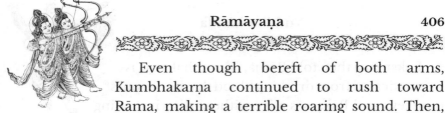

Even though bereft of both arms, Kumbhakarṇa continued to rush toward Rāma, making a terrible roaring sound. Then, with two arrows, Rāma cut off the Rākṣasa's feet. Still, Kumbhakarṇa opened his horrible mouth and hobbled frantically toward Rāma, hoping to devour Him. As Kumbhakarṇa steadily approached, Rāma filled his gaping mouth with so many arrows that the huge Rākṣasa began to gasp for breath. Finally Kumbhakarṇa began to topple, losing consciousness from extreme pain. Rāma then discharged another Aindra weapon that streaked across the sky, illuminating all directions, and tore off Kumbhakarṇa's head.

Kumbhakarṇa's gigantic body crashed into the sea, crushing to death huge fish and alligators. His head, shining like the full-moon, landed on the king's highway in Laṅkā, demolishing big palaces and huge sections of the defensive walls and gates.

From the sky, the demigods gave ecstatic shouts of joy, and the monkeys began talking of Rāma's victory as though they each had five mouths. As Kumbhakarṇa's relatives cried out in grief, Rāma experienced transcendental bliss in accomplishing His heroic feat.

Rāvaṇa was informed that Kumbhakarṇa's severed head was blocking the city gate, and his huge dead body was half submerged in the ocean. This was too much for Rāvaṇa, who simply fainted away. Upon regaining consciousness, he moaned, "Without Kumbhakarṇa I will not be able to go on living, for life has no more meaning. What a mistake I have made by not listening to Vibhīṣaṇa!"

One of Rāvaṇa's sons named Triśira said, "Father, do not lament. I have immense prowess and weapons awarded by Lord Brahmā. My brothers, Devāntaka, Narāntaka, and Atikāya are also expert in conjuring tricks, and can fight while flying in the sky. We shall all go together and kill Rāma, Lakṣmaṇa and the monkey warriors. Please give up your despair."

Rāvaṇa became enlivened by Triśira's assurances. After decorating his four sons with ornaments and garlands, the Rākṣasa king sent them out to fight, along with Mahapārśva and Mahodara. The six powerful warriors headed to the battlefield, followed by an enormous army of Rākṣasas. Thus the fighting began, as both sides roared impetuously.

Before long, the battlefield became difficult to traverse because of the piles of dead bodies, severed limbs, broken chariots and shattered mountain peaks and crags strewn about. monkeys that were previously struck down by Kumbhakarṇa reentered the fight, feeling refreshed, and at first seemed to gain the upper hand. Then, riding on horseback, Narāntaka slaughtered 700 monkey soldiers with his spear.

Sugrīva ordered Aṅgada to attack the son of Rāvaṇa. The unarmed Aṅgada thus approached Narāntaka, challenging, "Why are you wasting your time fighting with common monkeys? Throw your spear at my chest if you consider yourself to be a great hero!"

Biting his lip in rage, Narāntaka suddenly hurled his spear. However, when it struck Aṅgada, it broke into fragments and fell to the ground. Aṅgada darted forward and smashed his fist on the head of Narāntaka's horse. The horse fell dead with a fractured skull, and the infuriated Narāntaka jumped to the ground, retaliating by smashing Aṅgada's skull with his fist. As blood poured from his wound, Aṅgada reeled back, but quickly came to his senses. Again rushing forward with his fist clenched, Aṅgada brought it down with full force upon his adversary. The mighty blow crushed Narāntaka's entire chest, making him fall dead upon the battlefield.

Rāma was both pleased and astonished to witness Aṅgada's heroic feat. But Mahodara could not tolerate the death of his nephew. He angrily rushed at Aṅgada, along with Devāntaka and Triśira. When he saw the three Rākṣasas approaching, Aṅgada tore up a giant tree, hurling it at Devāntaka. Triśira easily cut the tree to pieces with his arrows. Aṅgada continued to shower trees and rocks, but to no avail.

Mahodara then approached Aṅgada while riding upon his elephant, and struck him in the chest with a spiked club. Aṅgada, however, was not even slightly disturbed by the blow, and violently struck the elephant with his hand. When the gigantic beast fell down dead, Aṅgada tore out one of its tusks and hurled it at Devāntaka, wounding him severely. However, Devāntaka quickly recovered and struck Aṅgada with his club, making the prince fall to his knees.

Even though Aṅgada sprang to his feet, Triśira struck him in the forehead with three arrows. Hanumān and Nīla rushed to the prince's aid. Nīla hurled a mountain peak at Triśira, and as the three-headed Rākṣasa smashed it to pieces, Devāntaka rushed at Hanumān with his club held

high. Hanumān leapt into the air to avoid Devāntaka's blow, simultaneously striking the Rākṣasa on the head with his clenched fist. With his skull completely smashed in, Devāntaka fell down dead on the battlefield.

Meanwhile, as Triśira released torrents of arrows at Nīla, Mahodara mounted another elephant and rejoined the fray. As all of his limbs became pierced, Nīla momentarily lost consciousness. Upon recovering, Nīla took up a mountain peak, sprang into the air, and smashed it upon Mahodara's head.

As Mahodara fell down, Triśira became mad with rage and began barraging Hanumān with streams of arrows. Hanumān retaliated with a mountain peak, but Triśira easily smashed it to pieces. Next, Hanumān released a continuous shower of trees, but the three-headed Rākṣasa tore them all to pieces, too. Hanumān became frustrated and angrily jumped on Triśira's horse and began tearing at its hide with his sharp nails. Triśira tried to pierce Hanumān with his spear, but the monkey hero grabbed it out of his hands and broke it in half. Triśira then quickly drew his sword and slashed Hanumān across the chest. But in spite of being wounded, Hanumān slapped the Rākṣasa in the chest, making him fall off his horse, dazed. Hanumān then jumped down from the horse and picked up the Rākṣasa's sword that had fallen from his hand and began roaring loudly. This was intolerable for Triśira, and he quickly jumped up and punched Hanumān in the chest. Hanumān flared with rage. Then, grabbing Triśira by one of his necks, he severed all three of the Rākṣasa's heads one after the other.

The monkeys began roaring triumphantly. However, Mahapārśva angrily took up his iron club and began to drive the monkeys from the battlefield. Ṛṣabha then came to challenge Mahapārśva, but the Rākṣasa immediately struck him in the chest with his club, throwing him to the ground unconscious. When Ṛṣabha regained his senses, he again rushed at Mahapārśva, striking him severely in the chest with his fist.

Mahapārśva collapsed to the ground, bathed in his own blood, and as he struggled to recover his strength, Ṛṣabha took away his spiked iron club. But before the monkey chief could attack, Mahapārśva got up and punched him, making him fall down in a daze. Ṛṣabha quickly recovered and again picked up the iron club, smashing it against Mahapārśva's chest. Blood gushed out from the wound, but still the Rākṣasa attempted to take the club from Ṛṣabha's hands. Before he could retake the club, the monkey chief smashed him over the head with it, causing the Rākṣasa to fall down dead, his eyes and teeth completely crushed in.

As the Rākṣasa army began to flee in fear, the giant Rākṣasa, Atikāya, attacked the monkeys from his chariot. Seeing Atikāya's colossal size, they thought that Kumbhakarṇa had come back to life, and fearfully ran for the shelter of Rāma.

Rāma was also amazed to see the gigantic Rākṣasa, and thus inquired about him from Vibhīṣaṇa. Vibhīṣaṇa explained, "This monstrous Rākṣasa, named Atikāya, is the son of Rāvaṇa and Dhanyamālinī. By performing severe austerities, he satisfied Lord Brahmā, thus receiving benedictions granting him immunity from death at the hands of demigods and demons. Lord Brahmā also awarded Atikāya weapons, armor and a chariot. He thus

became extraordinarily powerful. O Rāma, in previous battles, Atikāya was able to counteract the thunderbolt of Indra and the nooses of Varuṇa. You should kill him at once, before he eliminates the entire army of monkeys!"

While Vibhīṣaṇa was speaking, many of the monkey leaders attacked Atikāya, but the huge Rākṣasa tore to pieces all of the trees and mountain peaks that they hurled at him. As he began shooting the monkeys with his arrows, Atikāya appeared to be unconquerable, although he would not fight with any monkey that was not willing.

Leaving the monkeys aside, Atikāya rushed at Rāma, challenging Him with insulting words. This enraged Lakṣmaṇa, who took up His bow and rushed at the Rākṣasa. Although Atikāya was astonished to hear the twanging of Lakṣmaṇa's bow, he took his own arrow and said, "You are merely a youngster and should leave the battlefield while You are still able to do so. Why do You foolishly stand before me, acting as if You want to give up Your life?"

Lakṣmaṇa's anger flared even more after hearing his haughty words, and He replied with a similar challenge. As Atikāya placed an arrow on his bowstring, the demigods appeared overhead, anxious to see the upcoming duel. Atikāya released his arrow, and Lakṣmaṇa split it in half with His own, prompting the irritated Rākṣasa to quickly send five more. Lakṣmaṇa again cut them off, and responded with a powerful arrow that pierced Atikāya's forehead, causing him to tremble violently.

After recovering himself, Atikāya praised Lakṣmaṇa as a worthy opponent, and then released a deluge of arrows.

Lakṣmaṇa continued to foil Atikāya's arrows, causing the enraged Rākṣasa to shoot an especially powerful arrow that entered Lakṣmaṇa's chest. Although bleeding profusely, Lakṣmaṇa took out an arrow and empowered it with a mystic mantra from the fire-god, Agni. When Lakṣmaṇa released the arrow, Atikāya employed a Sūrya weapon to counteract it. The two arrows collided in the sky, reducing each other to ashes and falling to the ground.

Atikāya then released a Tvaṣṭā weapon, and Lakṣmaṇa counteracted it with an Aindra weapon. Atikāya then discharged a Yama weapon, and Lakṣmaṇa neutralized it with a Vāyu weapon. Lakṣmaṇa then released a steady stream of arrows, but they simply bounced off of Atikāya's armor and fell to the ground. Lakṣmaṇa shot 1,000 more arrows, but the undisturbed Atikāya was able to pierce Him with a single shaft in the chest, causing Him to fall unconscious.

When Lakṣmaṇa recovered, He was able to knock down Atikāya's flag, and then killed his horse and charioteer. However, despite releasing His most powerful arrows, Lakṣmaṇa could not even slightly wound the Rākṣasa.

At this time, Vāyu approached Lakṣmaṇa, saying, "The armor Atikāya wears was formerly given to him by Lord Brahmā, and is impenetrable. Therefore, You should employ Your *brahmāstra* to vanquish Your enemy."

Lakṣmaṇa fitted His ultimate weapon onto His bowstring, and fired it at Atikāya. The Rākṣasa shot many arrows to counteract the *brahmāstra*. When he saw that the weapon remained unimpeded, he began to hurl spears, clubs and axes, but to no avail. Indeed, the *brahmāstra* quickly knocked

off Atikāya's enormous head. As the severed head rolled on the ground, the dejected Rākṣasas rushed back to the shelter of Laṅkā, while the monkeys ran to congratulate Lakṣmaṇa.

Upon hearing the news of Atikāya's death, Rāvaṇa became deeply depressed. Feeling the situation hopeless, he brooded, "Rāma and Lakṣmaṇa are inconceivably powerful! With Their astonishing prowess They have already slain the best of my warriors. I can now understand that Rāma is Lord Nārāyaṇa Himself, appearing in a human form. Although I had previously been informed of this fact, I considered it to be merely the ravings of cowards and fanatics. Who can possibly defeat Rāma?"

Turning to his ministers, Rāvaṇa said, "Make certain that the city's gates are heavily guarded. Increase the security around the *aśoka* grove. I want everyone to remain on full alert to watch the enemy's movements."

Seeing his father with tears in his eyes and overwhelmed by grief and lamentation, Indrajit spoke up, "As long as I am still alive, there is no reason for you to grieve in this way. My dear father, I promise you that I will kill Rāma and Lakṣmaṇa this very day!"

With the blessings of his father, Indrajit went to his sacrificial altar. He then took a living goat by the neck and threw it into the sacrificial fire as an offering. At once, the fire flared up brilliantly, forecasting victory for Rāvaṇa's pet son. Then Agni himself came out of the flames to accept the offering.

Thereafter, Indrajit invoked the mantras that enabled himself, his donkey-drawn chariot, and all his paraphernalia to become invisible. After dispatching his army to attack the enemy, Indrajit took an invisible position in the sky and began raining down his arrows upon the monkey soldiers.

The monkeys attempted to retaliate by hurling numerous trees and rocks at the point where they thought the arrows had originated. But the Rākṣasa deflected all the missiles, while continuing to cut down as many as nine monkeys with a single arrow. Indrajit then invoked the *brahmāstra*, causing heaven and earth to tremble. That supreme weapon produced countless arrows, which knocked all the monkey warriors onto the ground. Millions fell dead instantly.

The invisible Indrajit continued to shower down spears, swords and axes. The bewildered monkeys could see the weapons as they fell from the sky, but were unable to sight their assailant. Even Hanumān, Sugrīva, Nīla and Jāmbavān fell to the ground wounded, and Rāma and Lakṣmaṇa appeared to be eclipsed by Indrajit's weapons.

Although covered by arrows, Rāma remained undisturbed, saying, "O Lakṣmaṇa, I can understand that Indrajit is releasing arrows surcharged with the power of Lord Brahmā. As long as this powerful Rākṣasa remains invisible, no one will be able to conquer him. Therefore it is best if We let Ourselves be overcome by his arrows. When Indrajit sees that We have fallen unconscious, he will surely consider himself victorious and return to Laṅkā to inform Rāvaṇa."

Rāma and Lakṣmaṇa became seriously wounded by Indrajit's arrows and fell down unconscious on the ground.

Seeing his enemies vanquished, Indrajit exulted with joy and returned to Laṅkā to tell his father.

The surviving monkeys became exceedingly depressed to see Rāma and Lakṣmaṇa's condition. Vibhīṣaṇa assured them, "O great heroes, do not lament, for Rāma and Lakṣmaṇa have voluntarily put Themselves in this helpless condition just to honor the weapons of Lord Brahmā. Very soon They will rise up and vanquish the enemy."

Hanumān then offered his respects to the *brahmāstra* and said, "The fighting has subsided and night has fallen. Therefore, our first business should be to restore the remaining monkeys to confidence." Hanumān and Vibhīṣaṇa then took up torches and began to wander over the battlefield. There they saw Sugrīva, Aṅgada, Nīla, Nala and some 6 million monkeys lying on the ground, all struck down by Indrajit's *brahmāstra*.

They found Jāmbavān severely wounded and unable to see. Jāmbavān inquired, "Is Hanumān still living?"

Vibhīṣaṇa asked him, "Why have you inquired about Hanumān, and not about Rāma, Lakṣmaṇa, Sugrīva and Aṅgada?"

Jāmbavān replied, "If Hanumān is living, then the army is still intact, even if it is apparently massacred. But if Hanumān is dead, then the entire army is destroyed, even if the soldiers are apparently alive."

Hearing this, Hanumān came forward. Clasping Jāmbavān's feet he said, "Rest assured that I am well."

Jāmbavān instructed him, "Go quickly to the Himālayas and locate the Ṛṣabha Mountain. Between Ṛṣabha and Kailāsa is an effulgent mountain covered with powerful medicinal herbs that illuminate all directions. You must gather four of these herbs and bring them back here. These herbs are Mṛta-sañjīvanī, which can restore even a dead man back to life; Viśalya-karaṇī, used for extracting weapons and healing wounds; Suvarṇa-karaṇī, which restores the body's original luster; and Sandhānī, which is used for healing fractured bones and joining severed limbs. If you can procure these herbs, then all the monkey heroes who have lost their lives can be revived."

Hanumān became enlivened, and swelled up with renewed energy. After going to the Trikūṭa Mountain, Hanumān squatted down in preparation for a tremendous leap. The mountain peak crumbled from his pressure, and trees burst into flames from the friction he generated. Likewise, Laṅkā's palaces and city gates began to collapse and the entire city trembled, striking all the citizens with fear.

Hanumān first jumped to the Malaya Mountains on the opposite side of the sea. Further expanding himself, Hanumān bowed to the sun god, then again leapt into the air, drawing up huge rocks and trees in his wake.

While soaring through the air at the speed of wind, Hanumān soon sighted the Himālayan Mountains with their golden peaks. After sighting Mount Ṛṣabha and Mount Kailāsa, Hanumān located the mountain situated between them that Jāmbavān had described, and was astonished to see its blazing effulgence.

Hanumān searched frantically all over the mountain for the required herbs. However, the creepers had hidden themselves upon sensing the arrival of an intruder, so Hanumān could not locate them. Hanumān roared ferociously and challenged, "O mountain, if you try to impede the service of Lord Rāma, I shall smash you into millions of tiny pieces."

Receiving no response, Hanumān decided that if he could not find the herbs, he had better bring the mountain and let Jāmbavān find them for himself. Breaking off the top of the mountain, Hanumān sprang into the air and quickly flew the 1,000 *yojanas* to Laṅkā. As he landed on the peak of Trikūṭa Mountain, all the monkeys shouted with joy.

Jāmbavān quickly gathered the required herbs and placed them below the nostrils of Rāma and Lakṣmaṇa for Them to inhale, upon which Their wounds were immediately healed. The herbs were then administered to the wounded monkeys, who all sprang to their feet as though rousing from a sound sleep. Even the monkeys that were previously killed were instantly revived by the herbs.

Hanumān then quickly returned to the Himālayas and put the mountain peak back in its place. Hanumān had completed the entire mission in just one day, and when he returned to Laṅkā, night had already fallen. Sugrīva told him, "My dear Hanumān, since all the dead Rākṣasas have been thrown into the ocean on Rāvaṇa's order, we cannot estimate how many of them have been killed. Nevertheless, of all Rāvaṇa's sons, only Indrajit still survives. Thus, Laṅkā is now defenseless. I suggest we take up torches and invade the city at night to throw the enemy into confusion."

The monkeys soon began their march to Laṅkā. When they approached the city gates, the Rākṣasa guards fled in fear. The monkeys were able to enter without a fight. With torches in hand, the monkey soldiers ran through the streets of Laṅkā, setting all the palaces, gates and walls ablaze. As the fire raged on all sides, thousands of burning buildings toppled to the ground. The whole of Laṅkā was in pandemonium. Burnt Rākṣasas and animals ran wildly in all directions, wailing in anguish.

Rāma and Lakṣmaṇa took up Their bows. When Rāma twanged His bowstring, the sound was heard above the clamor, striking terror into the hearts of the Rākṣasas. Rāma then destroyed Laṅkā's principal gate with a barrage of arrows. When Rāvaṇa saw the destruction, he became mad with rage.

The Rākṣasa king dispatched Kumbha and Nikumbha, the sons of Kumbhakarṇa, along with many other Rākṣasa heroes, including Yupakṣa, Sonitakṣa, Prajaṅgha and Kampana. Both the monkey and Rākṣasa armies were eager for combat. Thus, when the battle ensued outside the gates of Laṅkā, the fighting was especially fierce.

Amidst the slaughter of warriors on both sides, Aṅgada suddenly rushed at Kampana. But when the Rākṣasa struck him with his mace, Aṅgada fell backwards, bereft of consciousness.

The prince quickly recovered, and after picking up a huge mountain peak, he hurled it at Kampana, smashing him to death. The enraged Sonitakṣa then rushed at Aṅgada on his chariot, and riddled him with arrows. But without faltering, Aṅgada smashed the Rākṣasa's chariot and bow with his bare hands. Sonitakṣa was forced to jump down from his disabled carrier, and take up his sword and shield.

Aṅgada quickly went and captured Sonitakṣa, and after snatching the sword from his hand, slashed him with it. As Sonitakṣa fell wounded, Aṅgada rushed off to fight with the other Rākṣasa chiefs. Yupakṣa and Prajaṅgha came to intercept Aṅgada, while Sonitakṣa got up and followed him from behind. Mainda and Dvivida then rushed to Aṅgada's aid, and the three monkeys locked in a fierce battle with the Rākṣasa heroes.

As the monkeys bombarded the Rākṣasas with trees and mountain peaks, the Rākṣasas tore them to pieces with their weapons. Prajaṅgha rushed at Aṅgada, wielding a sword, but the son of Vāli struck him down with a tree before he could

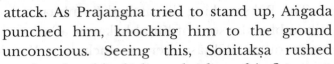

attack. As Prajaṅgha tried to stand up, Aṅgada punched him, knocking him to the ground unconscious. Seeing this, Sonitakṣa rushed forward and suddenly brought down his fist upon Aṅgada's forehead. Although he was momentarily dazed, Aṅgada quickly recovered, so that when Prajaṅgha rushed again with renewed vigor, the prince was able to decapitate him with a mere slap of his hand.

After witnessing the death of his uncle on the battlefield, Yupakṣa got down from his chariot. Then, with tear-filled eyes, he rushed impetuously at Dvivida, sword in hand. Dvivida caught hold of the onrushing Rākṣasa and began pounding him repeatedly in the chest. Seeing his brother captured, Sonitakṣa ran up to Dvivida and violently struck him in the chest with his mace. Dvivida reeled back in a daze, but as Sonitakṣa lifted his mace to strike again, Dvivida caught hold of the weapon and wrested it from the Rākṣasa's hands.

Meanwhile, Mainda arrived on the scene and struck Yupakṣa in the chest with his hand. Soon Dvivida and Mainda became locked in a wrestling match with Yupakṣa and Sonitakṣa. Dvivida tore at Sonitakṣa's face with his sharp nails, and after dashing him to the ground, crushed the Rākṣasa to death with his knees. Mainda then pressed Yupakṣa tightly in his arms, squeezing the life out of his body.

After the death of these two heroes, the Rākṣasa soldiers fearfully took shelter of Kumbha. The son of Kumbhakarṇa struck Dvivida down with an arrow, making him writhe on the ground in pain. Mainda then hurled a huge rock while rushing at Kumbha, but the Rākṣasa broke it to pieces with five arrows. Then, with another arrow, Kumbha struck Mainda in

the chest, making him fall unconscious. Seeing his two uncles fall, severely wounded, Aṅgada became enraged, and madly rushed at Kumbha, seeking revenge.

Although numerous arrows struck him as he advanced, Aṅgada remained unshaken. He released a shower of rocks upon Kumbha's head. However, Kumbha shattered the rocks and pierced Aṅgada's eyebrows with two arrows. Despite the flowing blood covering his vision, Aṅgada managed to grab a huge tree and hurl it at Kumbha. As the Rākṣasa cut it to pieces, Aṅgada fainted to the ground, too afflicted from his numerous wounds.

The monkeys then went to Rāma and told Him of Aṅgada's plight. Rāma dispatched Jāmbavān and other monkey leaders to go to Aṅgada's aid. As the monkey warriors approached, however, Kumbha checked them with a shower of arrows. Sugrīva then rushed at Kumbha, throwing numerous trees. The Rākṣasa, however, cut all the trees apart, and shot Sugrīva with numerous arrows. Still, Sugrīva remained undaunted, and he continued to advance within reach of Kumbha's chariot.

Suddenly, Sugrīva jumped up and snatched the bow from Kumbha's hands, breaking it in half. Then, quickly jumping down from the chariot, Sugrīva said, "O Kumbha, you have certainly exhibited great prowess on the battlefield today. Your father was naturally endowed with great power, whereas Rāvaṇa achieved superior prowess from the benedictions of Lord Brahmā. You, however, are powerful in both ways. O Rākṣasa, I would have killed you just now, but since you are exhausted after so much fighting, I request you to return to Laṅkā for rest. Thereafter, we can fight more under fairer conditions."

Kumbha appreciated Sugrīva's noble words, but without accepting the offer, suddenly grabbed the monkey king in his strong arms. As the two wrestled, the earth began sinking from the immense pressure upon it. Finally, Sugrīva lifted Kumbha up and threw him into the ocean, causing waves as high as mountains to swell up in all directions. Kumbha, however, sprang back onto the land and rushed at Sugrīva, then threw him to the ground and began beating him in the chest with his fists. Although his armor was smashed and blood gushed from his wounds, Sugrīva clenched his powerful fist and pounded Kumbha's chest with all his might. The son of Kumbhakarṇa was crushed by Sugrīva's blows, and he fell to the ground, mortally wounded.

Seeing his elder brother slain, Nikumbha began to roar so loudly and swing his club so wildly that all the monkeys and Rākṣasas became paralyzed with fear. As Hanumān came before him, Nikumbha struck him in the chest with his terrible club. But when the club hit mighty Hanumān, it merely shattered into one hundred pieces. Hanumān then smashed his clenched fist upon Nikumbha's chest, causing the Rākṣasa to stagger backwards. Upon recovering himself, however, Nikumbha captured Hanumān in his arms and began to carry him away.

Hanumān soon escaped Nikumbha's clutches and dashed his opponent to the ground. Hanumān then pounced upon his foe and began to crush him with his knees. At the same time, the heroic son of Vāyu grabbed Nikumbha by the neck and began twisting, until he tore the Rākṣasa's head from

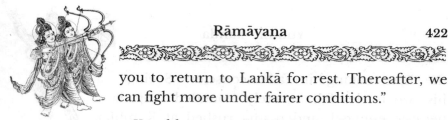

his trunk. Upon witnessing this ghastly feat, the monkeys shouted with joy.

When Rāvaṇa received news of Nikumbha's death, he ordered the son of Khara, named Maharakṣa, to fight with Rāma and Lakṣmaṇa. Maharakṣa approached the battlefield boasting of his prowess, but inauspicious omens suggested his coming defeat. The whip slipped from his charioteer's hands, and his flagpole fell to the ground. His horses faltered with tears in their eyes, seeming depressed. Likewise, a severe dust storm suddenly manifested, bringing gloom and darkness. Maharakṣa, however, ignored these omens and confidently approached the battlefield.

When the fighting began, Maharakṣa slayed many monkeys with his arrows. Then, as the Rākṣasas roared triumphantly, and the monkeys fled for their lives, Rāma took up His bow and began sending down torrents of arrows upon the Rākṣasas. The enraged Maharakṣa then challenged Rāma with harsh words. Rāma, however, merely laughed, exclaiming, "O proud fool, there has never been a war that was won merely by words!"

Maharakṣa then released a steady stream of arrows, but Rāma blasted them all to pieces with His own. Then, coming to close quarters, the two fought furiously, as demigods assembled overhead to witness the spectacular duel. Although Rāma and Maharakṣa deeply wounded each other, their strength seemed to only increase. Indeed, they shot so many arrows that the view of the battlefield was obscured.

Then, flaring with rage, Rāma split Maharakṣa's bow in half, smashed his chariot to pieces, and killed his driver and

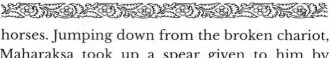

horses. Jumping down from the broken chariot, Maharakṣa took up a spear given to him by Rudra and pitched it at Rāma. Rāma, however, cut the spear to pieces with His arrows. Then, as Rāma fitted an Agni weapon to His bowstring, Maharakṣa madly rushed toward Him with an upraised fist. But before the Rākṣasa could reach Him, Rāma fired a celestial arrow that entered Maharakṣa's heart and killed him. When the Rākṣasa army saw their leader slain, they fled back to Laṅkā.

Thereafter, Rāvaṇa ordered Indrajit to re-enter the battle. The prince again went to his sacrificial altar, pouring libations of ghee on the fire so as to increase his potency unlimitedly. Indrajit took another goat by the neck and threw it into the fire as an offering. As before, Agni personally came before him to accept the offering, and the fire blazed up brightly. Indrajit then mounted his chariot, protecting it and all his weapons with the potency of Lord Brahmā.

Shortly thereafter, Indrajit began showering his arrows upon Rāma and Lakṣmaṇa from his invisible position in the sky. The sons of Daśaratha tried to counter-attack Indrajit with celestial weapons, but none could touch the powerful son of Rāvaṇa. Then, using his mystic power, Indrajit made everything dark, and assailed Rāma and Lakṣmaṇa with a barrage of arrows, severely wounding Them.

Firing toward the direction of the arrows that rained down, Rāma struck Indrajit, but the Rākṣasa hero appeared undaunted. Finally, Lakṣmaṇa became frustrated by Their seeming helplessness, and declared, "I will now invoke the *brahmāstra* and thereby destroy all the Rākṣasas, once and for all!"

Rāma replied, "My dear brother, while fighting with one enemy, it is not proper to kill others who are not taking part in the battle. I am also very eager to put an end to this powerful Rākṣasa. But have patience and let Us discharge more of our celestial weapons at him."

Indrajit could then understand that Rāma intended to finish him off quickly. Thus, he retreated hastily for Laṅkā. Soon afterwards, he set out again for the battlefield. However, this time he chose to remain visible, accompanied by an illusory Sītā.

Seeing Indrajit before them, all the monkeys, headed by Hanumān, rushed forward to attack. However, when they saw that Sītā was also seated upon the chariot, they became extremely depressed. Then, while the monkeys looked on helplessly, Indrajit drew his sword and grabbed Sītā by the hair. The illusory Sītā cried out, "Rāma! Rāma!" and Indrajit punched her with his fist. Feeling unbearable agony, Hanumān shouted, "You are the most abominable of all Rākṣasas. I promise that you will soon be punished in the hell reserved for the killers of women!" Saying this, Hanumān rushed at Indrajit, followed by many monkeys. However, the Rākṣasa repelled them with his arrows.

Indrajit declared, "Watch me now as I kill Sītā. A person who desires to win a war must be willing to give pain to the enemy!" At that, Indrajit took his sword and violently slashed the illusory Sītā's body diagonally, causing her to fall immediately to the ground in a pool of blood. Indrajit then taunted Hanumān, saying, "Sītā is now dead, proving all your endeavors to rescue her a useless waste of energy."

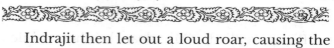

Indrajit then let out a loud roar, causing the monkeys to scatter. Hanumān chastised the fleeing monkeys for being cowards. Then the army rallied, and Hanumān began to massacre Rākṣasas with a vengeance. From a great distance Hanumān hurled a huge rock at Indrajit's chariot. The Rākṣasa quickly maneuvered to avoid the rock, and when it landed, it crushed many Rākṣasa soldiers, split the ground, and entered the bowels of the earth.

Hanumān continued to slaughter many Rākṣasas, while Indrajit attempted to check him with a storm of arrows. After some time Hanumān thought, "Since Sītā has been killed, it would be best for the monkey army to retreat so that I can report to Rāma and receive His instructions."

When Hanumān and the monkeys left the battle scene, Indrajit went to the sanctuary named Nikumbhila to make offerings into the sacrificial fire for the Rākṣasas. From a distant place, Rāma could see how the monkeys were fiercely fighting with Indrajit, and sent Jāmbavān to aid them. Jāmbavān met Hanumān and the monkeys as they retreated.

When Hanumān met Rāma, he informed Him of how Sītā had been mercilessly slain by Indrajit. Immediately, Rāma fell to the ground unconscious. The monkeys came quickly and sprinkled water to revive Him. Lakṣmaṇa picked up Rāma in His arms and lamented, "Oh what terrible misfortune! It appears that virtue and vice have changed roles. Perhaps virtue is simply not strong enough to give a good result without the assistance of sufficient prowess. Therefore, it is best to just depend on one's prowess and forget all so-called moral considerations. I hereby vow to

destroy all of Laṅkā, including Indrajit and Rāvaṇa! My dear Rāma, please remember Your divine position as the incarnation of Lord Viṣṇu, and thus give up Your excessive sorrow."

Vibhīṣaṇa then came forward, having restored the monkey soldiers to confidence. Seeing the grief-stricken Lakṣmaṇa with Rāma unconscious on His lap, he asked, "What has happened?"

As Lakṣmaṇa began to explain Sītā's death, Vibhīṣaṇa interrupted, saying, "It is not possible that Sītā has been killed by Indrajit, for Rāvaṇa would never voluntarily part with her. The Sītā you saw being killed was certainly an illusory creation of the Rākṣasa's mystic power. O Lakṣmaṇa, you should immediately go to Nikumbhila and kill Indrajit while he is busy making sacrificial offerings. If You do not attack him now, Indrajit will once again make himself invisible and become unassailable."

Rāma was too overwhelmed by grief to clearly understand what Vibhīṣaṇa had said. He asked him to repeat himself. Vibhīṣaṇa then explained further, "Long ago, Indrajit performed severe austerities to satisfy Lord Brahmā. Although the grandsire awarded Indrajit the *brahmāstra* and flying horses, he also predicted, 'You will be killed by an enemy while engaged in performing sacrifices at Nikumbhila.' Therefore Lakṣmaṇa must go at once to kill him. Otherwise he will become so powerful that all the monkeys will surely be slain."

Hearing this, Rāma ordered, "Lakṣmaṇa, take Hanumān, Vibhīṣaṇa and the rest of the monkey army." Lakṣmaṇa touched Rāma's feet, vowing to kill Indrajit as He departed.

When Lakṣmaṇa approached Nikumbhila, He saw innumerable Rākṣasas guarding it. Vibhīṣaṇa advised, "Let their army be attacked first. When the Rākṣasas are hard pressed, Indrajit will appear."

When the battle had begun, Indrajit saw how his army was being assailed, and mounted his chariot, even though his sacrifices remained incomplete. Hanumān was slaying many Rākṣasa soldiers, but when Indrajit appeared, they suddenly took heart and rushed at him. As Hanumān continued to massacre Rākṣasas, Indrajit released a torrent of arrows on Hanumān and the monkey soldiers.

Vibhīṣaṇa then took Lakṣmaṇa to a place beneath a banyan tree where Indrajit offered oblations into the sacrificial fire before entering the battlefield. Vibhīṣaṇa knew that Indrajit would soon come there to complete his rituals, and urged Lakṣmaṇa to wait there and kill Indrajit when he returned.

Lakṣmaṇa took His stand, and before long, Indrajit did return. As Lakṣmaṇa challenged him to fight, Indrajit rebuked Vibhīṣaṇa, saying, "Why does my own uncle come here to do me harm? I am the favorite son of your elder brother! Have you no feeling for your family members? You too, are born in the Rākṣasa dynasty. Have you no pride of your birth? Wicked fool, can't you see how you have betrayed your kinsmen? Is there no difference between living with one's own family and licking the feet of strangers? One's worst relative is always better than an outsider. Only you could act so treacherously!"

Vibhīṣaṇa answered, "O nephew, if you are truly concerned with dharma, then why do you reproach me, your elder? It is true that I have been born in a family of

Rākṣasas, but my nature is quite different. I hate impudence and cruelty. It is your father, not I, who caused this breach in our family. According to religious injunctions, It is one's duty to renounce all connections with sinful persons, even if they happen to be family relations. One who kidnaps another's wife is most abominable, and should be cast off like a snake that clings to one's body. To mistrust friends, to have sexual relations with the wife of another, or to steal others' property always lead to destruction. Rāvaṇa is doomed. Along with him, you and all of Laṅkā will be destroyed. O Indrajit, you are merely a proud, ill-mannered boy. Say whatever you like, but soon you will lay down your life, riddled by the arrows of Lakṣmaṇa!"

Lakṣmaṇa was mounted upon Hanumān, and after an exchange of challenges, Indrajit suddenly pierced Him with two arrows. Lakṣmaṇa responded by striking Indrajit in the chest with five arrows, and thus the fierce duel began. After some time Indrajit became pale and weakened from the onslaught of Lakṣmaṇa's arrows. Vibhīṣaṇa urged Lakṣmaṇa to make short work of the Rākṣasa. Lakṣmaṇa released more of His powerful arrows, causing Indrajit to become temporarily dazed. However, he quickly recovered, saying, "Remember how I previously defeated You," and pierced Lakṣmaṇa with seven arrows, Hanumān with ten, and Vibhīṣaṇa with 100.

Lakṣmaṇa, however, simply laughed, again covering Indrajit with arrows, and shattering his golden armor to pieces. However, when Indrajit retaliated with 1,000 arrows, Lakṣmaṇa's armor was also shattered. Thus, neither appeared to gain the upper hand.

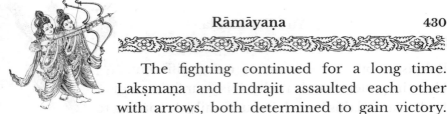

The fighting continued for a long time. Lakṣmaṇa and Indrajit assaulted each other with arrows, both determined to gain victory. Innumerable arrows pierced through their bodies and entered the earth, causing them to bleed profusely. The masses of arrows that had been counteracted were spread all over the ground like so much *kuśa* grass.

Neither Lakṣmaṇa nor Indrajit tired. As they fought, Vibhīṣaṇa attacked the other Rākṣasas, not wishing to fight with his nephew. The fighting between the two armies became very heated, as Jāmbavān went on a rampage. Hanumān had Lakṣmaṇa get down from his back so that he too, could join the melee, and proceeded to exterminate Rākṣasas by the thousands.

As the sun sank below the horizon, the sky became exceedingly dark, covered by the incessant flow of arrows shot by Lakṣmaṇa and Indrajit. Their two bows worked so quickly that the motion of their arms could not be discerned.

Lakṣmaṇa shot an arrow that beheaded Indrajit's driver, and the Rākṣasa had to drive his chariot and simultaneously shoot his arrows. This allowed Lakṣmaṇa the opportunity to pierce His adversary more easily, and after some time Indrajit began to lose strength. Four monkey warriors then jumped upon Indrajit's horses, ripping them to pieces with their sharp teeth and claws. The monkeys then proceeded to smash the chariot to pieces. Indrajit was forced to dismount.

In the dense darkness, Lakṣmaṇa began to close in on His foe. Indrajit ordered the Rākṣasas to keep the monkeys engaged while he reentered Laṅkā for a new chariot. After some time, Indrajit returned to the battlefield with renewed

enthusiasm, and began slaying monkeys by the thousands, causing the army to run to Lakṣmaṇa's shelter. Lakṣmaṇa then snapped Indrajit's bow and punctured his chest with five arrows. At that, Indrajit picked up a stronger bow, but Lakṣmaṇa counteracted all the arrows he released.

Lakṣmaṇa flared up with energy and proceeded to strike every Rākṣasa with two arrows, while wounding Indrajit at the same time. Indrajit responded with a flurry of arrows, and Lakṣmaṇa severed the charioteer's head and fired at the horses, throwing them into confusion. All the while, Indrajit's arrows bounced off Lakṣmaṇa's armor. Considering His armor to be impenetrable, Indrajit began to shoot Lakṣmaṇa in the forehead. Although wounded, Lakṣmaṇa quickly struck Indrajit in the face with five arrows.

Indrajit then stabbed Vibhīṣaṇa's face with three arrows, causing him to rush at his nephew in a fit of rage, wielding his club. As Vibhīṣaṇa pounded his horses to death, Indrajit jumped down from the chariot and hurled a spear at his uncle.

At that, Lakṣmaṇa intervened, chopping the spear to pieces with His arrows. Then, when Vibhīṣaṇa punctured Indrajit's chest with five arrows, Indrajit knocked a terrible Yama weapon onto his bowstring. Seeing this danger, Lakṣmaṇa took out a wonderful arrow awarded to Him by Kuvera in a dream.

When both weapons were released, they collided in mid-air, brightly lighting up the entire night sky, and causing a huge explosion as they shattered into hundreds of pieces amid crackling sparks and billowing smoke.

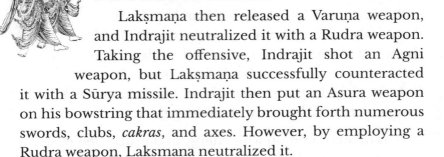

Lakṣmaṇa then released a Varuṇa weapon, and Indrajit neutralized it with a Rudra weapon. Taking the offensive, Indrajit shot an Agni weapon, but Lakṣmaṇa successfully counteracted it with a Sūrya missile. Indrajit then put an Asura weapon on his bowstring that immediately brought forth numerous swords, clubs, *cakras*, and axes. However, by employing a Rudra weapon, Lakṣmaṇa neutralized it.

Indrajit had gradually began to lose heart, when Lakṣmaṇa selected a wonderful weapon belonging to King Indra. As he placed the invincible weapon on His bowstring, drawing it back to his ear, Lakṣmaṇa prayed, "O chief of the celestials, if Rāma is truly the unrivaled Lord and the shelter of truth and virtue, let this weapon kill Rāvaṇa's son."

That effulgent arrow soared swiftly through the air and cut off the head of Indrajit, the Rākṣasa who had been the greatest impediment to Lord Rāma's army of monkeys. As the panic-stricken Rākṣasas ran in all directions, the monkeys shouted with joy, jumping up and down. In the sky, demigods and *ṛṣis* cried out ecstatically, praising Lakṣmaṇa's victory. Then, as the denizens of heaven showered flowers upon the heroes, the monkeys danced with joy, lashing their tails and shouting, "Jaya Rāma! Jaya Lakṣmaṇa!"

Exhausted and severely wounded, Lakṣmaṇa leaned upon Vibhīṣaṇa and Hanumān as He came before Rāma to circumambulate Him. Vibhīṣaṇa then narrated the entire story of Indrajit's defeat. Listening intently, Rāma experienced transcendental pleasure. After congratulating Lakṣmaṇa and smelling His head with great affection, Rāma said, "Indrajit was just like Rāvaṇa's right arm. Now that he

has been killed after three days and nights of battle, the Rākṣasa king will surely come out to fight."

Lakṣmaṇa was tormented with pain from the numerous wounds inflicted upon him by Indrajit's arrows. Therefore, Rāma ordered Suṣeṇa to treat Him and all the wounded monkeys. Later, when Suṣeṇa had Lakṣmaṇa inhale the vapors of a certain medicinal herb, Lakṣmaṇa was delighted to find that all His pain vanished, and His wounds suddenly healed.

Rāvaṇa's ministers informed him how Lakṣmaṇa had killed Indrajit with the assistance of Vibhīṣaṇa. Rāvaṇa fainted upon hearing the news, and only after a long time regained consciousness. Rāvaṇa lamented sorely over the death of his beloved heir apparent. Becoming possessed by mad anger, Rāvaṇa decided to take revenge by killing Sītā. As he announced this, his appearance was so fierce that the other Rākṣasas hid themselves out of fear.

Rāvaṇa called for his impenetrable armor, bow and arrows, all awarded him by Lord Brahmā. He declared, "I will now enact in reality what Indrajit merely did as a conjuring trick, simply to torment the enemy." Rāvaṇa violently unsheathed his sword, and rushed to the *aśoka* grove, followed by Mandodarī and several of his ministers. Although these well-wishers tried their best to restrain him, Rāvaṇa soon arrived before the terrified Sītā.

As he waved his sword menacingly, Sītā could understand that he intended to kill her. Sītā wondered, "What has happened to make the wicked Rākṣasa king come here like this before my allotted 12 months have elapsed? Has he

become too frustrated by my repeated refusals? Is he simply going to kill me out of desperation, being unable to defeat Rāma and Lakṣmaṇa? I should have taken Hanumān's advice and let him carry me back to Rāma on his back. Then I never would have been put into this ghastly situation."

Feeling compassion for the grief stricken Sītā, a pious minister named Supārśva addressed Rāvaṇa, "O lord, you have studied all the Vedas and observed the strictest vows. How can you even think of harming a woman like this? Let the lovely Sītā be. Instead, vent your wrath upon your real enemy. Today is the fourteenth day of the dark lunar fortnight. Tomorrow, as the new moon emerges, march against Rāma and His monkey hordes and obtain victory. I am sure that after killing Rāma, you will be able to enjoy Sītā to your heart's content. Why should you prematurely frustrate your ardent desire in this way?"

Rāvaṇa accepted this flattering advice. He then gave up the idea of killing Sītā and returned to his palace. Sitting morosely upon his throne, Rāvaṇa, still mourning the loss of his favorite son, gave the following order: "I want all remaining Rākṣasas to go at once and attack Rāma together. If they are unable to kill Him, then tomorrow I will go personally to fight with Him."

Just before dawn, the Rākṣasas rushed out from the city to fight with the monkeys, and a furious battle ensued. The incited Rākṣasas quickly butchered many monkey soldiers, causing those remaining to run to the shelter of Rāma's lotus feet. Rāma then employed a spectacular Gandharva weapon that shot forth unlimited streams of arrows upon the Rākṣasas. The showers of arrows were so dense that the

Rākṣasas could no longer see Rāma—all they could see was the decimation of innumerable Rākṣasa soldiers. Because of the Gandharva weapon, Rāma sometimes appeared invisible, and at other times the Rākṣasas saw 1,000 Rāmas standing before them in all directions. Within 90 minutes, Rāma massacred 200,000 foot soldiers, 18,000 elephant warriors, 14,000 cavalrymen, and numerous chariot fighters. The survivors then fled back to the safety of Laṅkā, as the demigods in the sky ecstatically praised Rāma for His victory. Rāma said, "O great monkey heroes, you should know that the ability to employ such celestial weapons is only possible for Myself and Lord Śiva."

Meanwhile in Laṅkā, the widows of the slain Rākṣasas grouped together and lamented over the death of their husbands. They wailed out, "We curse Śūrpaṇakhā, for she is the root cause of the enmity between Rāma and Rāvaṇa that has destroyed our race. Because Rāma has defeated Rāvaṇa many times in the past, Rāvaṇa should be well aware of His invincible prowess. Why couldn't our foolish king accept the advice of Vibhīṣaṇa and avoid this carnage?"

Hearing the womens' lamentation, Rāvaṇa suddenly boiled over with an uncontrollable rage. Hissing like a trampled serpent, he ordered his ministers, "Prepare my army for battle at once! Today I shall finally kill Rāma, Lakṣmaṇa and all the monkeys with my torrents of arrows. Bring my chariot, and make certain that every able-bodied Rākṣasa soldier follows me!"

At Rāvaṇa's command, 100,000 chariots, 300,000 elephants, 60 million horse soldiers and unlimited foot soldiers assembled. Rāvaṇa then mounted his chariot, drawn

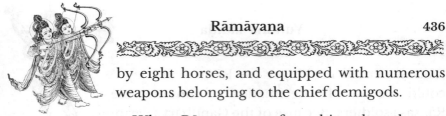

by eight horses, and equipped with numerous weapons belonging to the chief demigods.

When Rāvaṇa came from his palace, he was greeted with a tumultuous fanfare of blowing conchshells, trumpets and shouts of encouragement from the citizens. When the monkeys heard this uproar, feelings of fear and dread entered their hearts. Then, as Rāvaṇa exited from the northern gate, along with Mahodara, Mahapārśva, and Virūpākṣa, a gloomy atmosphere prevailed. Dark clouds obscured the sun and rained down blood, as Rāvaṇa's horses stumbled on the road. Rāvaṇa's left eye twitched, his left arm throbbed, his face grew pale and his voice became hoarse. Then, as meteors streaked across the sky, a vulture perched on Rāvaṇa's flagstaff. Rāvaṇa ignored these evil omens and continued on to meet his doomed fate.

When the fighting began, Rāvaṇa created havoc, for none of the monkeys could stand before his onslaught of arrows. As the enraged Sugrīva led the monkeys in a fierce counter-attack upon the Rākṣasa army, Rāvaṇa turned his attention toward Rāma.

Meanwhile, Virūpākṣa got down from his chariot and mounted an elephant. He rushed toward the monkeys while raining down arrows upon them. Sugrīva tore up a gigantic tree and violently smashed the elephant, throwing it backwards. Jumping from the wounded elephant, Virūpākṣa picked up his sword and shield and angrily rushed at Sugrīva. Although Sugrīva hurled a huge boulder at his onrushing foe, Virūpākṣa dodged it and slashed the monkey king with his sword. Momentarily dazed, Sugrīva fell to the ground, but he quickly sprang up and punched Virūpākṣa in the chest. This only enraged the Rākṣasa more. Virūpākṣa cut

off Sugrīva's armor with his sword and gave him a kick, making Sugrīva fall backwards. Again, Sugrīva sprang to his feet. When he tried to give the Rākṣasa a mighty slap, Virūpākṣa ducked the blow and punched Sugrīva in the chest. Flaring with rage, Sugrīva looked for an opportunity to strike, and suddenly brought the palm of his hand down on Virūpākṣa's forehead with all his might. Immediately blood gushed from all nine holes of the Rākṣasa's body, and he fell down dead.

Witnessing the death of Virūpākṣa and the loss of many Rākṣasa soldiers, Rāvaṇa became even more incensed. He urged Mahodara to vanquish the enemy. Fighting heroically, Mahodara began to consume the monkey soldiers in great numbers, making them run for the shelter of Sugrīva. Sugrīva rushed at Mahodara and hurled a huge rock, but the Rākṣasa broke it to pieces with his arrows. Boiling with rage, Sugrīva tore up a tall tree, but the Rākṣasa's arrows immediately cut it to pieces and pierced the monkey king. Sugrīva took up an iron club lying on the ground and rushed toward Mahodara. He struck down Mahodara's horses, forcing the Rākṣasa to jump from his disabled chariot. Mahodara then rushed at Sugrīva while launching his mace. Likewise, Sugrīva threw his club, and the two weapons collided in mid air, neutralizing each other.

Sugrīva and Mahodara both scrambled to pick up more clubs that were lying about and tossed the weapons at each other. Finally the two closed in on each other and began fighting hand to hand. Mahodara picked up a sword and cut deeply into Sugrīva's armor. However, the sword remained momentarily stuck, and as Mahodara struggled to free it, Sugrīva took advantage and knocked off the Rākṣasa's head.

Bereft of their leader, Mahodara's army fled from the battlefield. Meanwhile, Mahapārśva appeared on the scene and began slaughtering the monkey warriors. When Aṅgada saw his soldiers becoming disheartened, he took a heavy club and flung it at Mahapārśva with all his might. The Rākṣasa and his driver were struck so violently that they both fell to the ground unconscious. Jāmbavān then hurled a huge rock that shattered Mahapārśva's chariot and killed his horses. Thus, when the Rākṣasa hero regained consciousness, he was forced to continue fighting on the ground.

Mahapārśva immediately retaliated by penetrating Jāmbavān's chest with three arrows, and showering innumerable arrows upon Aṅgada. Aṅgada responded by throwing an iron club that knocked off Mahapārśva's golden crown and broke his bow and arrow. Then, rushing forward, Aṅgada soundly slapped the Rākṣasa on the head. This merely enraged the Rākṣasa further, however, who then picked up an ax and hurled it at the monkey prince. Aṅgada expertly dodged the weapon. He then charged Mahapārśva and smashed his chest with such force that the Rākṣasa's chest burst open, killing him instantly.

As Mahapārśva's army scattered in confusion, the monkeys and demigods shouted with joy, and Rāvaṇa seethed with rage. The king of the Rākṣasas then mounted his chariot and advanced toward Rāma, sending a continual stream of arrows. Rāma counteracted Rāvaṇa's arrows with His own, and thus a fierce battle gradually evolved between the two archenemies. Soon, their continuous volleys of arrows covered the sky, creating darkness all around.

The other monkey and Rākṣasa soldiers ceased fighting to witness the spectacular contest.

When Rāvaṇa struck Rāma in the forehead with an arrow, Rāma remained undaunted and retaliated with a Rudra weapon. Even though that missile discharged innumerable arrows, they simply bounced off of Rāvaṇa's impenetrable armor without harming him in the least. Rāvaṇa evoked a mystic Asura weapon, causing countless arrows with the heads of lions, tigers, vultures, serpents and alligators to rush at Rāma, their mouths open to devour Him. Although Rāma employed an Agni weapon that melted the arrows of Rāvaṇa in mid-air, thousands of monkeys were slain by them. Still, Rāma and the monkey chiefs were pleased, since the weapon Rāvaṇa employed was known to be one of his most powerful.

Rāvaṇa next evoked a Rudra weapon created by Maya Dānava, releasing maces, lances, thunderbolts and nooses in steady streams. Rāma quickly foiled the Rudra weapon with His Gandharva weapon. Rāvaṇa then discharged a brilliant Sūrya weapon that caused enormous, effulgent *cakras* to shoot out at Rāma. With a display of inconceivable skill, Rāma shattered all the *cakras* with His arrows, but while He was doing so, Rāvaṇa pierced Rāma's chest with ten powerful shafts. Rāma, however, did not flinch, and retaliated by shooting Rāvaṇa's limbs with numerous arrows.

Desiring to enter the fray, Lakṣmaṇa released seven arrows that cut down Rāvaṇa's flag. With another arrow, Lakṣmaṇa severed the head of Rāvaṇa's driver, and with five more, split the Rākṣasa king's bow. Then Vibhīṣaṇa also rushed forward, and killed Rāvaṇa's horses with his mace,

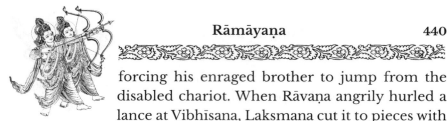

forcing his enraged brother to jump from the disabled chariot. When Rāvaṇa angrily hurled a lance at Vibhīṣaṇa, Lakṣmaṇa cut it to pieces with three arrows as it soared through the air. Rāvaṇa then picked up a magical spear manufactured by Maya Dānava. Seeing how Vibhīṣaṇa's life was in danger, Lakṣmaṇa quickly hailed so many arrows upon Rāvaṇa that he became stunned while standing with his spear in hand. Rāvaṇa shouted at Lakṣmaṇa, "Because You have dared rescue Vibhīṣaṇa, the spear that was meant for him will instead take Your life."

Rāvaṇa roared like a lion and hurled the magical spear. As it unerringly soared through the air toward Lakṣmaṇa, Rāma requested the spear to become ineffectual. Nonetheless, the spear shot through Lakṣmaṇa's chest and stuck into the ground, making the son of Sumitrā fall down seriously wounded.

When Rāma saw Lakṣmaṇa's pitiful condition, He became extremely despondent, with tears filling His eyes. Then, suppressing His intense grief, Rāma extracted the spear from Lakṣmaṇa's body, even as Rāvaṇa showered arrows upon Him.

Breaking the spear in half, Rāma raised Lakṣmaṇa in His arms and tearfully embraced Him. Then, after ordering Hanumān and Sugrīva to guard Lakṣmaṇa, Rāma angrily declared, "I shall now exhibit My full prowess against the wicked Rāvaṇa. I promise He will soon be slain on the battlefield! The monkeys may now go and sit at ease upon the mountain tops. Let them watch with the demigods as I perform a wonderful feat that will be glorified until the dissolution of the world!"

Rāma attacked Rāvaṇa with a vengeance. As they proceeded to cover one another with torrents of arrows, their twanging bows produced an astonishing clamor. The infuriated Rāma soon overwhelmed Rāvaṇa, causing the Rākṣasa to flee the battlefield in fear.

Rāma then went to Lakṣmaṇa, and with great anguish told Suṣeṇa, "Just by looking at My wounded brother, My strength immediately withers. Without Lakṣmaṇa, victory will have no meaning for Me. If He dies, I shall follow Him, just as he followed Me when I was exiled to the forest."

With a reassuring voice, Suṣeṇa replied, "O Rāma, Lakṣmaṇa is not dying. His facial luster has not faded and His eyes are still sparkling brightly. However, Hanumān must immediately be dispatched to the Mahodaya Mountain to collect the herbs called Viśalya-karaṇī, Sāvarṇya-karaṇī, Saṁjīva-karaṇī, and Saṁdhānī. By this medicinal treatment, Lakṣmaṇa can immediately be restored to perfect health."

Hanumān again leaped to the Himālayas. However, arriving at Mahodaya Mountain, he could not recognize the necessary herbs. In frustration he again tore off the mountain peak and, while holding it in both hands, returned to Laṅkā. Placing the mountain peak near Suṣeṇa, Hanumān laid down for a moment to rest, saying, "I could not recognize which herbs to bring, so I decided to carry the entire mountain here."

Suṣeṇa praised Hanumān and then went to look for the proper herbs. Thereafter, he crushed the herbs into powder, and when Lakṣmaṇa was given them to smell, His wounds instantly became healed. As Lakṣmaṇa stood up, Rāma

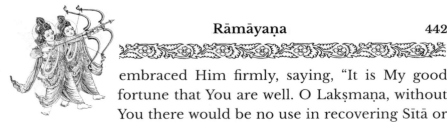

embraced Him firmly, saying, "It is My good fortune that You are well. O Lakṣmaṇa, without You there would be no use in recovering Sītā or even maintaining My life any longer."

Lakṣmaṇa replied, "My dear brother, please do not indulge in such grief any longer. Quickly make good Your vow to kill Rāvaṇa and install Vibhīṣaṇa as king of Laṅkā."

Meanwhile, Rāvaṇa mounted another chariot and rushed out from the city, eager to fight with Rāma. Rāma took up His bow and released a downpour of arrows upon Rāvaṇa. However, from the sky, the demigods exclaimed, "This battle is not being fairly fought. Rāma is standing on the ground while Rāvaṇa rides in a chariot!"

Taking this cue, Indra called to Mātali and ordered him to take his chariot to Rāma on the battlefield. Mātali thus came before Rāma, driving Indra's golden chariot, which was drawn by 1,000 greenish horses. The celestial charioteer then announced to Rāma, "My dear Lord, King Indra requests You to kindly accept this chariot for fighting with Rāvaṇa. Inside You will find Indra's bow and armor, along with an incomparable spear and various celestial arrows. O Rāma, please mount the chariot at once, for the demigods are most disturbed to see You having to fight standing on the ground."

After circumambulating Indra's chariot, Rāma mounted it, and a thrilling duel ensued. When Rāvaṇa released a Gandharva weapon, Rāma quickly neutralized it with another Gandharva weapon. Next, Rāvaṇa discharged a Rākṣasa weapon that took the form of innumerable serpents with blazing, wide-open mouths. In response, Rāma released a

Garuḍa weapon that transformed into countless golden eagles that quickly ate up all of Rāvaṇa's snake-arrows. This enraged the Rākṣasa king, who then rapidly discharged 1,000 arrows at Rāma. He also shot numerous arrows that hit Mātali, a single arrow that knocked down Indra's flag, and many more that afflicted the horses.

Rāvaṇa was putting Rāma in great difficulty, and the demigods and monkey warriors became quite anxious. Rāma then assumed a most frightening angry form, causing the entire earth, with its mountains and oceans, to quake. Many evil omens manifested, and all created beings, including Rāvaṇa, became afraid.

Numerous demons suddenly appeared in the sky to cheer Rāvaṇa toward victory. As if in response, Rāvaṇa picked up a fearsome dart and roared so ferociously that heaven and earth began to tremble. Then he shouted, "Rāma, prepare Yourself, for You shall now die!"

Rāvaṇa hurled the lethal dart. Soaring through the sky, it made a loud roaring noise, and was encircled by lightning. Rāma released innumerable arrows to counteract Rāvaṇa's awesome weapon, just as Indra tries to stop the fire of devastation by pouring down torrential rains. When Rāma saw all His arrows being consumed by the fearsome dart, He picked up the celebrated spear of Indra and hurled it. Soaring through the air, Indra's spear illuminated all directions, then collided with Rāvaṇa's dart, shattering it to pieces that fell harmlessly to the ground.

Rāma then punctured Rāvaṇa's chest, forehead and horses with arrows. Although Rāvaṇa was exhausted and

blood flowed from wounds all over his body, he continued to storm arrows upon Rāma in great anger. Indeed, Rāvaṇa riddled Rāma's chest with 1,000 arrows that covered Him with blood. The constant hail of arrows was so dense that Rāma and Rāvaṇa could no longer see each other clearly because of the darkness it produced. Still, Rāma remained undaunted. Laughing disdainfully, He rebuked Rāvaṇa, saying, "You are the most abominable of the man-eaters. Indeed, you are like their stool. O kidnapper of Sītā, you are a first class fool for considering yourself a great hero. Actually, you are a great coward, for you dared to take My wife away after deceptively luring Me far away. How can you be proud of overpowering a poor defenseless woman in the absence of her husband? You resemble a dog, for as a dog steals eatables from the kitchen in the absence of the householder, in My absence you kidnapped My wife, Sītā. Therefore as Yamarāja punishes sinful men, I shall also punish you. You are most abominable, sinful and shameless. Today, therefore, I, whose attempt never fails, shall punish you. O Rāvaṇa, today you will meet your deserved end. The body you are so attached to will become food for jackals and vultures!"

Thereafter, Rāma began to fire His arrows with redoubled energy and greater dexterity. This assault was combined with volleys of stones hurled by the monkeys. Rāvaṇa became so dazed that he could no longer take up and properly discharge his weapons. Seeing his master's death near at hand, Rāvaṇa's charioteer drove him swiftly away from the battlefield, beyond the reach of Rāma's arrows.

The charioteer then said, "O king, I took you away from the fighting only for your welfare. You appeared to

have lost all your strength and your horses were exhausted. Many inauspicious omens were visible, so I did what I considered to be my foremost duty."

Rāvaṇa became pacified by his driver's words, and then ordered, "Go quickly to where Rāma is! Once Rāvaṇa makes up his mind he does not turn back until he has completely vanquished his enemies!"

In Rāvaṇa's absence, Agastya Ṛṣi came before Rāma, knowing Him to be greatly fatigued from the fighting. After being properly honored and welcomed, Agastya said, "My dear Lord Rāma, kindly receive from me the Āditya-hṛdaya prayer meant for satisfying the sun god. This mantra bestows great blessings and cleanses all sins. One who chants this hymn prolongs his life and remains always fixed on the eternal path of religion. The mantra is as follows:

"'O presiding deity of the sun, I offer my obeisances unto you. You are the chief of all the demigods because of your unlimited effulgence, which maintains the entire universe. Indeed, both demigods and demons worship you for their ultimate welfare. You are the reservoir of all universal energy and the source of life for all beings. As such, you perfectly represent the Supreme Lord, Viṣṇu, as His empowered expansion. Men who are knowers of the Vedas therefore worship you as Lord Nārāyaṇa, situated within the sun, by chanting suitable prayers three times daily. It is you alone who destroy the dense darkness of this universe, and thus I bow down unto you, O splendorous one! Again and again I offer my obeisances unto you, O eye of the Supreme Lord and witness of the world's activities."

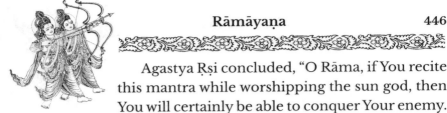

Agastya Ṛṣi concluded, "O Rāma, if You recite this mantra while worshipping the sun god, then You will certainly be able to conquer Your enemy. Anyone who is in difficulty and worships Sūrya with this prayer never comes to grief."

Agastya then left. Rāma already felt rejuvenated and thereafter, He sipped water three times while uttering the holy names of the Lord. Then, with His gaze fixed upon the sun, Rāma recited the Āditya-hṛdaya prayer, and experienced great transcendental bliss.

As Rāma again took up His bow and advanced toward Rāvaṇa, Sūrya spoke to Him from the sky, urging, "Do not delay! Go quickly!"

Rāma then ordered, "O Mātali, drive quickly to where Rāvaṇa is staying, but do so with great caution."

Remembering that He was speaking to Indra's charioteer, Rāma became embarrassed and apologized, saying, "I am sorry to have instructed you as if I were your master. I am simply eager to kill Rāvaṇa, and hope you will excuse My offense."

Mātali was touched by Rāma's display of humility, and soon brought Indra's chariot close to Rāvaṇa's side. Rāma and Rāvaṇa then exchanged arrows, and the fighting again became fierce. Evil omens came into view, foreboding the destruction of the Rākṣasa king. Clouds rained blood upon Rāvaṇa's chariot and a flock of vultures followed behind him. A huge meteor then fell close by, causing all the Rākṣasas to become despondent, convinced that Rāvaṇa would soon die.

Conversely, pleasing signs appeared before Rāma, indicating that victory would soon be His. Thereafter, Rāma and Rāvaṇa exhibited the entire wealth of their prowess. The competition became so intense that the armies were stunned with amazement. Indeed, the soldiers stood motionless like paintings. They were so absorbed in watching the fight that they did not even think of attacking each other.

When Rāvaṇa tried to cut Indra's flag, Rāma deflected his arrows with His own. Determined to match Rāvaṇa blow for blow, Rāma knocked down the Rākṣasa king's flag. Next, Rāvaṇa shot Indra's horses, but when the celestial steeds did not even stagger, Rāvaṇa became frustrated. Rāvaṇa resorted to using his Rākṣasa powers of illusion to shoot forth clubs, discs, trees and mountain peaks.

Rāma counteracted all these weapons before they reached His chariot, causing them to fall upon the monkey army. Both Rāma and Rāvaṇa continued to dispatch thousands of arrows at each other, and as they collided in the sky, the shafts fell down onto the battlefield. In this way, the fighting continued for nearly one hour as Rāma matched Rāvaṇa blow for blow. As all created beings looked on, their minds were filled with wonder.

Both chariot drivers also displayed great skill, but then, as the chariots came side by side, Rāma forced Rāvaṇa's four horses to turn away by cutting them with four arrows. This increased Rāvaṇa's anger, and he repeatedly assailed Rāma with his arrows in retaliation. Rāma remained undisturbed. Thus, the exchange of weapons became so feverish that the fighting was unparalleled in the history of warfare.

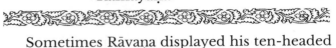

Sometimes Rāvaṇa displayed his ten-headed feature, and at others he appeared in his normal persona with only one head. Suddenly Rāma severed Rāvaṇa's head with an arrow. However, as the severed head fell to the ground, a duplicate miraculously appeared in its place. Rāma then severed that head, but another replaced it, too. Again and again, Rāma continued to sever Rāvaṇa's heads, until 100 of Rāvaṇa's heads had fallen on the battlefield. Each time a new head appeared in place of the old one, Rāma wondered, "With these arrows I previously killed Mārīca, Khara, and Viradha. I pierced seven mighty trees and slayed the invincible Vāli. These arrows have humbled great mountains and agitated the fathomless ocean. How is it that they are now ineffectual against Rāvaṇa?"

The duel thus continued at a fierce pace, both combatants obsessed with killing the other. Indeed, several days and nights passed without a gap in the fighting. Finally, when Mātali saw that Rāma was not gaining His desired victory, he inquired, "Why are You only fighting in a defensive manner? My Lord, are You not aware of Your limitless potencies? The hour of doom has now arrived for the king of the Rākṣasas. Why do You not employ the divine *brahmāstra*?"

Reminded of His ultimate weapon, Rāma took up the arrow that Agastya Ṛṣi had formerly given Him at the time of their meeting in the Daṇḍakāraṇya forest. Lord Brahmā had personally created this arrow for Indra's use, and later it was presented to Agastya. The feathers of the wonderful arrow were supplied by Garuḍa and presided over by Vāyu. The razor sharp head was created with the combined energy of the fire god, Agni, and the sun god, Sūrya. Mount Meru

and Mount Mandara contributed their gravity, becoming the arrow's weight, and its shaft was made from a subtle, ethereal element. The wonderful *brahmāstra* arrow was omnipotent and infallible, and its dazzling effulgence rivaled the sun's.

Empowering the arrow with the required mantras, Rāma placed the terrible *brahmāstra* upon His bowstring. While gazing upon the flaming arrow, the monkeys became filled with delight, while dread penetrated the hearts of the Rākṣasas. As Rāma pulled the bowstring back to His ear, the earth began to shudder and the heavens appeared to be thrown into confusion. At last, when Rāma released the *brahmāstra*, it sped through the air like death itself, striking violently the chest of the Rākṣasa king. Piercing through Rāvaṇa's heart like a thunderbolt, the fierce arrow then entered into the earth, taking Rāvaṇa's sinful life along with it. Then, as the wonderful *brahmāstra* reentered Rāma's quiver, Rāvaṇa dropped his bow from his hand. Vomiting blood from his ten mouths, he fell down dead upon the ground.

Upon seeing this, Rāvaṇa's followers raised a tumultuous sound, crying, "Alas! Alas! What has happened? What has happened?" With great transcendental ecstasy, the monkey warriors loudly proclaimed Rāma's victory and pursued the fleeing Rākṣasa army. From the sky the demigods shouted, "Well done! Excellent!" as they covered Rāma's chariot with showers of flowers and beat upon celestial drums. With Rāvaṇa dead, the *ṛṣis* and demigods felt blessed relief and peace of mind that they had not enjoyed for a very long time. A gentle, cool, fragrant breeze then began to blow, and the sun serenely spread its rays, so that happiness appeared to pervade all directions.

Sugrīva, Aṅgada, Vibhīṣaṇa and Lakṣmaṇa were the first to come and pay homage to Rāma. However, when Vibhīṣaṇa saw his elder brother lying dead on the battlefield, he broke down and cried in an outburst of grief.

Meanwhile, news of Rāvaṇa's death spread throughout the inner apartments of the royal palace. All of Rāvaṇa's wives came out of the city to the battlefield. Their hair disheveled and ornaments in disarray, the ladies approached the dead body of their husband, wailing loudly. Overcome with unbearable grief, some of the women rolled in the dust, while others embraced different parts of Rāvaṇa's body. Crying out, "O lord, O my husband!" one of the ladies hung around Rāvaṇa's neck while others clutched at his feet, rubbed his wounded chest, and threw their arms up in despair. Others fainted away, unable to bear the grief.

Amidst the sounds of loud wailing, they could be heard lamenting, "O, dear husband, by ignoring our good advice and that of Vibhīṣaṇa, you have brought about your own destruction. Now that you are dead, we too are vanquished, for the wife has no other support than the husband. This is the inevitable end, however, for such a cruel and hard-hearted person like you. Who else would have dared to kidnap Sītā and keep her against her will?"

Rāvaṇa's favorite queen, Mandodarī, then lamented, "O my lord, O master! You epitomized trouble for others, and therefore you were called Rāvaṇa. But now that you have been defeated, we also are defeated, for without you the state of Laṅkā has been conquered by the enemy. To whom will it go for shelter? My dear husband, although you were so powerful, you could not stand before Lord Rāma.

You were too confident of your acquired prowess. Thus, you became a great burden to the earth. You could not understand that Lord Viṣṇu Himself has descended upon the earth as Lord Rāma to relieve that burden. O Rāvaṇa, your sinful passion for Sītā has become the cause of destruction for all Rākṣasas.

"You always masqueraded as a great hero, yet you were proven to be a coward when you deceitfully kidnapped Sītā. You came under the influence of lusty desires, and therefore you could not understand the influence of mother Sītā. Now, because of her curse, you have been reduced to this state, having been killed by Lord Rāmacandra. O pleasure of the Rākṣasa dynasty, because of you the state of Laṅkā and also we ourselves now have no protector. By your deeds you have made your body fit to be eaten by vultures and your soul fit to go to hell. But even though your character was abominable, I do not see how I will go on living in your absence."

Finally, Mandodarī fainted with her head against Rāvaṇa's chest. Then her co-wives lifted her up and revived her to consciousness. Rāma then ordered Vibhīṣaṇa, "Begin the funeral rites for your brother without further delay. It will only be possible to comfort Rāvaṇa's widows after his body has been cremated."

Vibhīṣaṇa replied, "I do not wish to perform the funeral ceremonies for a man who kidnapped the wives of others, who was merciless and tyrannical, and who was inclined toward irreligion. Since he was my elder brother, it is my duty to respect Rāvaṇa, but at the same time his actions were those of an enemy, and thus he does not deserve my worship."

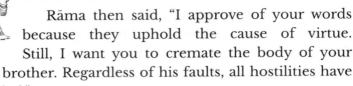

Rāma then said, "I approve of your words because they uphold the cause of virtue. Still, I want you to cremate the body of your brother. Regardless of his faults, all hostilities have now ended."

Vibhīṣaṇa then went to Laṅkā to make preparations for Rāvaṇa's funeral. After bringing his maternal grandfather, Mālyavān, Vibhīṣaṇa placed the body of Rāvaṇa upon the funeral carrier and proceeded with numerous other Rākṣasas carrying the firewood. Going toward the south, the party arrived at a consecrated place, where they cremated Rāvaṇa's body according to Vedic injunctions. Thereafter, Rāvaṇa's wives were consoled and everyone returned to Laṅkā.

Having given up His transcendental anger, Rāma assumed a gentle countenance and laid aside His bow, arrows and armor. With the fighting concluded, the demigods left from the sky overhead and went back to their abodes. While going, they chanted the glories of Lord Rāma with great satisfaction. Then, after receiving due honor from Rāma and permission to depart, Mātali ascended into the sky upon Indra's chariot and returned to the heavenly kingdom.

Returning to His military camp, Rāma ordered Lakṣmaṇa to perform the installation ceremony for Vibhīṣaṇa. In turn, Lakṣmaṇa gave golden vessels to the chief monkeys and ordered them to quickly fetch water from the four seas.

Lakṣmaṇa performed the installation ceremony strictly according to Vedic injunctions. All of Laṅkā's citizens came to the sacrificial arena with presentations of auspicious articles. After receiving these gifts, Vibhīṣaṇa offered them

to Rāma. Rāma then told Hanumān, "Please go and find out how Sītā is. Inform her that I have killed Rāvaṇa and return here with any message she may have for Me."

Hanumān then went to the *aśoka* grove and found the grief-stricken Sītā, still surrounded by hideous Rākṣasīs. Standing meekly before her, Hanumān said, "Your husband has sent me here to give you the following message: 'After many sleepless months I have fulfilled My vow to rescue you. Now that your oppressor, the king of the Rākṣasas is dead, you may give up your anxiety.'"

Hearing the news of Rāvaṇa's death and Rāma's well being, Sītā became so overwhelmed with joy that she could not speak for some time. When Hanumān asked her why she did not make any reply, Sītā said, "I can hardly speak because I am so elated. O Hanumān, what you have told me is unlimitedly more valuable than any amount of gold or jewels."

With folded hands, Hanumān suggested, "If you so desire, I can kill all of these hideous Rākṣasīs who have tortured you for so long. Indeed, I would take great pleasure in avenging all the suffering you have had to undergo. I simply wait for your permission."

The compassionate Sītā replied, "They are only foolish maidservants who were compelled to carry out the orders of their king. Whatever I have suffered was due to my own past misdeeds. These Rākṣasī women only acted as instruments in the hands of destiny. O Hanumān, perhaps you have heard this: 'A great man never takes into account the offenses that are committed against him by another person. Indeed, he vows at all costs not to return evil with evil.'

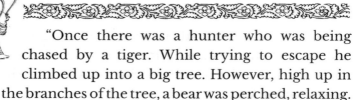

"Once there was a hunter who was being chased by a tiger. While trying to escape he climbed up into a big tree. However, high up in the branches of the tree, a bear was perched, relaxing. Upon seeing the bear, the tiger called to him, saying, 'This hunter is our common enemy. You should push him out of the tree so that I can eat him.' The bear, however, replied, 'Because this hunter has taken shelter of my home, I will not do anything to harm him. To do so would be unrighteous.' Saying this, the bear went to sleep. The tiger then said to the hunter, 'If you push the bear out of the tree so that I can eat him, I will promise not to harm you.'

Swayed by the tiger's words, the hunter pushed the sleeping bear. However, as he was falling, the bear grabbed another branch and saved himself. The tiger said to the bear, 'Since this hunter tried to kill you, you should retaliate by pushing him out of the tree.'

"But even though the tiger appealed to the bear like this repeatedly, the bear refused, saying, 'A great person never takes into account the sins of a person who has offended him. Instead, at all costs, he keeps his vow never to return evil for evil, knowing that good conduct is the ornament of virtuous persons.'"

Being thus admonished, Hanumān asked Sītā if she had a message to give Rāma. She replied, "My only words are this: I long to see my dear husband, who is known to be always very affectionate to His unalloyed devotees."

Hanumān said, "Be assured that you will see Rāma and Lakṣmaṇa this very day. Please allow me to leave so that I may deliver your message without delay."

Hanumān returned to Rāma and related Sītā's message. He urged Rāma to meet with Sītā, saying, "Because Sītā has suffered so much, always longing to see You, please go to the *aśoka* grove at once."

When Rāma heard this appeal, tears came to His eyes. Then, His eyes cast down, He ordered Vibhīṣaṇa, "Let Sītā be brought before Me after bathing, dressing and adorning herself with celestial ornaments."

Vibhīṣaṇa then went to the *aśoka* grove, and through the Rākṣasī, made his presence known to Sītā. Humbly approaching her, Vibhīṣaṇa said, "Rāma desires to see you. Please mount this palanquin I have brought. Rāma asks that you suitably prepare yourself by bathing, dressing, and adorning yourself with celestial ornaments."

Sītā then went to bathe, and after dressing herself nicely, she was placed upon the palanquin and brought before Rāma. When Vibhīṣaṇa first approached Rāma, he saw that the Lord's head was bent low, as if He were absorbed in thought. Vibhīṣaṇa then announced Sītā's arrival. Rāma requested she be brought before Him at once.

Out of natural curiosity, hordes of monkeys had come to catch a glimpse of Sītā. However, Vibhīṣaṇa and his assistants began pushing them back, and there arose a great commotion. Because of strong affection for His servitors, Rāma became annoyed by seeing this, and told Vibhīṣaṇa, "Do not harass these monkeys. There is nothing wrong if a chaste woman is seen in public during a time of adversity or war, at a *svayaṁvara*, at sacrifices or a wedding. Therefore, please allow the monkeys to see Sītā if they so desire."

Rāma then ordered, "Let Sītā come down from the palanquin and come before Me on foot." As Vibhīṣaṇa escorted Sītā, the monkey chiefs could understand that Rāma was in an angry mood. They were surprised not only that Rāma was upset, but He was making Sītā walk in public view, His manner stern and grave.

Sītā approached Rāma with great shyness, seeming to shrink into herself. Then, when Sītā saw the moon-like handsome face of her beloved husband, her miseries immediately disappeared, causing her natural shining effulgence to return. Sītā was exceedingly happy to see her beloved, and her lotuslike mouth showed her joy. But Rāma was in a different mood.

Rāma's heart was tormented by fear of a public scandal. Therefore, He addressed Sītā in an angry tone, "I have fulfilled My vow to win you back and thus avenge Rāvaṇa's insult to My honor. However, you should understand that My great endeavor to kill the Rākṣasa king was not really for your sake, but to vindicate My good name and the reputation of the Ikṣvāku dynasty. In truth, your appearance before Me is not at all pleasing. Thus, I now grant you leave to go wherever you desire. No cultured man will accept a wife who has been embraced by another, or who has dwelt in the house of someone else for so long. I am sure that no woman could have remained with Rāvaṇa for such a long time without being enjoyed by him. Rāvaṇa was obsessed by lust for you. How could he have controlled himself and refrained from ravishing you by force? By killing Rāvaṇa I have regained My honor. However, there is no need to have any more attachment for you. You are now free to do as you like. Fix your mind upon Lakṣmaṇa, Bharata or anyone else you choose."

As Sītā heard Rāma's speech, her hair stood on end and her head bent low in shame. Since before she had only heard loving words from her husband, Rāma's words entered her heart like sharp arrows. She began to weep bitterly. Since she was in the presence of innumerable witnesses, it was difficult for her to endure her husband's reproaches.

Then, wiping tears from her eyes, Sītā replied in a faltering voice, "How can You dare speak about me in such an irresponsible manner? Never for a moment have I given up my chastity, either by body, mind or words. My character is pure. You should not judge me as though I were an ordinary woman. Although I am called Jānakī, the daughter of King Janaka, my birth was transcendental, for I appeared from the earth itself.

"O Rāma, if it was Your plan all along to cruelly reject me in this way, why didn't You inform me when Hanumān came as Your messenger? If I knew that You did not intend to take me back, I would have immediately given up my life, thus avoiding many months of unbearable pain. Likewise, You could have avoided this ghastly war that has taken the lives of countless Rākṣasas and monkeys. What was the need of demanding so much service from Your allies? O Rāma, why are You acting like this? Does my pure devotion to You mean nothing?"

Sītā then addressed Lakṣmaṇa, saying, "Please build a large fire for me to enter. This is the only path that remains for one who has been rejected by her husband in public."

Suppressing His agitation, Lakṣmaṇa looked at Rāma, and saw that His elder brother approved of Sītā's words. Thus,

Lakṣmaṇa went to prepare the fire. Rāma appeared so stern and intense that no one dared to even speak to Him, what to speak of pacifying Him.

When the fire was built and blazed up brightly, Sītā circumambulated Rāma. Then, coming before the fire with folded hands, Sītā bowed to the *brāhmaṇas* and demigods. Next, Sītā aloud offered a prayer to Agni, "O god of fire, because my heart has never turned away from Rāma, please grant me protection. Although I have never been unfaithful to Rāma in thought, word or deed, He accuses me of being polluted. Therefore, O god of fire, seer of all within the three worlds, I request you to become the witness of my purity."

Saying this, Sītā circumambulated the fire. Then, as the huge crowd looked on in wonder, Sītā entered into the flames with a fearless mind. Within the blazing fire, Sītā, who was adorned with dazzling gold ornaments, shone with wonderful golden effulgence. As soon as Sītā entered the fire, all the women present screamed with horror, and a cry of anguish arose from the assembled monkeys and Rākṣasas.

In the midst of the great wailing, Rāma appeared to become thoughtful. Meanwhile, the chief demigods appeared before Him, riding upon their celestial vehicles. As Rāma stood before them with folded hands, the demigods, headed by Lord Brahmā and Lord Śiva, said, "O Supreme Personality of Godhead, Lord Rāmacandra, we are very pained to see how You are neglecting Your eternal consort, Mother Sītā. You are the creator of the universe and the Lord of all demigods. Why do You ignore Your divinity and reject Sītā as though You were a common man?"

Rāma then replied, "I consider Myself to be an ordinary human being, the son of Mahārāja Daśaratha. However, if there is something more to be said, then perhaps you, Lord Brahmā, can disclose it to Me."

Lord Brahmā said, "My dear Lord Rāma, You are directly Lord Nārāyaṇa Himself, and thus You are identical with all

the forms of Nārāyaṇa. You are a plenary expansion of Lord Śrī Kṛṣṇa, the original Supreme Personality of Godhead. You are the cause of all causes. You are the universal form and the support of the cosmic manifestation. All the demigods are Your parts and parcels and Your eternal servants. Moreover, Sītā is none other than Lakṣmī herself, the Supreme Goddess of Fortune. Both of you have appeared on the earth to destroy Rāvaṇa. Now that this mission has been accomplished, O Lord, You may return to Your transcendental abode in the spiritual sky after ruling over the earth for as long as You desire."

As soon as Lord Brahmā finished speaking, the fire-god, Agni, emerged from the flames with Sītā. As Agni presented Sītā before Rāma, everyone could see how her body, bright red dress, ornaments and hair showed no sign of being even slightly burned. In his capacity as a universal witness, Agni announced, "O Rāma, here is Your dear wife, Sītā. She is devoid of even the smallest tinge of sin. Sītā was never the slightest bit unfaithful to You by mind, word, or glance, what to speak of any action. Therefore, my dear Rāma, You must accept Sītā without reservation, giving up Your harsh words and demeanor."

Rāma was pleased to hear Agni's testimony, and as tears of joy fell from His eyes, He replied, "O Agni, it was necessary for Sītā to undergo this trial by fire, just to convince the masses of her spotless purity. If I had prevented her from entering the fire, people would have criticized Me for accepting her without first proving her chastity. They would have concluded that I was simply motivated by lust. In truth, I already knew of Sītā's chastity and that Rāvaṇa could never pollute her. She is always fully protected by the power of her righteousness. It

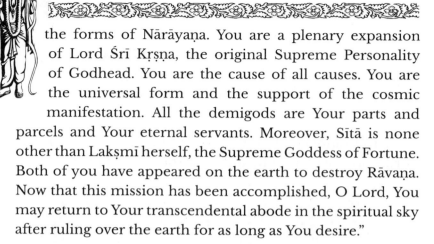

was only to prove Sītā's chastity to the world that I appeared to neglect her. Indeed, Sītā is non-different from Me, for she is directly My internal potency. Just as sunlight, being nondifferent from the sun, is inseparable from the sun, so too, there is no possibility of My being separated from Sītā.[8]

Rāma felt great transcendental bliss in being reunited with Sītā. His pastimes are all manifestations of His internal potency, enacted for the purpose of relishing spiritual exchanges.

Lord Śiva then embraced Rāma, saying, "My dear Lord, by slaying the incomparably powerful Rāvaṇa, You have performed a wonderful feat that will be glorified throughout the three worlds until the time of dissolution.

Pointing to the sky, Lord Śiva said, "O Rāma, see how Your father is waiting there, seated upon his celestial chariot. Having been delivered by Your mercy, he now resides on

8. Śrīla Prabhupāda explains and comments: "It was actually impossible for Rāvaṇa to take away Sītā. The form of Sītā taken by Rāvaṇa was an illusory representation of mother Sītā—*māyā-sītā*. When Sītā was tested in the fire, this *māyā-sītā* was burnt, and the real Sītā came out of the fire. A further understanding to be derived from this example is that a woman, however powerful she may be in the material world, must be given protection, for as soon as she is unprotected she will be exploited by Rākṣasas like Rāvaṇa. Before mother Sītā was married to Lord Rāmacandra she was protected by her father, and when she was married she was protected by her husband. Therefore the conclusion is that a woman should always be protected. According to the Vedic rule, there is no scope for a woman's being independent, for a woman cannot protect herself independently.

Indra's planet. Go quickly with Lakṣmaṇa and be reunited with Mahārāja Daśaratha, for he has come here just to see You."

Rāma and Lakṣmaṇa went and bowed down before Their father. Feeling extremely delighted, Mahārāja Daśaratha took Rāma upon his lap and said, "My residence in heaven does not give me any real pleasure. O Rāma, only now that I am able to see You do I feel happy. All along, Kaikeyī's words demanding Your exile remained imprinted upon my heart. Only now that Your period of banishment has come to an end do I feel somewhat relieved. However, I still yearn to see You return to Ayodhyā and be installed as emperor of the world after being reunited with Bharata. I can now understand that You are the Supreme Lord Viṣṇu Himself, and that You have descended upon the earth just to vanquish Rāvaṇa."

Rāma replied, "My dear father, I too feel greatly relieved that My exile has come to an end and My mission is accomplished. However, I have one request to make of you. Please withdraw your harsh words spoken at the time of My banishment, disowning Kaikeyī and Bharata."

Mahārāja Daśaratha readily consented, saying, "Let it be so." He then fondly embraced Lakṣmaṇa and declared, "My dear son, because of the dedicated service You have rendered to Rāma, I am eternally indebted to You. Please know that Your elder brother is directly the Supreme Personality of Godhead, appearing in human form for the welfare of the world. He is worshipable even by the greatest of demigods, what to speak of ourselves."

Mahārāja Daśaratha then told Sītā, "Please bear no grudge toward Rāma for having tested your purity. Know

that your remarkable behavior will earn you a place in history as the most glorious woman the world has ever seen."

Having thus spoken, Mahārāja Daśaratha mounted his celestial chariot and ascended towards heaven. As Rāma stood with folded hands, Indra said, "My audience can never go in vain. Thus, I wish for You to take a benediction from me."

Rāma was pleased to hear Indra's statement and thus requested, "O king of the celestials, please bring back to life all the monkey warriors who died in My service. Additionally, let all the trees in the places where these heroes dwell become full of fruits, even when out of season."

Indra replied, "Although this boon is very difficult even for me to grant, I shall happily do so."

Just then, all the monkeys who had died in the battle began to rise up from the ground, their wounds completely healed. It seemed to them as if they were awakening from a long sleep. However, when they saw Rāma and all the demigods before them, the monkeys could understand they had got back their lost lives, and thus felt supremely delighted.

Indra then departed, followed by the demigods, while Rāma and the monkeys spent the night in that place. The next morning, Vibhīṣaṇa came before Rāma with numerous maidservants, carrying paraphernalia for His bath. However, Rāma ordered, "My dear Vibhīṣaṇa, summon all the monkeys, headed by Sugrīva. Let them enjoy this royal luxury. As long as I am separated from Bharata, who is

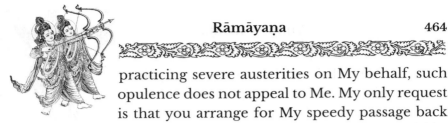

practicing severe austerities on My behalf, such opulence does not appeal to Me. My only request is that you arrange for My speedy passage back to Ayodhyā. Indeed, to travel there by foot would be an arduous journey."

Vibhīṣaṇa replied, "If You will ride in the Puṣpaka chariot, You can reach Ayodhyā this very day. However, I humbly request that Yourself, Sītā and Lakṣmaṇa remain here for some time with the army of monkeys so I may royally entertain everyone before Your departure."

Rāma said, "I certainly cannot refuse your hospitality. However, I am growing increasingly anxious to meet Bharata, Kauśalyā and My stepmothers. Therefore, I beg you to permit Me to depart without delay."

Vibhīṣaṇa went quickly and brought Rāma the Puṣpaka chariot. This wonderful chariot originally belonged to Kuvera before Rāvaṇa stole it from him. The chariot was constructed from gold by Viśvakarmā, with seats of gems. The wonderful spaceship could travel anywhere, following the mental indication of its driver. Thus, when Rāma and Lakṣmaṇa saw the chariot hovering before Them, awaiting Their command, They were quite astonished.

Before departing, Rāma requested Vibhīṣaṇa to present gifts of gold and jewels to all the monkey soldiers. Then Rāma mounted the Puṣpaka chariot with Sītā and Lakṣmaṇa. Addressing the assembly, Rāma said, "My dear monkey warriors, there is no way I can repay you for your heroic fighting on My behalf. Your unflinching devotional service will always serve as an inspiration for future devotees. Thus, your glories will forever shine brightly. Now please return

to Kiṣkindhyā and live there happily under Sugrīva's leadership. Vibhīṣaṇa, you should accept responsibility for ruling over Laṅkā immediately, since the citizens are now bereft of their king."

Then, standing before Rāma with folded hands, Sugrīva and Vibhīṣaṇa pleaded, "O Lord, please allow us to accompany You to Ayodhyā. After seeing the coronation ceremonies, we shall return home."

Rāma replied, "Nothing would please Me more than to return to Ayodhyā with all of My dear friends. Therefore, you and all the other monkey heroes can board the Puṣpaka chariot and we will embark immediately."

Finally, after all were comfortably seated, the Puṣpaka chariot rose majestically into the air. While all the monkeys and bears were enjoying the flight, Rāma pointed out the sights to Sītā: "Look there at the battlefield where all the heroic Rākṣasas lay dead, all killed for your sake. Look, there is where Rāvaṇa fell, there is the spot where Kumbhakarṇa was slain, there is where Indrajit was defeated, and there is where Prahasta died. Over there is the bridge called Nala-setu, by which we crossed the ocean to Laṅkā. There, on the far shore, is the place called Setubandha (Rāmeśvaram), where the bridge construction began. From this time onward, Setubandha will be a most sacred place, capable of washing away all of one's accumulated sinful reactions."

Then, as Rāma pointed to Kiṣkindhyā, Sītā said, "I would be pleased if I could return to Ayodhyā in the company of the wives of the monkey chiefs."

Happy to grant Sītā's request, the chariot halted as Rāma instructed Sugrīva and the other warriors to quickly bring their wives. When everyone was seated, their journey continued.

Rāma pointed out to Sītā, "There is Mount Ṛṣyamūka, where I met Sugrīva, and nearby you can see heavenly Lake Pampā, which abounds with bluish lotus flowers. There you can see the River Godāvarī, and on its banks is the *āśrama* of Agastya Ṛṣi. O Sītā, there is the spot where Rāvaṇa kidnapped you! There is Citrakūṭa, where Bharata came to meet Me. Over there is the River Yamunā, and there is the mighty Gaṅgā, where King Guha's capital lies on the river's banks."

In this way Rāma, Sītā and Lakṣmaṇa's entire forest life was displayed in reverse order as they retraced their way back to Ayodhyā. Finally, the river Sarayū came into view, and at last, the outskirts of Ayodhyā.

Before entering the city, however, Rāma stopped at the *āśrama* of Bharadvāja Ṛṣi to inquire about His relatives' welfare before meeting them. After happily welcoming Rāma, Bharadvāja replied to His inquiries, saying, "In Your absence, Bharata has been living a life of severe renunciation, wearing deerskin and tree bark and keeping matted hair. He has been ruling the kingdom as Your subordinate by keeping Your shoes on the royal throne. O Rāma, by dint of my mystic power, I know that You have removed the burden of the earth. Therefore, I would be pleased to award any benediction You desire."

Rāma happily replied, "Let all of the trees along the way to Ayodhyā become filled with fruits and flowers. Let streams of honey flow down from the trees, exuding the fragrance of nectar."

As soon as His words were spoken, the trees along the way to Ayodhyā immediately filled up with sumptuous fruit. Seeing this miraculous transformation, thousands of monkeys quickly jumped down from the Puṣpaka chariot and began feasting to their full satisfaction.

Rāma was always thinking of how He could reward the monkeys for their selfless service. Thus, it pleased Him to see them satisfied in this manner. Turning to Hanumān, Rāma said, "Please inform Guha of My arrival. Then go to Nandīgrāma and describe to Bharata all the events

concerning Sītā's abduction and her subsequent recovery. Watch carefully the expression on Bharata's face when He hears of My arrival. Then, report back to Me before we depart from this *āśrama.* If Bharata wishes to rule the kingdom Himself, whether due to attachment for position, power, or royal luxury, or even from Kaikeyī's urging, I will be happy to allow Him to do so."

Hanumān took a human form and departed, traveling through the air. He first informed Guha that Rāma would come to meet him after spending the night at Bharadvāja's *āśrama.*

Upon his arrival at Nandīgrāma, Hanumān saw Bharata, dressed in tree-bark and wearing matted hair. Bharata was living in a small cottage, subsisting only on fruits and roots, and He appeared to be very miserable and emaciated.

Hanumān then approached Bharata, announcing, "I have come as a messenger from Rāma. He inquires about Your welfare, and wishes to inform You that He will soon return to Ayodhyā."

When He heard these glorious words, Bharata's face immediately lit up with great delight. Then, becoming exhilarated with transcendental emotion, He fainted to the ground. Upon coming to His senses, Bharata stood up and embraced Hanumān with great satisfaction. Then, while bathing Hanumān with torrents of tears, Bharata said, "Because you have brought Me this good news, I shall immediately reward you with 100,000 cows, 100 villages and sixteen virgin girls to marry. Now, please sit down and tell Me everything that happened during Rāma's exile."

Once Hanumān had finished telling Bharata everything of Rāma's exile, up to the point of His imminent return, Bharata exclaimed, "My long cherished wish has finally been fulfilled!"

Bharata then ordered Śatrughna to make all arrangements for Rāma's reception. Thus, Sumantra and the other ministers soon arrived at Nandīgrāma, riding elephants. Kauśalyā, Sumitrā and Kaikeyī then arrived on palanquins, while engineers hurriedly constructed a new road connecting Nandīgrāma with Ayodhyā.

After all arrangements had been made, Bharata picked up Rāma's sandals, a white royal umbrella and *cāmaras*. Then, accompanied by many *brāhmaṇas*, He left His cottage amidst the blowing of conchshells and the beating of drums.

The news of Rāma's arrival had spread instantly, and almost the entire population of Ayodhyā came to Nandīgrāma hoping to see Him. Bharata was accompanied by ministers, priests and other respectable citizens, by professional musicians vibrating pleasing musical sounds, and by learned *brāhmaṇas* loudly chanting Vedic hymns. Following in the procession were chariots drawn by beautiful horses with harnesses of golden rope. These chariots were decorated by flags with golden embroidery and by other flags of various sizes and patterns. There were soldiers bedecked with golden armor, servants bearing betel nut, and many well-known and beautiful society girls. Many servants followed on foot, bearing an umbrella, whisks, different grades of precious jewels, and other paraphernalia befitting a royal reception.

However, when after some time there was no sign of Rāma, Bharata anxiously said to Hanumān, "I pray you were

not exhibiting your frivolous monkey nature by joking with me."

Hanumān then pointed to the distance where clouds of dust were being raised by the approaching monkeys. Just then, a far off roaring came to be heard. When Hanumān suddenly sighted the Puṣpaka chariot in the distance, he shouted, "Here comes Śrī Rāma!"

A loud, spontaneous cheer suddenly arose from the crowd as they too sighted the Puṣpaka chariot, which appeared to be just like the full moon rising in the sky. Everyone respectfully got down from their chariots, elephants and horses, as Bharata began worshipping Rāma from a distance.

With folded hands, Bharata recited prayers in glorification of Lord Rāma, and He offered water and other paraphernalia in worship. Finally, when Bharata could clearly see Rāma glowing magnificently at the front of the Puṣpaka chariot, He bowed down with great reverence.

As the celestial airship landed, Bharata rushed forward and climbed onto the chariot to greet His older brother. Rāma immediately got up from His seat to embrace Bharata, taking him on His lap. Bharata, His heart softened in ecstasy and His eyes full of tears, approached Lord Rāmacandra and fell at His lotus feet with great ecstatic love.

Lord Rāmacandra saw that Bharata was much emaciated and heard that in His absence His brother was eating only barley cooked in the urine of a cow, covering His body with the bark of trees, wearing matted locks of hair, and lying on a mattress of *kuśa*. The most merciful Lord Rāma very much lamented this. Afterwards, Bharata greeted Lakṣmaṇa and Sītā, showering them with praise. He then greeted Sugrīva

by embracing him, saying, "Although We are four, you are now just like Our fifth brother."

Meanwhile, Rāma approached His mother, Kauśalyā, and lovingly clasped her feet. Then, one after another, Rāma greeted Sumitrā, Kaikeyī, and Vasiṣṭha while all the citizens came forward with folded hands to welcome Him. Accompanied by Sītā and Lakṣmaṇa, Lord Rāmacandra then offered His respectful obeisances unto the learned *brāhmaṇas* and the elderly persons in the family, and all the citizens of Ayodhyā offered their respectful obeisances unto the Lord. The citizens of Ayodhyā, upon seeing their King return after a long absence, offered Him flower garlands, waved their upper cloths, and danced in great jubilation.

Thereafter, Bharata came before Rāma, with Rāma's wooden shoes in hand. While carefully placing the slippers upon Rāma's lotus feet, Bharata said, "Here is the kingdom I have overseen in Your absence. By Your mercy, Ayodhyā is flourishing, and the treasury, storehouses and army have all increased tenfold. My duty is now over, and I hereby relinquish everything unto You." After offering the wooden shoes before Lord Rāmacandra, Lord Bharata stood with folded hands, His eyes full of tears, and Lord Rāmacandra bathed Bharata with tears while embracing Him with both arms for a long time.

After this, Rāma ordered the Puṣpaka chariot to return to its rightful owner, the god of wealth, Kuvera. Thus, the celestial vehicle ascended into the sky, heading toward the north. Then, as Rāma sat at the feet of His spiritual master, Vasiṣṭha, Bharata came before Him and requested, "My dear

elder brother, please install Yourself upon the royal throne without further delay, and resume a life of royal luxury."

Lord Rāmacandra then entered Ayodhyā in the midst of a great festival. He was greeted on the road by the princely order, who showered His body with beautiful, fragrant flowers, while great personalities like Lord Brahmā and other demigods glorified the activities of the Lord in great jubilation.

The family priest, Vasiṣṭha, had Lord Rāmacandra cleanly shaved, freeing Him from His matted locks of hair. After bathing, Rāma at last again dressed in royal style, and was decorated with a garland and ornaments. The three mothers similarly adorned Sītā, and the wives of the monkeys were similarly dressed and ornamented.

Next, at Śatrughna's command, Sumantra came before Rāma with a lavishly decorated chariot. Rāma graciously mounted it and Bharata took up the reins while Śatrughna held the royal white umbrella. On either side of Rāma stood Lakṣmaṇa and Vibhīṣaṇa, waving a fan and *cāmara*, while from the sky, the demigods and celestial *ṛṣis* glorified Rāma with carefully chosen words.

As Rāma proceeded toward Ayodhyā, a huge procession followed Him, as all the monkeys, appearing in human form, rode elephants. Thereafter, when Rāma entered His capital, He saw how all the citizens had come out of their houses, lining the streets to welcome Him. Men and women, children and the elderly gazed upon Rāma as though they were getting back their lost lives. While waving their cloths and jumping with excitement, the people shouted, "Our

beloved prince has returned! All glories to Lord Rāma, the maintainer of His devotees!"

Amid the playing of musicians and the chanting of Vedic hymns, Rāma glanced lovingly over His subjects. Rāma greeted His ministers and described to them His political alliances with the monkeys and Vibhīṣaṇa. Thus He came to His father's palace.

Rāma ordered that His own palace be given for Sugrīva's use. Bharata then took the monkey king by the hand and led him there. At Bharata's request, Jāmbavān, Hanumān, Gavaya and Ṛṣabha brought water from the four seas, while five hundred powerful monkeys brought water from five hundred sacred rivers. The vessels of water were then placed before Vasiṣṭha, and thereafter, the *ṛṣi* seated Rāma and Sītā upon a throne made of valuable jewels.

Assisted by Vāmadeva, Jābāli, Kaśyapa, Katyāyana, Suyajña, Gautama and Vijaya Ṛṣis, Vasiṣṭha performed the bathing ceremony, with the first ablutions performed by the *brāhmaṇas*. Next Rāma was bathed by a virgin girl, followed by His minister, the leading warriors, and *vaiśyas*, one after another. After the final bathing, Vasiṣṭha ordered the four Lokapālas and other chief demigods witnessing the coronation from the sky to sprinkle Rāma with herbs.

Then, as Rāma sat upon a golden throne bedecked with valuable gems, Vasiṣṭha placed the royal crown upon His head and decorated His body with golden ornaments. The crown, formerly worn by all the kings in the Ikṣvāku dynasty, was made by Lord Brahmā especially for the coronation of Vaivasvata Manu. At Indra's prompting, Vāyu placed a garland made from 100 golden lotus flowers around Rāma's neck, and presented Him with a celestial necklace of pearls

and gems. Śatrughna held the royal umbrella over Rāma's head, as Sugrīva and Vibhīṣaṇa fanned Him from both sides.

Thereafter, as Gandharvas sang and Apsarās danced in ecstasy, Rāma gave in charity 100,000 cows, 300 million gold coins and all varieties of precious jewels to the *brāhmaṇas*. Rāma presented Sugrīva with a celestial necklace and gave Aṅgada a pair of bracelets adorned with diamonds and precious stones. Rāma presented Sītā a necklace previously given to Him by Vāyu, along with many lavishly decorated dresses.

Sītā desired to present Hanumān with a gift, as a token of her appreciation for all he had done for her. With this in mind, she unclasped the necklace Rāma had given her and looked toward Rāma questioningly. Understanding her intention, Rāma requested Sītā to present the necklace to Hanumān. Thus she happily placed it around his neck.

Thereafter, all the monkey chiefs were given valuable clothing and ornaments. In this way, Rāma's coronation came to a successful conclusion. Completely satisfied at heart, the monkeys returned to their respective kingdoms, while Vibhīṣaṇa returned to Laṅkā. When everyone had taken their leave, Rāma said to Lakṣmaṇa, "My dear brother, now that I have been installed upon the throne, I wish to install You as My heir apparent."

Despite being urged repeatedly in this way, Lakṣmaṇa remained silent, for He refused to accept the proposal. Rāma could well understand the mind of Lakṣmaṇa. Thus, He finally conferred the honor upon Bharata.

Rāma ruled the earth from His capital, Ayodhyā, for 11,000 years. During that time He performed many sacrifices, including 100 horse sacrifices. During the reign of Lord Rāma, the forests, the rivers, the hills and mountains, the states, the seven islands and the seven seas were all favorable in supplying the necessities of life for all living beings. All bodily and mental suffering, disease, old age, bereavement, lamentation, distress, fear and fatigue were completely absent. There were no widows to lament the loss of their husbands; nor were there diseases or thieves. Indeed, even wild animals gave up their natural enmity, and thus did not kill one another. All the citizens were fully righteous, always looking toward Rāma as their lord and master. Beyond that, they saw Rāma as their life and soul. Everyone lived for thousands of years and had thousands of sons. There was even no death for those who did not want it. All talk centered around Rāma alone. Thus, the entire earth appeared as if transformed into the kingdom of God, Vaikuṇṭha.

Lava and Kuśa then concluded their narration: "Anyone who listens daily to this wonderful story, known as the *Rāmāyaṇa,* will become free from all sinful reactions. This sacred narration grants prowess, longevity and victory to those who subdue their passions and hear it with faith. The reader of this *Rāmāyaṇa,* if a woman, will receive sons; if a king, will conquer the earth; if a traveler, will reach his destination; and if a sinful person, will be purified."

Uttara-kāṇḍa

Soon after Rāma's coronation, all the great *ṛṣis* came to Ayodhyā to personally worship Him and glorify His wonderful transcendental pastimes. The *sapta-ṛṣis*—Vasiṣṭha, Kaśyapa, Atri, Viśvāmitra, Gautama, Jamadagni and Bharadvāja—arrived at the royal palace, as did Kauśika, Kaṇva, Agastya and Dhaumya. When the gatekeeper informed Him that these exalted *ṛṣis* had arrived, Rāma had them escorted into the royal court and stood with folded hands to greet them. Rāma arranged comfortable seats for the sages and then offered them ceremonial worship and innumerable cows in charity.

When the *ṛṣis* were seated at ease, Rāma respectfully inquired of their welfare. The *ṛṣis* said, "O Rāma, You have certainly satisfied us by descending on earth to exhibit Your magnanimous pastimes. Now that Rāvaṇa is dead, we feel relief and happiness, for he was a great impediment to the progressive welfare of the world. Indeed, not only Rāvaṇa, but also many others, such as Khara, Mārīca, Kumbhakarṇa, Atikāya, Nikumbha and Kumbha, were terrorizing all living beings. Thus, we are very grateful to You for destroying them. We are especially thankful that Indrajit is dead. There was no one comparable to Indrajit, even among the demigods, demons and Rākṣasas. Except for Yourself and Lakṣmaṇa, he could not be slain by anyone within the three worlds."

Interrupting the sages, Rāma curiously inquired, "O best of the *ṛṣis*, why do you praise Indrajit even more than Kumbhakarṇa or Rāvaṇa? How is it that he became more

powerful than his father and was able to defeat Indra, the king of heaven?"

On behalf of the sages, Agastya replied by narrating the following history: "Long ago, in the Satya-yuga, there lived a great *brahmārṣi* named Pulastya, who was a son of Lord Brahmā. Once upon a time, Pulastya went to the *āśrama* of the great sage Trinabindu on the slopes of Mount Meru to perform severe austerities. Because of the scenic beauty of this celestial place, the Apsarās frequently came there. Thus, along with Trinabindu's daughter, they would play, sing and accompany themselves with musical instruments.

"It so happened that one day, while enjoying themselves in this way, the Apsarās unintentionally disrupted Pulastya's meditation. Becoming highly angered, the *ṛṣi* cursed the girls, saying, 'Whoever I see coming nearby again will become pregnant, simply by my glance!'

"The Apsarās fearfully ran away, never daring to return to that place. The daughter of Trinabindu, however, was not present that day, and was unaware of the *ṛṣi's* curse. Thus, the next day when she went to play with her friends in the usual manner, she came within sight of Pulastya. Consequently, she soon found that she was pregnant, although without any apparent cause, and became extremely pale with fear. Returning home, she stood before her father, hanging her head in shame.

"Trinabindu was quite surprised to see how his daughter's body had become transformed, and he anxiously inquired, 'How has this happened, my child?'

"The girl replied, 'I wandered near the *āśrama* of Pulastya in search of my friends, when suddenly I found myself to be pregnant. I do not know why.'

"Trinabindu then entered a trance of meditation, and by dint of his mystic vision, he was able to perceive how Pulastya's curse was the cause of his daughter's pregnancy. Trinabindu then took his daughter to Pulastya and requested him to accept her as his wife. Since he was already inclined to have her, Pulastya agreed. Thus, from that time onward,

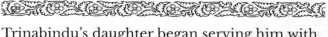

Trinabindu's daughter began serving him with great love and devotion.

"Later, after becoming pleased with his wife's service, Pulastya said, 'I shall now give you a son who will be my equal, insuring that my hereditary line will continue. Because you always listen to the Vedas while I am engaged in reciting them, your son's name will be Viśravā.'

"Soon Pulastya's wife gave birth to a son, and because the boy was pure and detached, he spent his time engaged in austerities. In consideration of Viśravā's exalted qualities, the great sage Bharadvāja later gave his daughter, Iḍaviḍā, to him in marriage. Then, after some time, Viśravā desired to beget a son who would promote the spiritual welfare of the masses of people. Thereafter, an exalted son was born to Iḍaviḍā. This child was given the name Vaiśravana by the sages, who understood that in the future he would take the post of Kuvera, the lord of wealth.

"When he grew up, Vaiśravana began performing austerities, maintaining his body with only water. Gradually, Vaiśravana reduced his intake to only air, and finally, he even stopped breathing. In this way, 1,000 years passed quickly, seeming like a single year.

"Lord Brahmā became pleased with Vaiśravana's austerities, and appeared before him, accompanied by all the demigods. When offered a benediction, Vaiśravana expressed his desire to become a Lokapāla. Lord Brahmā then replied, 'Indeed, I was already prepared to appoint a fourth Lokapāla. I therefore grant your wish. You may assume the post of Kuvera, the lord of wealth, thus becoming equal in

greatness to the other three Lokapālas, namely, Yamarāja, Indra and Varuṇa. Additionally, I shall award you a celestial vehicle befitting your exalted position. Here is the Puṣpaka chariot.'

"Lord Brahmā departed, and because the universal grandsire had not designated a place of residence for him, Vaiśravana went to his father, Viśravā. Viśravā said, "My dear son, you may reside at the city of Laṅkā, located on the Trikūṭa mountain. Viśvakarmā built this place for the habitation of Rākṣasas. However, Laṅkā is now vacant, since the Rākṣasas long ago fled in fear of Lord Viṣṇu and have taken up their residence in Rasātala.

"Following his father's order, Vaiśravana took up residence at Laṅkā. In due course, because of his good rule, that place came to flourish and was filled with citizens known as the Nairṛtas. Now and then, Vaiśravana would mount his chariot and visit his parents."

Rāma sat listening to Agastya's discourse with great pleasure. However, He again politely interrupted, saying, "While I am anxious to hear the continuation of this story, I am curious to understand some points. Under what circumstances had the Rākṣasas previously come to inhabit Laṅkā? I have heard that the Rākṣasas were originally born from the eyebrows of Pulastya. However, it now appears that their origin must be different. Who is the actual ancestor of the original Rākṣasas? How powerful were they in comparison to Rāvaṇa? Why were they driven away from Laṅkā by Lord Viṣṇu and made to reside below the earth?"

Agastya continued his narration in sweet words. "In the beginning of the cosmic manifestation, Lord Brahmā

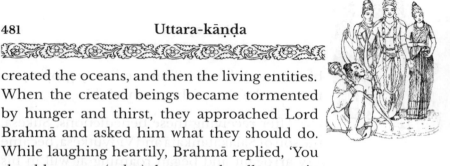

created the oceans, and then the living entities. When the created beings became tormented by hunger and thirst, they approached Lord Brahmā and asked him what they should do. While laughing heartily, Brahmā replied, 'You should protect (*rakṣa*) the ocean by all means.'

"Some of the created beings responded by saying, 'We shall protect' (*rakṣa*) while others said, 'We shall eat' (*yakṣa*). Lord Brahmā then proclaimed that the former group would be known as the Rākṣasas, and the latter as Yakṣas.

"There were two leaders of the Rākṣasas, named Heti and Praheti. Praheti was naturally inclined toward virtue. Thus he retired to the forest to perform austerities. Heti wanted to marry, and on his own initiative, married Bhaya, Yama's sister. Also being the sister of Kāla, Bhaya was a most fearsome personality. Through her, Heti begot a son named Vidyutkeśa. When Vidyutkeśa grew up, Heti arranged his marriage to the daughter of Sandhyā, named Salakatankatā. Later on, Salakatankatā gave birth to a son on the slopes of Mount Mandara, but since she had only desired to enjoy sex with her husband and not to bear a child, she abandoned the baby after delivery.

"When the neglected child began to cry, he was seen by Lord Śiva, who happened to be passing on his bull-carrier along with his wife, Pārvatī. At the request of the compassionate Umā, Lord Śiva made the child immediately grow up, and benedicted him with immortality. Then, to further please his wife, Lord Śiva gave the child a flying city. Pārvatī also awarded a benediction to the entire Rākṣasa race, saying, 'Henceforth, the women of your dynasty will deliver their babies at the time of conception. And upon

birth, the children will immediately grow up to become the size of the mother.'

"After receiving these benedictions, Sukeśa, the son of Salakatankatā and Vidyutkeśa, became very arrogant and began roaming at will in his airplane. Considering Sukeśa's opulence, the Gandharva named Grāmani gave his beautiful daughter, Devāvatī, to him in marriage. Thereafter, Sukeśa begot three sons by Devāvatī: Mālyavān, Sumāli, and Māli. Knowing that their father had become powerful by obtaining benedictions, the three sons went to Mount Meru, determined to gain success by the performance of severe austerities.

"The severe penances of the three sons of Sukeśa became fearful for all living entities. Lord Brahmā appeared before the three brothers to fulfill their desires and make them desist from their austerities. Thus, when Lord Brahmā offered them benedictions, the brothers replied, 'O lord, may we become long-lived, and become so powerful that we will strike terror into the hearts of our enemies. Give us the ability to become invisible at will, and let us three always have love for each other.'

"Lord Brahmā gave his consent and departed. Due to their benedictions, Mālyavān, Sumāli and Māli became so fearless that they began to harass the demigods and demons alike. Enlivened by their leaders' prowess, the Rākṣasas approached Viśvakarmā in a group, requesting him to build them a place equal to the demigods. Viśvakarmā informed the Rākṣasas of Laṅkā, surrounded by golden walls, which he had previously constructed under the order of Indra. Then, at Viśvakarmā's urging, the Rākṣasas took up residence there.

"Soon thereafter, the Gandharva woman, Narmadā, gave her three daughters in marriage to Mālyavān, Sumāli and Māli. Through his wife, Mālyavān begot many children, including Virūpākṣa and Durmukha. The wife of Sumāli gave birth to Prahasta, Akampana, Dhumrakṣa, Supārśva and Prahasa. Through his wife, Māli begot Anala, Anila, Hara and Sampāti, who became Vibhīṣaṇa's four ministers. All these offspring became proud like their fathers, and began to harass the demigods.

"Finally, the demigods and *ṛṣis* went to Lord Śiva and complained that the descendants of Sukeśa were practically driving them out of heaven. When the demigods and *ṛṣis* requested Lord Śiva to kill the three Rākṣasas, however, he replied, 'Due to Lord Brahmā's benedictions, the sons of Sukeśa are immune to death at my hands. Therefore, I suggest you approach Lord Viṣṇu, the Supreme Infallible Person.'

"Thereafter, the demigods and *ṛṣis* went to see Lord Viṣṇu, the master of everyone and the Supreme Personality of Godhead. After offering their obeisances, the demigods prayed, 'My dear Lord, we are Your eternal servants and You are our eternal master. Because we desire the welfare of all living entities, we are busily engaged in the management of universal affairs. O Lord, You are our only shelter. Thus, we have come to inform You of our plight. The sons of Sukeśa named Mālyavān, Sumāli and Māli have become invincible by the benedictions of Lord Brahmā and are harassing us greatly. Even Lord Śiva has refused to fight them. Thus, we are now forced to approach Your lotus feet for protection.'

"Lord Viṣṇu replied, 'My dear demigods and great *ṛṣis*, do not fear. I know about Sukeśa's sons. Because they have

proudly overstepped the bounds of propriety, I have already decided to kill them.'

"Being thus restored to confidence, the demigods again offered prayers of glorification and departed for their respective abodes. Soon thereafter, Mālyavān came to learn of Lord Viṣṇu's assurance to the demigods that He would kill him and his brothers. Mālyavān went to consult with Sumāli and Māli. Mālyavān said, 'Since Lord Viṣṇu has already killed Hiraṇyakaśipu, Kālanemi and many other powerful demons, He must be exceedingly difficult to conquer.'

"Sumāli and Māli replied, 'There is no need for us to fear anyone, even Lord Viṣṇu. Indeed, Lord Viṣṇu has no personal enmity with us. He has simply been poisoned by the words of the demigods. Therefore, let us kill the demigods in retaliation, for they are our real enemies.'

"Coming to this conclusion, all the Rākṣasas left Laṅkā to fight with the demigods. While they were en route to heaven, however, many evil omens manifested, indicating the imminent destruction of the Rākṣasas. When Lord Viṣṇu heard that Mālyavān was leading an attack on the demigods, He quickly took up His Śārṅga bow and other weapons, and mounted the back of His carrier, Garuḍa.

"As the Lord approached, part of the Rākṣasa army was blown away by the fierce wind generated by Garuḍa's flapping wings. Regardless, thousands of other Rākṣasas took courage and surrounded Lord Viṣṇu, attacking Him with innumerable weapons. With His Śārṅga bow, the Lord soon dispersed the enemy soldiers by releasing showers of arrows that issued forth at the speed of mind.

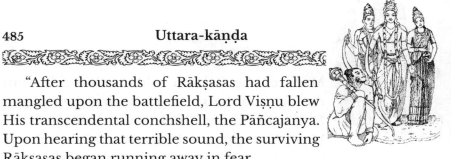

"After thousands of Rākṣasas had fallen mangled upon the battlefield, Lord Viṣṇu blew His transcendental conchshell, the Pāñcajanya. Upon hearing that terrible sound, the surviving Rākṣasas began running away in fear.

"Sumāli then angrily rushed forward, and with a shower of arrows appeared to check Lord Viṣṇu. This caused the Rākṣasas behind him to become enlivened, and they rallied again. Elated at his success, Sumāli roared with delight. Just then, however, Lord Viṣṇu cut off the head of Sumāli's charioteer, making the horses carry him wildly away from the battlefield. Māli then rushed forward, piercing the Lord with thousands of arrows. However, without being the least bit pained, Lord Viṣṇu responded with His own volley of arrows, forcing Māli to retreat from the battlefield. While driving Māli off, Lord Viṣṇu cut down his flag, broke his bow and killed his horses, depriving him of his chariot. Māli then grabbed his club and jumped to the ground. He rushed forward and violently struck Garuḍa on the forehead. Feeling acute pain, Garuḍa turned away from the blow. Thus, Lord Viṣṇu was also forced to turn His back upon the enemy.

"Upon witnessing Māli's wonderful feat, the Rākṣasa warriors roared with delight. However, hearing the Rākṣasa's jubilant reaction, Lord Viṣṇu became enraged. Thus, even though facing backwards, He released His Sudarśana *cakra*. The blazing disk then swiftly severed Māli's head. Upon seeing the death of their brother, Sumāli and Mālyavān became overwhelmed with grief and turned back toward Laṅkā.

"Thereafter, as the demigods came to congratulate Lord Viṣṇu in great happiness, Garuḍa recovered and began dispersing the remaining Rākṣasas by flapping his wings.

Many of the Rākṣasa soldiers thus fell from the sky into the sea. Upon seeing their plight, Mālyavān turned back and challenged, 'O Viṣṇu, You appear to be ignorant of the rules of combat, for You are attacking those who have given up their intent to fight. Please stay on the battlefield a while longer so I may punish You for Your wicked behavior.'

"Lord Nārāyaṇa replied, 'Your accusation is unjust. I am merely making good My promise to give protection to the demigods—and I shall keep My promise at all costs.'

"At this, Mālyavān hurled a great spear. However, when it pierced His chest, Lord Viṣṇu merely pulled it out and threw it back at the Rākṣasa. When the spear hit Mālyavān's chest, it shattered the Rākṣasa's armor, making him faint on his chariot. Mālyavān, however, soon recovered, and quickly hurled a club that hit the Lord's chest. Then, coming very close by, Mālyavān struck Lord Viṣṇu on the chest with his mighty fist, and began beating Garuḍa. The enraged Garuḍa then quickly drove Mālyavān away with a blast of air from his wings.

"Seeing his brother's plight, Sumāli fled back toward Laṅkā, with the ashamed Mālyavān following. Thereafter, because of their fear of Lord Viṣṇu, the Rākṣasas gave up their residence at Laṅkā and entered the nether regions."

Agastya continued, "Mālyavān, Sumāli and Māli were more powerful than Rāvaṇa and the other Rākṣasas that were killed by You. However, since the Rākṣasas You faced in battle were all descendants of Pulastya, they were incomparably strong. Therefore, my dear Rāma, it can only be concluded that You are none other than Lord Nārāyaṇa

Himself, for no one else could have killed these Rākṣasas."

Agastya continued, "While Sumāli wandered throughout the netherworld in fear of Lord Viṣṇu, Vaiśravana took up his residence at Laṅkā under his father's order. Some time later, Sumāli took his beautiful daughter with him and left the lower regions to wander the earth in search of a suitable husband for her. It so happened that one day Sumāli saw Vaiśravana flying overhead in his Puṣpaka chariot. Sumāli was struck with wonder upon seeing the celestial vehicle. Soon he returned to the nether regions to ponder the fate of the Rākṣasa race's welfare. Then, coming to a firm decision, Sumāli called for his daughter Kaikasī, and requested her to accept Viśravā as her husband.

"Thereafter, Kaikasī obediently went to Viśravā's residence and stood shyly before him, her head bent downward as she scratched the ground with her toes. It happened that Viśravā was in the midst of performing a horse sacrifice, and Kaikasī did not realize that she had approached at an inauspicious time. Still, the magnanimous sage inquired, 'My dear young girl, who are you? What is your purpose in coming here?'

"Kaikasī replied, 'I am the daughter of Sumāli and my name is Kaikasī. Whatever else you may wish to know, I request that you ascertain by your spiritual prowess.'

"Viśravā then entered a trance of meditation, and after reading Kaikasī's mind, he said, 'I can understand that you desire to receive sons from me. Your wish my be granted, but because you have approached me at an inauspicious time, your sons will become fierce Rākṣasas.'

"Kaikasī replied, 'I do not wish to have such sons from you. Therefore, please be merciful unto me.'

"Viśravā then granted, 'As a concession, your youngest son will come to be famous as a pious man.'

"In due course of time, Kaikasī gave birth to a hideous child with ten heads and twenty arms, a huge mouth and long teeth. At the time of his birth, the earth trembled, meteors fell from the sky, and fierce winds blew, bringing terror to the hearts of all living beings. Because of his ten heads, Viśravā named the child Daśagrīva. Then, after some time, Kumbhakarṇa was born. This child possessed the largest body on earth. After Kumbhakarṇa came a daughter named Śūrpaṇakhā, who had a very ugly face. The last child was Vibhīṣaṇa. When this noble son was born, the demigods uttered exclamations of joy and showered down flowers from heaven.

"Thereafter, Kumbhakarṇa wandered all over the universe devouring *ṛṣis*, while Vibhīṣaṇa engaged himself in studying the Vedas. Then, one day, Kuvera came to see his father, while riding in the Puṣpaka chariot. When Kaikasī saw Vaiśravaṇa, she urged her own son, Daśagrīva, to become as powerful and glorious as his half-brother. Hearing these words from his mother, Daśagrīva became envious of Kuvera, vowing to become greater than him in all respects. Then, with his mind fixed on performing severe austerities, Daśagrīva set out for the holy site of Gokarṇa, along with his younger brothers.

"Daśagrīva began executing unprecedented austerities. Because of this, Lord Brahmā became very pleased with him and his brothers."

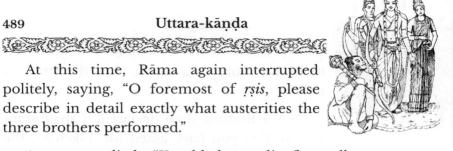

At this time, Rāma again interrupted politely, saying, "O foremost of *ṛṣis,* please describe in detail exactly what austerities the three brothers performed."

Agastya replied, "Kumbhakarṇa lit fires all around him during the heat of summer, while in the winter he remained submerged in cold water. In this way he passed 10,000 years without wavering from his determination. Vibhīṣaṇa stood on one leg for 5,000 years, and for another 5,000 years he kept his arms above his head while worshipping the sun god. Daśagrīva went without food for the entire 10,000 years, and at the end of each 1,000-year period, gave one of his heads as an offering into the sacrificial fire. Indeed, it was just when Daśagrīva was about to offer his last head in sacrifice that Lord Brahmā appeared to reward him for his austerities.

"When he saw Lord Brahmā standing before him, Daśagrīva bowed down with great respect. Then, when Lord Brahmā urged him to accept a benediction, Daśagrīva replied in a voice choked with joy, 'O my lord, I only have one fear, and that is death. Therefore, please fulfill my desire by granting me the boon of immortality.'

"However, Lord Brahmā replied, 'It is not possible for anyone within the material creation to have absolute immortality. Even I shall one day have to die. Thus, I request you to ask for something else.'

"Daśagrīva begged, 'Please grant me immunity from death at the hands of the Nāgas, Yakṣas, Daityas, Dānavas, Rākṣasas and demigods. I do not require immunity from others like human beings and animals, for I consider them

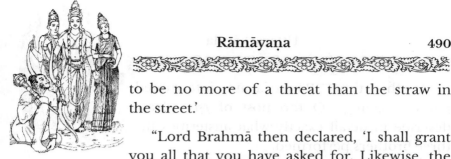

to be no more of a threat than the straw in the street.'

"Lord Brahmā then declared, 'I shall grant you all that you have asked for. Likewise, the heads you previously offered in sacrifice will be restored. I will also give you one more benediction, allowing you to assume any form you like, simply by willing.'

"Lord Brahmā then said to Vibhīṣaṇa, 'You may also accept a benediction from me according to your desire.'

"Vibhīṣaṇa replied, 'My dear lord, since you are pleased with me, the goal of my life has already been achieved. My only wish is that my mind may always remain steadily fixed upon the path of virtue, even amidst the greatest of difficulties. In addition, if you so desire, please grant that the knowledge of the *brahmāstra* appear to me upon command, even though untaught.'

"Being very pleased, Lord Brahmā replied, 'Since you are by nature inclined toward righteousness, although born a Rākṣasa, I shall grant you immortality on the level of the chief demigods.'

"Next, when Lord Brahmā was about to offer Kumbhakarṇa a benediction, all the demigods accompanying him pleaded with folded hands, 'This Rākṣasa is evil-minded. He has already devoured seven Apsarās and ten attendants of Indra, along with numerous *ṛṣis* and human beings. His only business is to terrorize the entire universe. Since he has already created so much havoc without any benediction, we think that after he receives benedictions from you, he will surely devour the three worlds. O lord, we request that you somehow cast a spell of delusion over Kumbhakarṇa on the

pretext of granting a benediction.'

"After carefully considering the demigods' request, Lord Brahmā mentally summoned his consort, the goddess Sarasvatī, who came to his side. When the goddess inquired, 'Of what service can I be, O lord?' Brahmā replied, 'I want you to become the speech within Kumbhakarṇa's mouth.'

"Thus, it so happened that when Lord Brahmā requested Kumbhakarṇa to take a benediction, the gigantic Rākṣasa replied, 'If you wish to fulfill my desire, then allow me to sleep for many, many years.'

"Lord Brahmā immediately replied, 'Let it be so!' Then, just as the universal grandsire was about to depart with the goddess Sarasvatī and the demigods, Kumbhakarṇa came to his senses and wondered, 'How did these disastrous words come from out of my mouth? I must have been bewildered by the demigods!'

"Thereafter, the three brothers began to live happily within a forest. When Sumāli learned that his three grandsons had received benedictions, he gave up all fear and came out from the nether regions. He was accompanied by his followers, including Mārīca, Prahasta, Virūpākṣa and Mahodara.

"Sumāli immediately went to Daśagrīva, and embracing him he said, 'By your mercy, our fear of Lord Viṣṇu, which caused us to flee Laṅkā, is now gone. Although Kuvera is now occupying the kingdom of Laṅkā, it originally belonged to the Rākṣasas. Therefore, my dear grandson, you should approach your half-brother and take back your rightful kingdom, by request, gift, or, if necessary, by force. If you

can retrieve Laṅkā, then I promise to make you the king of the Rākṣasas.'

"However, Daśagrīva replied, 'My dear maternal grandfather, you should not speak like this, for Kuvera is my elder half-brother.'

"Being so admonished, Sumāli remained silent. Later, Prahasta approached Daśagrīva, saying, 'You should know that for great heroes, there is no question of so-called brotherly feelings getting in the way of self-interest. My dear Daśagrīva, you should not have criticized Sumāli, for he truly gave you good advice. Just consider the sisters, Diti and Aditi, who are both wives of Kaśyapa and mothers to demigods and demons. Long ago, the Daityas controlled the universe, then later, with the help of Lord Viṣṇu, the three worlds came under the control of the Ādityas. Thus, O foremost of Rākṣasas, you would not be the first to fight against your brother for sovereignty.'

"In truth, the idea of conquering Laṅkā appealed to Daśagrīva. After considering Prahasta's words for a time, he went with him to Trikūṭa. Daśagrīva first employed Prahasta as his diplomat, who politely requested Kuvera to return Laṅkā to its rightful owners. However, after receiving Prahasta and hearing his proposal, Vaiśravana replied, 'This place was given to me by my father. Therefore I am unwilling to give it up. However, if Daśagrīva likes, he may certainly come here and share Laṅkā with me, allowing us to live without enmity.'

"After Prahasta's departure, Kuvera went to his father and explained Daśagrīva's intentions. Viśravā then replied, 'Daśagrīva has already come here, asking me to give him the kingdom of Laṅkā. However, I harshly rebuked him for his

greediness. I warned him that if he went ahead with his plan to conquer and displace you, he would ultimately meet with destruction. Because of receiving benedictions from Lord Brahmā, Daśagrīva has become too proud, and thus fails to discriminate between persons he should respect and those he need not. Now, due to my displeasure, he has become even more wicked-minded. Therefore, I recommend that you and your followers leave Laṅkā. Take up residence in Kailāsa and avoid antagonizing your arrogant half-brother.' Thereafter, Kuvera vacated Laṅkā. When Prahasta informed Daśagrīva, he entered the city and began to rule as king, being installed upon the throne by the Rākṣasas.

Some time later, Daśagrīva gave his sister, Śūrpaṇakhā, in marriage to the Dānava king, Vidyujjihva. Once thereafter, while roaming in the forest, Daśagrīva happened to meet Maya Dānava and his daughter. When Daśagrīva's asked him how he had come there, Maya Dānava explained, 'Long ago, the Apsarā named Hemā was given to me in marriage. Thereafter, I lived with her for thousands of years. Being very attached, I built a wonderful city for Hemā, made of gold and jewels. However, fourteen years ago, she left me to fulfill some purpose of the demigods. Overcome by grief, I left my beautiful city and am now wandering the forest hoping to find a suitable husband for my daughter. Besides this girl, I have begot two sons through Hemā: Mayavi and Dundhubhi. Now, if I may ask, who are you, and what is your purpose in coming here?'

"When Maya Dānava learned his new acquaintance was the son of an eminent *ṛṣi*, he decided to give him his daughter in marriage. Thus Mandodarī married Daśagrīva. Then Maya Dānava gave his son-in-law the wonderful spear

he had acquired after executing great austerities, which was later to severely wound Lakṣmaṇa.

"After some time, Daśagrīva arranged for Vajrajvalā, Bali Mahārāja's granddaughter, to marry Kumbhakarṇa, and the daughter of a Gandharva king to wed Vibhīṣaṇa. Mandodarī then gave birth to Meghanāda, who later came to be known as Indrajit.

"Some time later, drowsiness began overtaking Kumbhakarṇa because of Lord Brahmā's curse. He then requested Daśagrīva to build him a palace that was sixteen miles long and eight miles wide, with crystal and golden columns and stairways made of valuable gems. Thereafter, Kumbhakarṇa entered his palace and began sleeping for thousands of years.

"Meanwhile, the proud Daśagrīva began killing demigods and *ṛṣis* without restraint, and destroying many of the heavenly pleasure gardens. Kuvera soon learned of the degradation of his half-brother. Thus, out of family affection, he sent a messenger to Daśagrīva, advising him to mend his evil ways, saying, 'Once I happened to see Lord Śiva and his wife seated on a mountain peak in the Himālayas, engaging in austerities. I was curious to see the goddess Umā, but as soon as my left eye fell upon her, it was immediately burnt, while my right eye turned gray. In fear, I quickly left that place and proceeded to perform austerities at another location in the Himālayas, hoping to appease Lord Śiva.

"'Finally, after the passage of eight hundred years, Lord Śiva was pleased to appear before me and offer his sincere friendship. Although the vision in my left eye was fully restored, the lord informed me that my right eye would forever have to remain gray.

"'O Daśagrīva, upon my return home from performing these austerities I came to learn of your misdeeds. Now, as your well-wisher and relative, I must warn you that the demigods are already planning to destroy you. You must rectify your behavior before it is too late.'

"Upon hearing Kuvera's message, Daśagrīva became inflamed with rage. He declared, 'It was only out of respect for my elder half-brother that I have remained patient hearing these insults. However, because of this rebuke, I am now determined to not only conquer the three worlds, but to kill the four Lokapālas as well!'

"Saying this, Daśagrīva drew his sword and mercilessly struck down the messenger. Then, after feeding the messenger's body to the Rākṣasas, Daśagrīva mounted his chariot and started for the abode of Kuvera, followed by the six ministers: Mahodara, Prahasta, Mārīca, Śuka, Sāraṇa and Dhūmrākṣa. After flying through the sky for about one hour, Daśagrīva came to Mount Kailāsa. Thus, when the Yakṣas saw the Rākṣasas, they approached Kuvera and took his permission to fight.

"A fierce battle ensued. When it appeared that the Yakṣas were getting the better of his ministers, Daśagrīva took up his club and began smashing the enemy. Then, when the surviving Yakṣas came to Kuvera and informed him of their defeat, Kuvera sent out another army. The Rākṣasas again emerged victorious, and Daśagrīva then entered the abode of Kuvera. At the gate, a guard boldly blocked Daśagrīva's entrance, and when Daśagrīva attempted to push his way in, the guard smashed him over the head with a wooden post, causing him to bleed profusely. However, because of

the benediction from Lord Brahmā, Daśagrīva could not be killed. He recovered, and smashed the guard into a formless lump of flesh, causing the other Yakṣas to flee in fear.

"Kuvera then sent forth his chief commander, Manibhadra, along with four thousand Yakṣa soldiers. During the battle that followed, Prahasta soon killed one thousand Yakṣas, Mahodara killed one thousand, and Mārīca killed two thousand. Still, Manibhadra attacked Dhūmrākṣa, making him fall down unconscious. Daśagrīva then retaliated by striking Manibhadra's crown, forcing him to turn sideways. Just then, Kuvera appeared on the scene, club in hand. He was accompanied by two of his ministers, Śukra and Prauṣṭhapada, along with two deities that preside over wealth: Padma and Śankha. Kuvera challenged Daśagrīva, saying, 'Because you have proudly ignored all propriety, and thus acted most sinfully, I shall soon send you to the hellish planets so you may receive what you deserve.'

"As the Rākṣasa ministers fled, losing heart after hearing their master chastised in this manner, Kuvera rushed forward and struck Daśagrīva on the head with his club. Daśagrīva, however, was not disturbed in the least, and the two continued exchanging blows. Finally, when neither could gain the upper hand, Daśagrīva resorted to using Rākṣasa illusions. He assumed different forms, such as a tiger, a cloud, a hill, the sea, and a Yakṣa. Finally, Daśagrīva struck Kuvera on the head with his gigantic club, causing the lord of wealth to fall unconscious, bleeding profusely. Then Padma, Śankha and other Yakṣas quickly removed Kuvera from the battlefield, bringing him back to consciousness.

"Pleased with his victory, Daśagrīva took possession of the Puṣpaka chariot. He mounted it and set out for the place of Kartikeya's birth, a clump of golden reeds in the Himālayas. Suddenly, however, the Puṣpaka chariot stopped ascending the mountains and would proceed no further. Then, as Daśagrīva stood with a look of amazement, Nandīśvara suddenly appeared before him. This confidential servant of Lord Śiva was dwarfish, misshapen in appearance, bald, and altogether fearful to look at. Nandīśvara ordered Daśagrīva, 'You must turn back at once, for Lord Śaṅkara is sporting on this mountain.'

"At this Daśagrīva became enraged. While getting down from his chariot, he demanded, 'Who is this Śaṅkara?' Then, as he looked up, Daśagrīva saw Nandī with the face of a monkey, standing near Lord Śiva and holding a flaming spear in his hand. Upon seeing the bull-carrier of Lord Śiva in this feature, Daśagrīva laughed with great disdain.

"Nandī angrily cursed Daśagrīva, saying, 'In the future, powerful monkeys will take birth who will annihilate your entire race. I could kill you at once if I so desired, but I will let you be destroyed by your own misdeeds instead.'

"Daśagrīva did not care for Nandī's words, however, and replied, 'Because you have rudely stopped my chariot, I shall now retaliate by killing your master, Lord Śaṅkara.' Daśagrīva placed his hands underneath the mountain and began lifting it up. Then, as the mountain shook violently, Pārvatī stumbled, and clung tightly to her lord. Mahādeva then pressed down the mountain with his big toe, crushing Daśagrīva's arms beneath it. As Daśagrīva cried out in great pain, the entire three worlds trembled, so much so that King Indra stumbled while walking on the road.

"Upon seeing their master's plight, Daśagrīva's ministers advised him to take shelter of Lord Śiva, also known as Āśutoṣa, because he is easily pleased. With no other alternative, Daśagrīva bowed down and began glorifying Lord Mahādeva by reciting hymns from the Sāma Veda.

"One thousand years passed as Lord Śiva remained seated on top of the mountain. Then, Mahādeva became pleased to relieve the pressure of his toe so that Daśagrīva could remove his arms. Because of the fierce cries uttered by Daśagrīva when his arms were being crushed, Lord Śiva gave him the name Rāvaṇa. Thus, from that time forward, Daśagrīva became known as Rāvaṇa, because his loud crying had made all the demigods also cry out in fear.

"Thereafter, Rāvaṇa began to wander over the earth on the Puṣpaka chariot, challenging the heroic *kṣatriyas*. The prudent kings surrendered to Rāvaṇa without a fight, and the Rākṣasa king easily defeated all the others.

"One day, Rāvaṇa arrived at a forest near the Himālayas and saw a beautiful young girl with matted hair and a deerskin dress. Upon seeing her, Rāvaṇa became afflicted by lust, and while laughing aloud, exclaimed, 'The practice of austerities in the forest is contradictory to your youthful beauty. My dear young girl, who are you? Why have you decided to come here to live a life of penance?'

"The girl replied, 'I am the daughter of the *brahmarṣi*, Kuśadhvaja, the son of Bṛhaspati. My name is Vedavatī because I am considered to be an incarnation of the Vedas. Many demigods and other highly qualified men have approached my father, asking for my hand in marriage.

However, he has turned them all down, for he feels only Lord Viṣṇu would make a suitable son-in-law. When Sambhu, king of the Daityas, heard this, he came and killed my father in his sleep. My mother then entered the fire of cremation, carrying the body of her husband in her arms. Since that time, I have installed Lord Nārāyaṇa within my heart and have performed austerities, hoping to attain Him as my husband. O Rāvaṇa, by dint of my ascetic merit, I know everything about you. Therefore, please take your leave and depart without further ado.'

"Getting down from his chariot, Rāvaṇa said, 'My dear lovely girl, I request you to become my wife. Indeed, in comparison to me, who is Lord Viṣṇu?'

"At this, Vedavatī indignantly replied, 'Who, other than you, would dare speak disrespectfully of Lord Nārāyaṇa?'

"As she spoke, Rāvaṇa grabbed Vedavatī by the hair. Inflamed with rage, the girl immediately transformed one of her arms into a sword, then cut off her hair, thus setting herself free. Then, while lighting a fire, Vedavatī said, 'After being touched by you, I no longer desire to live. I shall not curse you, for that would decrease my ascetic merit. However, I shall take another birth in a divine manner, just to encompass your destruction.'

"As Vedavatī entered the fire, flowers showered down upon her from heaven. Then, giving up her body, Vedavatī next appeared from a lotus flower. Rāvaṇa, however, quickly caught her, forced her onto the Puṣpaka chariot and took her back to Laṅkā.

"Thereafter, when Rāvaṇa showed the reborn Vedavatī to his ministers, he was warned that if he kept the girl, she would become the instrument of his destruction. Taking heed, Rāvaṇa threw Vedavatī into the sea. Then, upon reaching the other shore, by employing her mystic power she came to the sacrificial ground of King Janaka. As King Janaka was leveling the ground with a plow, the girl appeared from the furrow as a baby. Thus, it came to be that the Vedavatī who had appeared in Satya-yuga, became Jānakī in Treta-yuga.

"Rāvaṇa continued to roam over the earth in the Puṣpaka chariot, until one day he arrived at the place called Uśīrabīja. There he saw King Marutta engaged in a sacrificial performance under the direction of the *brahmarṣi*, Saṁvartana, a brother of Bṛhaspati. All the demigods were present in the sacrificial arena, but out of fear of Rāvaṇa, they transformed themselves into animals. Indra became a peacock, Kuvera became a chameleon, Yamarāja became a crow, and Varuṇa became a swan.

"After entering the sacrificial arena like an unclean dog, Rāvaṇa approached King Marutta and challenged, 'Either fight with me or surrender!'

"Marutta inquired, 'Who are you? What do you want from me?'

"Rāvaṇa laughed derisively, saying, 'I am the younger half-brother of Kuvera. My name is Rāvaṇa and I have already defeated my illustrious relative in battle.'

"Marutta sarcastically replied, 'As the conqueror of your elder brother, you are certainly very virtuous. Therefore, I

consider you most worthy of being pierced by my arrows!' Marutta angrily grabbed his bow, rushing at the king of the Rākṣasas.

"Saṁvartana, however, blocked his disciple's way, saying, 'This sacrifice, performed for Lord Śiva, is not yet complete. My dear king, if it is spoiled, this glorious sacrifice will become the cause of destruction for your entire dynasty. Rāvaṇa is very difficult to conquer. Moreover, one who has been sanctified for a sacrificial performance should never become angry or engage in fighting.' Becoming pacified, King Marutta threw aside his bow. As he again sat down, Rāvaṇa proceeded to devour many of the *ṛṣis* who had come there to attend the ceremony.

"Only after Rāvaṇa's departure did the demigods resume their normal features. Indra then benedicted the peacocks to never again fear snakes. He also made marks appear on the peacocks' formerly all blue bodies, to resemble his 1,000 eyes. Thus, whenever Indra showers down rain, the peacocks dance as a symbol of their love for him.

"Yamarāja benedicted the crows to no longer contract the diseases common to other living entities. Additionally, the crows were granted that they would live for as long as humans did not kill them. Now, when crows are fed, people residing in the abode of Yamarāja become satisfied by that act.

"Formerly, swans were not all white. However, by the benediction of Varuṇa, they became white as foam and began enjoying great pleasure sporting in the water. Lastly, Kuvera blessed the chameleon with a golden complexion. Thereafter, the demigods departed for their abodes.

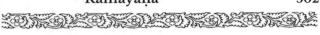

"Rāvaṇa continued challenging great kings to fight or surrender unto him. Many prominent rulers accepted defeat without a fight.

"One day, Rāvaṇa came to Ayodhyā, and when he challenged Mahārāja Anaraṇya, the king came out of his capital with a huge army. Although Anaraṇya's army was completely massacred by the Rākṣasas, the king himself was able to seriously wound Mārīca, Śuka, Sāraṇa and Prahasta, forcing them to flee from the battlefield. Mahārāja Anaraṇya then proceeded to shower 800 arrows upon Rāvaṇa's head, but the Rākṣasa king was not even slightly injured from the attack. Rāvaṇa rushed forward quickly and struck Anaraṇya on the head with his hand, causing him to fall to the ground, fatally wounded.

"As the king lay dying, he cursed Rāvaṇa, saying, 'In the future, a descendent in my dynasty named Rāma will become the cause of your destruction.' While the king uttered this oath, flowers showered down from heaven, and the demigods could be heard beating their celestial drums. As king Anaraṇya gave up his body, Rāvaṇa left that place.

"Thereafter, one day, Rāvaṇa happened to meet the great sage Nārada while traveling through the sky. Rāvaṇa greeted him most politely, and in turn, Nārada praised the exploits of the Rākṣasa monarch. Nārada said, 'O king, since you are so powerful that you can conquer even the great demigods, why are you trying to annihilate the human beings? The poor humans do not deserve to be killed by you, for they are already most unfortunate, being plagued with so many miseries in life.'

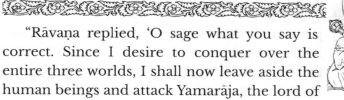

"Rāvaṇa replied, 'O sage what you say is correct. Since I desire to conquer over the entire three worlds, I shall now leave aside the human beings and attack Yamarāja, the lord of death.'

"Making up his mind in this way, Rāvaṇa immediately departed for the southern quarter. Narada's curiosity was aroused. He wondered, 'Can Rāvaṇa actually defeat Yamarāja? If he does, I wonder what sort of universal order he will institute to replace the old one.'

"Thus, to witness the impending battle, Nārada quickly went to the abode of Yamarāja, arriving before Rāvaṇa. The lord of death greeted Nārada and then inquired, 'O best of the celestial *ṛṣis*, what is the object of your visit?'

"Nārada replied, 'Rāvaṇa is on his way here, desiring to defeat you in battle.'

"As the Puṣpaka chariot entered the domain of Yamarāja, Rāvaṇa could see how all the living entities were reaping the results of their previous pious and impious activities. Some poor souls were suffering various hellish torments, while others were enjoying a high standard of material comfort. Then, by his own prowess, Rāvaṇa freed all those who were suffering in hell. Enraged at this audacious act, thousands of Yamadūtas attacked Rāvaṇa and attempted to demolish the Puṣpaka chariot. However, regardless of being attacked so viciously, the chariot remained intact, due to the prowess of Lord Brahmā.

"When the Yamadūtas showered their arrows upon Rāvaṇa, his armor became smashed, with his limbs becoming

pierced all over. Covered with his own blood, Rāvaṇa finally began losing consciousness and fell from the Puṣpaka chariot to the ground. However, after quickly recovering, Rāvaṇa took up an arrow of Lord Śiva and with it, began annihilating all the Yamadūtas. At this, Rāvaṇa and his ministers began roaring loudly, and when Yamarāja heard the uproar, he could understand that the Rākṣasa king had emerged victorious.

"After calling for his chariot, Yamarāja took up his rod of death, death nooses and other weapons, and angrily set out to fight. When Yamarāja entered the battlefield, the entire three worlds became agitated, and Rāvaṇa's ministers became so overwhelmed with fear that they began to flee in all directions. Rāvaṇa, however, remained undisturbed, and as Yamarāja approached, Rāvaṇa deluged him with arrows.

"The fierce duel that ensued went on for seven days and nights uninterrupted. The king of the Rākṣasas then released 100,000 arrows, and at that time, Mṛtyu (Death personified) begged Yamarāja, 'O Lord, please grant me permission to kill Rāvaṇa. I cause the destruction of the entire cosmic manifestation. Thus, what will be the difficulty in slaying an entity like Rāvaṇa?'

"Yamarāja, however, wished to kill Rāvaṇa himself, and as a last resort, took up his rod of death. As soon as they saw this terrible weapon, all the Rākṣasas except Rāvaṇa turned and ran away. Lord Brahmā then hastily appeared before Yamarāja, and while remaining unseen by others, he said, 'O lord of death, please do not nullify the benediction I have awarded Rāvaṇa. If you release this rod of death, it will not

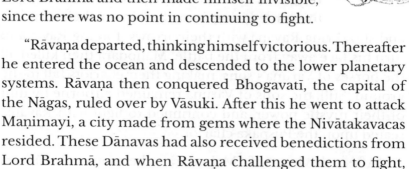

only destroy your enemy, but will kill all created beings, too. Therefore, please give up your intention.' Yamarāja yielded to the authority of Lord Brahmā and then made himself invisible, since there was no point in continuing to fight.

"Rāvaṇa departed, thinking himself victorious. Thereafter he entered the ocean and descended to the lower planetary systems. Rāvaṇa then conquered Bhogavatī, the capital of the Nāgas, ruled over by Vāsuki. After this he went to attack Maṇimayi, a city made from gems where the Nivātakavacas resided. These Dānavas had also received benedictions from Lord Brahmā, and when Rāvaṇa challenged them to fight, they were happy to oblige him.

"The Dānavas and the Rākṣasas fought for one full year, but neither could gain the upper hand. Finally Lord Brahmā came there to stop the fighting, advising the two parties to establish an alliance of friendship. Thus, Rāvaṇa spent the next years as the Dānavas' guest, and during that time he learned 100 conjuring tricks from them.

"From Maṇimayi, Rāvaṇa went to Rasātala, searching for Varuṇa's abode. When, in the course of his wanderings, he came to the city called Aśmanāgara, Rāvaṇa defeated the Kālakeyas residing there, and during the battle accidentally cut to pieces his brother-in-law, Vidyujjihva.

"After some time Rāvaṇa finally sighted the abode of Varuṇa, and there he came upon the Surabhi cow, whose milk created the great ocean of milk. After circumambulating Surabhi, Rāvaṇa entered Varuṇa's city. Then, after announcing his challenge to the waters, he killed all the warriors that came to oppose him.

"Incited with rage, Varuṇa's sons and grandsons came out with a large army, but they were soon routed by Rāvaṇa's ministers. Having retreated, Varuṇa's sons again came out to fight, this time rising into the air on their chariots and showering Rāvaṇa with their arrows, forcing Rāvaṇa to turn his face away from the battle. Mahodara then killed all the horses of Varuṇa's sons, making their chariots fall to the ground. Still, the sons of Varuṇa remained airborne by dint of their mystic power, and continued to fight with Rāvaṇa, seated upon the Puṣpaka chariot.

"After driving off Mahodara, the sons of Varuṇa surrounded Rāvaṇa and again assaulted him with torrents of arrows. Rāvaṇa suddenly flared up with rage. He pierced Varuṇa's sons with his weapons, and they fell to the ground wounded. As Varuṇa's sons were being carried away from the battlefield by their own men, Rāvaṇa ordered one of Varuṇa's ministers, 'Go convey my challenge to your master. Now that his sons are vanquished, let the lord of the waters himself come out to fight.'

"The ministers informed Rāvaṇa, 'Varuṇa has gone to Brahmaloka to attend a concert given by the Gandharvas. Therefore, O king of the Rākṣasas, be satisfied that you have defeated Varuṇa's sons.'

"Rāvaṇa soon returned to Laṅkā. Along the way he kidnapped the virgin daughters of many kings, *ṛṣis*, demigods and demons. If Rāvaṇa saw any girl that he found attractive, he would first kill all of her relatives, and then forcibly take her on his chariot. In this way, Rāvaṇa's chariot became filled with hundreds of girls, all crying out pitifully from

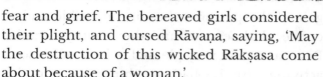

fear and grief. The bereaved girls considered their plight, and cursed Rāvaṇa, saying, 'May the destruction of this wicked Rākṣasa come about because of a woman.'

"As soon as the girls uttered these words, flowers fell from the heavens and celestial drums resounded in the sky. Thus cursed by the virtuous women, Rāvaṇa's bodily luster immediately began to fade.

"Shortly after Rāvaṇa's return to Laṅkā, Śūrpaṇakhā came and fell down at her brother's feet. With tears in her eyes she wailed, 'O how cruel you are to your sister! By killing my husband you have made me a widow!'

"To pacify Śūrpaṇakhā, Rāvaṇa replied, 'My dear sister, please do not give way to grief. I promise to gratify all your desires. Please forgive me, for in the heat of battle I could not distinguish between friend or enemy. Thus, I accidentally killed Vidyujjihva.'

"Rāvaṇa sent Śūrpaṇakhā to live under the protection of her cousin, Khara. He also dispatched an army of 14,000 Rākṣasas so that his brother could firmly establish his supremacy in the Daṇḍakāraṇya forest. Rāvaṇa then went to his sacrificial arena at the Nikumbhila grove. There he saw his son, Meghanāda, wearing a deerskin. With surprise, Rāvaṇa inquired, 'My dear boy, what are you doing?'

"Meghanāda was engaged in performing a sacrifice. Thus, to insure that his vow of silence was not broken, Uśanā, the family priest, replied on his behalf, 'In your absence, Meghanāda has already performed seven great sacrifices for the pleasure of Lord Viṣṇu. Thus, he has received a celestial chariot and various weapons from Lord Śiva. He has also

gained the power to become invisible and to create darkness within the enemy's ranks.' Rāvaṇa was not very pleased to hear of his son's activities, for he had worshipped one of his enemies—Lord Viṣṇu.

"When Vibhīṣaṇa learned that Rāvaṇa had kidnapped so many girls, he approached his brother and said, 'This act of yours is very sinful and is unfit for a member of our good family. Already, as a reaction to your wickedness, your mother's cousin, Kumbhīnasī, has been kidnapped by the Rākṣasa Madhu.'

"Kumbhīnasī was the unmarried granddaughter of Mālyavān, the uncle of Rāvaṇa's mother, Kaikasī, who was residing in Rāvaṇa's palace in his absence. When Rāvaṇa heard about Kumbhīnasī's abduction, he flared with rage and prepared to kill the offender at once. Calling together all his Rākṣasa chiefs, Rāvaṇa left Laṅkā with 4,000 *akṣauhiṇīs*, for he intended to attack the demigods after dealing with Madhu.

With Meghanāda at the front and Kumbhakarṇa at the rear, Rāvaṇa entered Madhu's city. His mother's cousin quickly came out to meet him, and fell at Rāvaṇa's feet. He thus assured her, 'I shall do whatever you request of me. Please get up, for there is nothing to fear.'

"Kumbhīnasī then begged Rāvaṇa to spare her husband. The Rākṣasa king replied, 'Yes, it shall be so. Now let Madhu come forward, for I want him to accompany me in my conquest of the demigods.' Kumbhīnasī awakened her husband and informed him that Rāvaṇa had come to solicit his help in conquering the demigods. Madhu immediately

came and paid his respects to Rāvaṇa, and the next morning the Rākṣasa army departed.

Rāvaṇa reached Kailāsa just as the sun was setting, and had his army make camp there. While sitting at leisure on top of the hill, Rāvaṇa surveyed the beautiful forests and lakes that served as the demigod's sporting grounds. Indeed, he could hear the singing of Apsarās coming from Kuvera's palace. The entire atmosphere was extremely pleasing and enhanced by fragrant breezes.

"At that time, the Apsarā Rambhā chanced to pass by. When Rāvaṇa saw Rambhā's beautiful bodily features, enhanced by her attractive dress and tinkling ornaments, he became so lusty that he immediately jumped from his seat and grabbed her by the hand. Pierced by Cupid's arrows, Rāvaṇa said, 'O exquisitely beautiful one, your sweet smiling face, your full, well-rounded breasts and your shapely hips and thighs have combined together to steal away my mind. Now that I have seen you, I cannot bear to let you go. Who is there superior to me that you are now on your way to meet? Accept me as your husband and remain with me. It would surely be a waste of your incomparable beauty to have it enjoyed by anyone else.'

"Rambhā, however, angrily replied, 'You should not speak to me like this, for you are just like my father and I, your daughter-in-law.'

"Rāvaṇa then argued, 'Only the wife of one's son can be considered to be a daughter-in-law.'

"At this, Rambhā countered, 'Yes, what you say is correct. Still, you should know that I am the lawful wife of your

brother's son, Nalakūvara, and I am on my way to meet him now. Therefore, O king of the Rākṣasas, please follow the path of righteousness and let me go at once.'

"Not interested in good advice, Rāvaṇa replied, 'Your reasoning only applies to women who have one husband. However, since the Apsarās have no actual husbands, just as the demigods are not committed to a single wife, I do not have to consider you in the light of such morality.'

"Saying this, Rāvaṇa forcibly pulled Rambhā down onto a flat rock and began copulating with her. When she was finally released, her hair and dress disheveled, Rambhā ran to her husband, Nalakūvara, and told him everything that happened. Upon hearing of Rāvaṇa's misconduct, Nalakūvara became outraged. Then, to verify Rambhā's story, he entered a trance of meditation. Thereafter, having ascertained the truth of the matter, Nalakūvara touched water and pronounced the following curse: 'The head of Rāvaṇa will split into seven pieces if he ever again tries to enjoy a woman against her will.'

"The demigods were overjoyed to hear this declaration, and showered flowers down upon Kuvera's son. Similarly, when the women at Laṅkā kidnapped by Rāvaṇa heard of Nalakūvara's oath, they too, experienced great happiness. And when Rāvaṇa heard of the curse, he gave up all inclination to have sexual relations with women who were not inclined toward him.

"The next morning, Rāvaṇa mobilized his army and approached the abode of Indra. The king of heaven, being afraid of Rāvaṇa, became dejected upon seeing the army of

Rākṣasas approaching. Indra quickly sent out all the demigods to fight and then approached Lord Viṣṇu. After offering his obeisances to the Lord, Indra explained, 'Because of Lord Brahmā's benedictions, I feel helpless in battling Rāvaṇa. My dear Lord, I request that You either empower me with sufficient energy to kill the Rākṣasa king, or else take up the matter Yourself.'

"Lord Viṣṇu reassured Indra, 'There is no need for you to be afraid. Go and fight with Rāvaṇa, even though it is not possible for you to conquer him. I do not wish to kill him just now. However, please know that when the time is right, I shall slay not only the wicked Rākṣasa king, but all of his relatives too.'

"Thereafter, a fierce battle ensued between the demigods and the Rākṣasas, supported by their allies, the Dānavas. Rāvaṇa's maternal grandfather, Sumāli, led the Rākṣasa army and soon routed the demigod soldiers. Then Savitra, the eighth Vasu, suddenly entered the battlefield, striking fear into the hearts of the Rākṣasas. After destroying Sumāli's chariot, Savitra picked up the Rākṣasa's mace and smashed it over his head, striking him down dead.

"Being leaderless, the Rākṣasa soldiers began to flee. Meghanāda then came forward, and the powerful son of Rāvaṇa began to scatter the demigods. Indra, however, admonished the fleeing warriors and sent forth his own son, Jayanta, to fight. An equally matched duel thus began between the two princes. However, when Meghanāda resorted to creating darkness on the battlefield through his mystic potency, Jayanta became ill at ease. In the darkness,

the fighting became gruesome and confused. Pulomā, ruler of the Daityas and father of Śacī, the wife of King Indra, came and forcibly grabbed his grandson by the hair. Dragging him away from the battlefield for his protection, Pulomā dove deep into the sea with Jayanta.

"Seeing that Jayanta was gone, the demigods panicked and ran away. Indra then immediately called for his chariot. As Indra went out to join the battle, surrounded by other Ādityas, a fierce wind began blowing and huge meteors streaked across the sky. Meanwhile, inspired by Indra's presence, the demigods slaughtered the Rākṣasas, so that eventually only one tenth of their forces remained alive. Kumbhakarṇa was also wounded by the combined attack of the Rudras and other celestials.

"Now highly enraged, Rāvaṇa began penetrating the ranks of the enemy army and approached the heavenly king, Indra. As the two rulers proceeded to shower their arrows upon each other, darkness set in, bewildering everyone but Indra, Rāvaṇa and Meghanāda. Rāvaṇa was determined to destroy all the demigods. Indra understood that he could not kill the Rākṣasa king, and thus advised his warriors to capture him instead.

"Rāvaṇa suddenly rushed at Indra, but the king of heaven drove him back with torrents of weapons. The fear-stricken Rākṣasas considered themselves to be defeated. Meghanāda was outraged, and thus invisibly entered the demigod army and came before the heavenly king. Sending forth incessant streams of arrows, Meghanāda was able to exhaust Indra, and thereupon bound him up by the mystic

power he had acquired from Lord Brahmā. Seeing how Rāvaṇa was being overpowered by the demigods, the invisible Meghanāda announced to his father, 'You should retreat from the battle, for I have already taken Indra captive. Since victory is yours, there is no need to continue fighting.'

"Hearing this, the demigods became disheartened and at once desisted from battle. Rāvaṇa then instructed Meghanāda, 'Go ahead of me and take Indra to Laṅkā. I will join you there shortly.'

"In this way Indra, the king of heaven, became a prisoner of the Rākṣasas within their capital city. Lord Brahmā then took all the demigods with him and went to Laṅkā. While remaining stationed in the sky, the universal grandsire addressed Rāvaṇa as follows: 'The prowess and valor exhibited by your son is wonderful indeed. Because of his dramatic victory over the king of heaven, let Meghanāda from this day onward be known as Indrajit. O king of the Rākṣasas, I request you to release Indra. In exchange, I shall reward your son with an incomparable benediction.'

"Indrajit exclaimed, 'I shall give up Indra for the boon of immortality.'

"Lord Brahmā, however, replied, 'It is not possible for any of the created beings to have unconditional immortality. Therefore, my dear prince, please ask for something else.'

"Indrajit said, 'As an alternative, grant me the following—At the time of battle, if I offer oblations into the sacrificial fire according to Vedic injunctions, let a huge chariot emerge

from the flames. Then, as long as I remain seated upon that chariot, let me be immune to death. Thus, only if I engage in battle without having finished the chanting of mantras and offering of oblations, will I be subject to destruction. Some people seek immortality through the performance of austerities, but I have acquired it simply by exhibiting my prowess. Lord Brahmā granted Indrajit's request, and in return, the Rākṣasas released Indra.

"After this incident, Indra became morose and his bodily luster faded. Lord Brahmā approached him and asked, 'What grievous sin did you commit in the past that is now causing you to suffer so much?'

"Without waiting for Indra to reply, the all-knowing Brahmā narrated the following story: 'In the beginning of creation there was only one type of human being. There was no distinction in their bodily features. Then to create diversity and increase the population, I created the first woman, giving her the name Ahalyā, which means, "One who does not possess even the slightest ugliness."

"'While contemplating whose partner this girl would be, I kept her in the care of Gautama Ṛṣi for many years. O Indra, during this time you confidently assumed that I would give Ahalyā to you as a consort. However, when Gautama later returned the girl to me, I was impressed by his self-control. I decided that Ahalyā could become his wife.

"'All the demigods, especially yourself, were upset by my decision. Thus, being overcome by lust and anger, you went to Gautama's *āśrama,* and when you saw the beautiful Ahalyā,

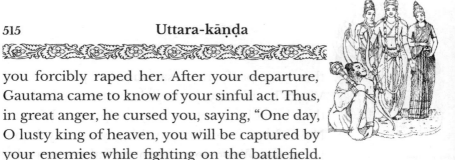

you forcibly raped her. After your departure, Gautama came to know of your sinful act. Thus, in great anger, he cursed you, saying, "One day, O lusty king of heaven, you will be captured by your enemies while fighting on the battlefield. Furthermore, when this abominable act that you have initiated becomes prevalent in human society, anyone who commits this sin will get only half of the reaction, and you will get the other half. Thus, from now on, the position as the king of heaven will never be secure—not only for you, but future Indras also."'

"'After chastising Indra, Gautama cursed his wife for her infidelity, saying, "From now on you must remain in this *āśrama* as a stone pillar. Additionally, you will no longer have the distinction of being the only woman. All other women will receive a share of your beauty."'

"'Ahalyā then pleaded, "My dear husband, Indra came here disguised as you and then forcibly raped me. Please be merciful unto me, for I am faultless."'

"'Gautama then informed his wife, "In the future, Lord Viṣṇu will take birth in the Ikṣvāku dynasty, and He will be known as Rāma. In the course of performing His transcendental pastimes, He will come here in the company of Viśvāmitra. By seeing Lord Rāma and offering Him your hospitality, you will become free from my curse and reinstated as my wife."'

"Brahmā continued, 'My dear Indra, you should know that all of your present difficulties are due to the curse of Gautama. To counteract the effects of that curse, I suggest

that you perform a sacrifice to please Lord Viṣṇu. In this way, you will become purified and thus be able to return to your post in heaven. Now, there is one more thing you may know from me. Your son has been taken away by Pulomā and is being kept deep within the ocean.' Thereafter, by following Lord Brahmā's directions, Indra regained his heavenly position, and became free from all anxieties."

While hearing about the extraordinary prowess of Indrajit, Rāma and Lakṣmaṇa uttered exclamations of great wonder. Then Rāma again inquired, "O best of the *ṛṣis*, was there ever an instance of a *kṣatriya* who defeated Rāvaṇa?"

Agastya replied, "Once, while wandering over the earth, Rāvaṇa came to the city of Māhiṣmatī, ruled by Kārtavīryārjuna, king of the Haihayas. That day, Kārtavīryārjuna had gone to the River Narmadā to enjoy himself in the water with many attractive women. Thus, when Rāvaṇa inquired from a minister about Kārtavīryārjuna's whereabouts, he was informed that the king had gone out.

"Rāvaṇa departed, and after going to Vindhya Mountain, he came to the banks of the Narmadā. Stepping down from the Puṣpaka chariot, Rāvaṇa sat down on the shore with his ministers and said, 'This holy river is very glorious. You should all take a ritualistic bath to relieve yourselves of all sinful reactions. Meanwhile, I shall engage in the worship of Lord Śiva. Bring me some flowers for an offering.'

"While the ministers looked for mountain flowers for Rāvaṇa's offering, Rāvaṇa took his bath and chanted the Gāyatrī mantra. Coming out of the water, Rāvaṇa took off

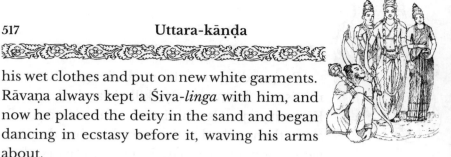

his wet clothes and put on new white garments. Rāvaṇa always kept a Śiva-*linga* with him, and now he placed the deity in the sand and began dancing in ecstasy before it, waving his arms about.

"Kārtavīryārjuna was a short distance downstream, sporting with his female companions. Desiring to test the strength of his one thousand arms, Kārtavīryārjuna began to block the water's flow. Thus, the water backed up, overflowing its banks and washing away Rāvaṇa's flowers, just as he was about to offer them in worship. At this, Rāvaṇa angrily summoned Śuka and Sāraṇa, ordering them to find out the cause of the river's unnatural flow.

"Rising into the air, the ministers went down stream. When they had gone only four miles they saw Kārtavīryārjuna playfully blocking the river's flow. When Rāvaṇa heard this, he immediately set out for battle, accompanied by all his ministers. While going along, Rāvaṇa saw numerous inauspicious omens. Still, without being deterred in the least, Rāvaṇa soon came within Kārtavīryārjuna's vicinity. When Kārtavīryārjuna's ministers approached him, Rāvaṇa ordered, 'Announce my arrival to your king and tell him I have come to challenge him to fight.'

"One of the ministers replied, 'It is not proper for you to challenge Kārtavīryārjuna while he is intoxicated and in the company of women. Therefore, please spend the night here, and in the morning, you can fight. However, if you are so impatient that you cannot wait, then you will have to defeat us before approaching our master.'

Responding to their challenge, Rāvaṇa's ministers immediately killed and devoured Kārtavīryārjuna's ministers. Kārtavīryārjuna's army then rushed at the intruders, but they too were soon exterminated. The survivors then hastily went to report what happened to Kārtavīryārjuna. Hearing this, Kārtavīryārjuna got out of the water, grabbed his club, and began to drive away the Rākṣasas. Prahasta daringly stood up to Kārtavīryārjuna and hurled a flaming mace. The Haihaya king deftly deflected it with his own mace, and then severely struck Prahasta, knocking him to the ground. Seeing Prahasta fallen, Rāvaṇa's other ministers ran away in fear.

"Rāvaṇa then rushed at Kārtavīryārjuna, and they proceeded to violently strike each other with their clubs. However, neither grew tired. Then Kārtavīryārjuna hurled his club against Rāvaṇa's chest. Although the club broke into pieces, Rāvaṇa was thrown backwards a bow's length, crying out as he fell to the ground in agony.

"Kārtavīryārjuna quickly rushed forward, and after catching hold of Rāvaṇa, tied him up with strong rope. The demigods were elated to witness this heroic feat. Thus, they showered Kārtavīryārjuna with flowers while continually praising him.

Prahasta and the other Rākṣasas then rushed forward while throwing torrents of weapons. However, Kārtavīryārjuna simply caught all these weapons in his hands and drove away the Rākṣasas. He then took the captive Rāvaṇa and entered Māhiṣmatī. When Pulastya heard that his grandson was being held captive, he went to meet Kārtavīryārjuna.

When the ministers saw the great *ṛṣi* descending from the heavens, they hurriedly informed the Haihaya king of his arrival. Kārtavīryārjuna then came before Pulastya with folded hands. After providing him with a royal reception, he asked, 'O foremost of illustrious personalities, of what service can I be?'

"Pulastya replied, 'Kindly release the Rākṣasa king, for you have proven that your power far excels his.'

"Without uttering a word, Kārtavīryārjuna released Rāvaṇa. The ruler of the Haihayas also gave the Rākṣasa king various presents, thus forming an alliance between the two. Finally, Kārtavīryārjuna bowed down before Pulastya and entered his palace, while the son of Lord Brahmā (Pulastya) ascended into the sky.

"Although Rāvaṇa was embarrassed because of his defeat, he continued to wander over the earth, defeating countless *kṣatriyas*. Finally, he came to Kiṣkindhyā, ruled by Vāli, who wore a golden necklace presented to him by King Indra. When Rāvaṇa expressed his desire to fight, Suṣeṇa, Aṅgada, Sugrīva and the minister Tāra replied, 'Vāli is not here now, but will be returning shortly. O great Rākṣasa hero, just look at this heap of bones. This is all that remains of those who challenged Vāli in the past. We can assure you that you will come to a similar end. My dear king, if you are very impatient, not wishing to wait, then you can find Vāli on the shore of the southern ocean.'

"Rāvaṇa then mounted the Puṣpaka chariot and flew to the Southern Sea. There he saw Vāli absorbed in saying prayers. Rāvaṇa wanted to capture the monkey king alive,

and began to creep up silently from behind. Vāli, however, was able to see Rāvaṇa from the corner of his eye. Remaining undisturbed, Vāli thought, 'I shall capture this Rākṣasa when he comes close by and keep him under my arm. Then, leaving him dangling, I will complete my worship by visiting the three other oceans.'

"Vāli could hear Rāvaṇa's footsteps. When he drew close, Vāli suddenly whirled about and caught him. Then, pressing Rāvaṇa tightly under his arm, Vāli sprang into the air toward his next destination. Rāvaṇa's ministers quickly came to his rescue, but they could not catch Vāli. Thus, Vāli continued his tour of the four seas and finally returned to Kiṣkindhyā.

Vāli was exhausted from carrying Rāvaṇa such a great distance, and thus put him down in a park. Then, laughing disdainfully at Rāvaṇa, Vāli asked the dazed Rākṣasa who he was. With genuine admiration, Rāvaṇa introduced himself and said, 'The astonishing speed that you travel through the air is only matched by three others: the mind, Vāyu and Garuḍa. O king of the monkeys, you truly are an exceptional hero. Therefore, I want to establish friendly relations with you. Please accept me as your ally.'

"Thereafter, a sacrificial fire was lit, and when their friendship was thus formalized, Rāvaṇa and Vāli warmly embraced. Rāvaṇa continued to reside at Kiṣkindhyā for one month as the honored guest of the monkey chief."

At this point, Rāma said, "O *ṛṣi,* Rāvaṇa and Vāli were certainly powerful heroes, but I feel that Hanumān's prowess exceeds both of them. Indeed, during My conquest of Laṅkā,

it was he alone who enabled Me to become victorious and recover Sītā. I cannot properly express My debt to Hanumān, the best of My unalloyed servitors. O great sage, I still have some doubt that I pray you can dispel. Why is it that when there was enmity between Vāli and Sugrīva, that Hanumān did not vanquish Vāli? I think Hanumān could not have been aware of his own prowess. Otherwise, how could he have stood by idly and watched Sugrīva suffer? O foremost of *ṛṣis*, you are the knower of all mysterious truths. Therefore, please explain the transcendental pastimes of Hanumān so My doubt can be removed."

Hanumān was also present in the assembly, listening to the conversation, and he experienced great transcendental bliss upon hearing Rāma's statement. The great sage Agastya then answered, "It is true that no one can equal Hanumān in strength, speed or intelligence. However, it so happened that he forgot his actual prowess. I will recount the story of his life to explain why.

"Hanumān was begot by Vāyu through Añjanā, the wife of Kesari, a monkey chief who used to reside on Mount Meru. After delivering the child, Añjanā went to gather some fruit for him. In her absence, however, the hungry baby started to cry. At that time the sun began to rise. When the baby monkey saw the luminous orange globe, he thought that it was a fruit, and suddenly sprang upwards to catch it.

"When the demigods saw the son of Vāyu flying swiftly through the air, they became astonished, declaring, 'Not even the mind or Garuḍa can move so fast. If this monkey shows so much ability as a baby, what will he be like when he grows up?'

"Vāyu followed his son to protect him from the scorching heat of the sunshine. Then, as the baby monkey approached, Sūrya refrained from consuming him, in consideration of his childish innocence, and the future mission he would perform on behalf of Rāma. Thus, the son of Vāyu was able to take his seat upon the chariot next to Sūrya.

"Just at that time, Rāhu happened to come to attack the sun god. Instinctively, the baby monkey grabbed Rāhu, but in the next moment, Rāhu, the worst of the planetary controllers, slipped from his clutches.

Rāhu fearfully approached Indra and complained, 'Although I have been allotted the sun and moon as the means for appeasing my hunger, it appears that my share has been appropriated by another. Just now, when I approached the sun god, I saw that another Rāhu was attacking him.'

"Indra was quite astonished to hear this, and he thus mounted Airāvata and set out toward the sun. Rāhu had gone ahead, and when the son of Vāyu saw him coming, he considered him to be a type of gigantic fruit, and sprang from Sūrya's chariot to catch him. Rāhu immediately began to flee, crying out for Indra's protection. Thus, the king of heaven, who approached from nearby, gave him assurance. Then, when the hungry baby sighted Airāvata, he took the elephant to be an enormous white fruit and rushed toward him.

"When Indra saw the son of Vāyu approaching, he immediately released his thunderbolt. The baby monkey crashed down on a mountain, broke his jaw, and thus gave up his life. This enraged Vāyu, who then took his son and withdrew into a mountain cave. Vāyu ceased acting as the air

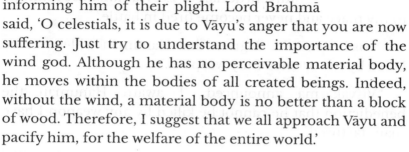

of respiration, and all living entities began to suffocate, their bowels and bladders becoming obstructed. With bloated bellies, the demigods hurriedly approached Lord Brahmā, anxiously informing him of their plight. Lord Brahmā said, 'O celestials, it is due to Vāyu's anger that you are now suffering. Just try to understand the importance of the wind god. Although he has no perceivable material body, he moves within the bodies of all created beings. Indeed, without the wind, a material body is no better than a block of wood. Therefore, I suggest that we all approach Vāyu and pacify him, for the welfare of the entire world.'

"Lord Brahmā led the demigods to Vāyu's cave. The wind god was tormented by the death of his son, whose body he still held in his arms. After Vāyu offered his obeisances, Lord Brahmā affectionately placed his hand upon the baby monkey's head, and immediately brought him back to life.

"Upon the revival of his son, Vāyu resumed circulating within all creatures. Thus, the living entities again became joyful. Lord Brahmā then told the assembled demigods, 'In the future, this child will act for your welfare. Thus, all of you should award him benedictions.'

Hearing Lord Brahmā's command, Indra took off his garland of lotus flowers and placed it around Hanumān's neck. Indra declared, 'Because of his broken jaw, this child will henceforward be known as Hanumān. He need no longer fear my thunderbolt, for he will be immune to its effects.'

"The sun god announced, 'I hereby donate one percent of my brilliance to Hanumān. Furthermore, I grant him full knowledge of the scripture and benedict him with eloquent speech.'

"Yamarāja then said, 'I hereby grant Hanumān immunity from my rod of death and from all diseases.'

"Kuvera declared, 'Let Hanumān be immune to my mace and never become tired in battle.'

"Lord Śiva said, 'I grant that Hanumān will never be killed by me or one of my weapons.'

"Viśvakarmā announced, 'I award Hanumān the benediction that he cannot be killed by any weapon I have manufactured.'

"Lastly Lord Brahmā said, 'I grant Hanumān a long life, magnanimity, immunity to the *brahmāstra*, and immunity to the curses of the *brāhmaṇas*.'

"Lord Brahmā then said to Vāyu, 'This child will be able to change his form at will and shall be unconquerable. He will be able to travel wherever he likes and at any speed he chooses. In the future, he will perform glorious activities that will aid in the destruction of Rāvaṇa. Thus, he will become very pleasing to Lord Rāma.'

"The demigods departed, and Vāyu placed Hanumān under the care of his mother, Añjanā. After receiving so many benedictions, Hanumān was bursting with energy. He began acting fearlessly. Sometimes he even offended prominent *ṛṣis* by interrupting their sacrifices and breaking their paraphernalia. While Hanumān indulged in these pranks, the *ṛṣis* tolerated him, for they knew that he was immune to death from their curses, due to Lord Brahmā's benediction.

"Hanumān's foster father, Kesari, and his natural father, Vāyu, tried their best to discipline him. Still, Hanumān continued to transgress the bounds of propriety. Thus, the *ṛṣis* became a little angered at him, and declared that, 'For now you shall remain ignorant of your true prowess. At the proper time, you will again become aware of your full potency.'

"Thereafter, Hanumān began wandering through the forests in a peaceful mood. At this time, the king of the monkeys, Ṛkṣarāja, succumbed to death from old age. His eldest son Vāli assumed the throne, while Sugrīva became heir apparent. From childhood, Hanumān and Sugrīva were best friends. However, when hostility broke out between the two brothers, Hanumān was not aware of his true prowess, and thus he did not help Sugrīva fight Vāli.

"Because of his ignorance of his great power, Hanumān became more interested in the cultivation of knowledge than the exhibition of force. To learn all areas of Vedic knowledge, he would follow the sun god the full distance from where he rises to where he sets. Hanumān would put forward innumerable questions, and eventually he became as learned in the Vedas as Bṛhaspati."

In this way Agastya Ṛṣi described the glories of Hanumān. Rāma, Lakṣmaṇa and the monkey chiefs were amazed and delighted to hear them. When the assembled *ṛṣis* decided to go, Rāma said, "Now that I have been installed as emperor, I want to perform many sacrifices for the welfare of the world. I request that you all return home so that the sacrifices may be performed under your supervision."

Happily giving their consent, the *ṛṣis* departed. The next morning, awakened by the professional singers who recited His glories, Rāma bathed and sat down to perform fire sacrifices. Thereafter, Rāma visited the palace temple and proceeded to the royal court. Seated upon the royal throne and surrounded by His ministers, servants and twenty of the monkey chiefs, Rāma administered the state government in an exemplary manner.

King Janaka was one of many great kings that came to Ayodhyā to attend Rāma's coronation. After some time, Rāma approached him, saying, "My dear father-in-law, you should now return to your kingdom, Vidarbha, lest it become neglected. Bharata and Śatrughna will escort you there with a large army."

Janaka consented, and Rāma honored him with many valuable presentations. Janaka gave all the presents to his beloved daughter, Sītā, and happily departed for home. Rāma then addressed His maternal uncle, the Kekaya king, Yudhājit: "Because your father is now very old, you too should return to your kingdom to take care of him. Lakṣmaṇa will accompany you with a large army."

Yudhājit gave his consent, and after his departure, Rāma bid farewell to His friend, the king of Kāśī. Altogether, Rāma bade farewell to three hundred kings and princes that had come to Ayodhyā to celebrate His coronation. After returning home, all these kings sent their escorts back with many valuable presentations for Rāma. When He received all these gifts, Rāma immediately gave them away to Sugrīva, Vibhīṣaṇa and the other monkeys and Rākṣasas.

One day, Rāma took Hanumān and Aṅgada upon His lap and told Sugrīva, "These two great heroes deserve every possible honor." Rāma then took off the ornaments from His body and decorated Hanumān and Aṅgada with them. The other monkey heroes were also present, and so Rāma sweetly said, "You are all not only My dear friends, but are just like My brothers." Rāma embraced all the monkeys and gave them various presents.

All the monkeys remained in Ayodhyā for more than one month, happily spending their time feasting and relishing the association of the Supreme Personality of Godhead, Lord Rāmacandra. However, due to their great love for Rāma, the time passed so quickly that it seemed to the monkeys to be less than one hour. After the month had passed, Rāma requested Sugrīva to return to Kiṣkindhyā and Vibhīṣaṇa to return to Laṅkā. At that time Hanumān came before Him and offered the following prayer: "O my Lord, may my devotion for You always remain steady, and may my love for You never become diverted toward anyone else. In addition, may my life continue for as long as the narration of Your transcendental pastimes is recited upon the earth. Indeed, only by hearing the recitation of the *Rāmāyaṇa* will I be able to mitigate the unbearable pangs of separation from You."

Rāma then got down from His throne, and while embracing Hanumān declared, "Your life shall continue for as long as the *Rāmāyaṇa* is recited. Indeed, the *Rāmāyaṇa* will be recited for as long as the earth continues to exist. My dear Hanumān, I shall never be able to repay you for the service you have rendered unto Me. I will remain eternally indebted."

Rāma took off the necklace of pearls and precious stones that decorated His chest and placed it around Hanumān's neck. All the monkeys then got up, and one by one, bowed down to Lord Rāma.

Thereafter, Rāma embraced Sugrīva and Vibhīṣaṇa, and the monkeys' eyes became filled with tears, their minds bewildered from ecstatic feelings of impending separation, and their speech indistinct. Finally the monkeys departed. Rāma felt great separation from His servants, but He was also happy that the heroes would be reunited with their families.

Later that afternoon, Rāma suddenly heard a voice from the sky. Looking up He saw that the Puṣpaka chariot was addressing Him. The chariot told Rāma, "I returned to Kuvera as You ordered. However, the lord of wealth told me, 'Because Rāma has conquered Rāvaṇa, you now rightly belong to Him.' Thus, I have been sent back by Kuvera to render service unto You. O Lord, please accept me without hesitation."

Rāma worshipped the Puṣpaka chariot with flowers, incense and sandalwood paste, and then ordered him, "If I am ever in need of your service, you can appear to Me when called for. In the meantime, you are free to go wherever you please." Being so directed, the Puṣpaka chariot departed to wander on its own.

Some time after this incident, Bharata came one day before Rāma and began to glorify His rule of the kingdom, saying, "Although little more than one month has passed since Your coronation, there is already a complete absence of disease, untimely death and labor pains for women. The clouds are showering rain at the proper time, and all the people are in a joyous state of mind." Rāma felt great bliss listening to Bharata's praise, for He understood that all living entities can attain the highest fulfillment of life in a God conscious kingdom.

The winter passed, and with the arrival of spring, Rāma passed much of His time with Sītā in the lovely palace gardens. During the day, Rāma would dutifully carry out the state administration, and in the evenings He would sit with Sītā in the shade of a large *aśoka* tree. Surrounding them, the Apsarās sang and danced among the flowering trees.

Rāma, the Supreme Personality of Godhead, and Sītā, the goddess of fortune, passed each day enjoying newer and newer delights. Their pleasure in each other's association expanded unlimitedly.

One day Rāma understood that Sītā was pregnant. He expressed His great pleasure, saying, "O lovely princess, is there any desire within your heart that you feel has not yet been gratified? Please inform Me if there is, for I shall fulfill your every wish without fail."

Sītā replied, "O Lord, in Your association all my desires have been abundantly fulfilled. However, since You are asking, I admit I have a strong desire to visit the *āśrama* of the *ṛṣis* situated on the banks of the Gaṅgā, and offer my obeisances to the great saints living there."

Rāma assured her, "My dear Sītā, please know that very soon you will have the opportunity to visit the *ṛṣis* in the forest."

Thereafter, Rāma entered the royal assembly, and engaged in joking and light conversation with His advisors. Rāma then asked Bharda, "What do the citizens talk about these days? What do they say about Sītā, Lakṣmaṇa, Bharata and Śatrughna? How do they feel about Our mother, Kaikeyī, and Myself? Indeed, kings are always the topic of criticism for the people."

With folded hands, Bharda replied, "O Lord, everyone praises Your victory over the ten-headed Rāvaṇa. They acclaim You as the greatest of all heroes."

Rāma, however, urged, "Tell Me truthfully what they say.

Only by knowing matters as they are can one curtail his faults, and thus endeavor for self-improvement. O Bharda, there is no need for you to be afraid. I have already understood that envious people are spreading rumors about Me through Ayodhyā. I have even personally heard some people criticize Me for taking back a woman who remained so long in the house of another."

Hearing this, Bharda bowed to Rāma and replied, "Whether good or bad, I do not know. However, this is what people are saying in the marketplaces and in the city streets: 'Rāma has performed an extraordinary feat by bridging the ocean and vanquishing the powerful Rāvaṇa. However, has it occurred to Him that He has brought home a woman who was abducted by the Rākṣasa king and forced to sit upon his lap? Does Rāma not feel disgust at enjoying a woman who remained with Rāvaṇa for almost one entire year?' O Lord, these are the things people are speaking about You."

Shocked and dismayed to hear this, Rāma then asked the other ministers if what Bharda had said was true. They all confirmed it was so. Rāma was fully aware of Sītā's complete purity and innocence, but He could not tolerate the shame of having to hear that people were mocking Him in this way. Rāma made up His mind to abandon His unsuspecting wife, and called for Lakṣmaṇa.

Rāma addressed His brother with great agitation, "O Lakṣmaṇa, please listen with great attention, for what I have to say is most painful. I have just learned that some citizens of Ayodhyā condemn Me for taking Sītā back from the kingdom of Laṅkā. Just see how distressed I have become! I have appeared in the royal dynasty of Ikṣvāku; thus any

taint of dishonor to My name brings Me more grief than the thought of death.

"After killing Rāvaṇa. I also considered, 'How can I take Sītā back to Ayodhyā?' It was just to allay these doubts that I made the princess of Vidarbha enter the fire in the presence of all the demigods and *ṛṣis*. Vāyu and Agni declared that Sītā was pure, and within My heart, I also knew she was chaste, so I accepted her back. Now, however, rumors are spreading everywhere, and I am being blamed in My own kingdom.

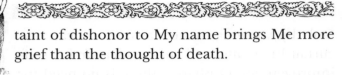

"O Lakṣmaṇa, a person who is the target of rumors suffers great humiliation and defamation. Ill deeds are always condemned, and that is what motivates the noble-minded toward good acts. I am ready to give up My life if necessary, to avoid public scandal. Indeed, I am ready to renounce You, My dear brother, for insuring My good name and reputation. Thus, what can be said of Sītā? I am drowning in an ocean of sorrow. Never before have I experienced such misfortune!

"Lakṣmaṇa, tomorrow at dawn You must take Sītā to the banks of the Gaṅgā and take her on a tour of the āśramas of the great *ṛṣis*. Then abandon her near the hermitage of the great sage Vālmīki, on the banks of the River Tamasa, and return to Ayodhyā alone. My dear brother, You must carry out this order without any argument, for any slight hesitation on Your part will bring Me the greatest displeasure. Indeed, let it be known that anyone who objects to My decision immediately becomes My most bitter enemy! Just a little while ago Sītā told Me she is very eager to visit all the *āśramas* along the banks of the Gaṅgā. Now go and fulfill her desire.[9]

---

9. It is often queried why Lord Rāma banished Sītā simply because of some small criticism. It appears that Lord Rāma was harsh and cruel to His chaste wife. However, Lord Rāma, as an ideal king, had to uphold the honor of His dynasty and set an impeccable example for all generations to follow. Had He not banished Sītā, lesser monarchs in the future could have used this as an excuse not to respond to valid criticisms by their citizens. Rāma's decision may seem harsh, but to properly rule it is required that a king sometimes be harsh. His first duty is to rule the people; other considerations are secondary, even if they affect his personal happiness or that of his own family members.

Lakṣmaṇa became brokenhearted to hear Rāma speak like this. However, since He was the obedient servant of his elder brother, He assented without hesitation. Then, early the next morning, Lakṣmaṇa went to Sītā and said, "Your husband has ordered me to fulfill your desire. I shall escort you to the banks of the Gaṅgā so that you can worship the great *ṛṣis* residing there. Sumantra is ready with the chariot, so I request you come at once."

Sītā was delighted, and after putting on her finest dress and most exquisite jewelry, she told Lakṣmaṇa, "I shall distribute these and other gifts to the wives of the great sages."

Lakṣmaṇa helped Sītā onto the chariot and they quickly departed. However, while going along, Sītā began to speak anxiously, saying, "O Lakṣmaṇa, my left eye has suddenly begun to twitch and my mind feels strangely uneasy. Suddenly I feel very weak, and the earth seems to have taken a gloomy aspect. I hope Rāma is all right."

Sītā prayed to the demigods for the welfare of her husband and other relatives. Lakṣmaṇa then said in a voice choked with tears, "I hope you too will not meet with misfortune."

By evening, Sītā, Lakṣmaṇa and Sumantra reached the banks of the River Gomati and spent the night there. Early the next morning, they continued their journey. By afternoon they came to the banks of the Gaṅgā. Upon dismounting their chariot, however, Lakṣmaṇa broke down and cried, for he could no longer contain his grief. Feeling great concern, Sītā inquired, "O Lakṣmaṇa, what is wrong? Now that we have reached our destination You should be happy. Indeed,

Your sadness makes me uneasy. Have just two days of separation from Rāma brought You so much anguish? I love Rāma dearly, yet I have not become so disturbed. Please compose Yourself, for we must now cross the Gaṅgā to have the audience of the great *ṛṣis*. Thereafter, we can quickly return to Ayodhyā, for I also long to see Rāma!"

After wiping the tears from His eyes, Lakṣmaṇa arranged for a boat and escorted Sītā across the Gaṅgā. Upon reaching the other side, Lakṣmaṇa tearfully confessed, "O princess of Vidarbha, the all-good Lord Rāma has entrusted Me with a most painful task. Indeed, by performing this duty I shall become infamous in the eyes of the world. It would have been better if I had died rather than execute your husband's order! O noble lady, please forgive Me for what I am being forced to do!"

Lakṣmaṇa fell to the ground, weeping bitterly. With great indignation, Sītā asked, "O Lakṣmaṇa, what is the matter? I cannot understand what You are saying. Please tell me clearly what is troubling You. Has some great misfortune befallen Rāma that You do not have the courage to tell me?"

With His head bowed low, Lakṣmaṇa replied in a voice choked with tears, "While sitting in the royal court, Rāma learned that rumors were circulating throughout Ayodhyā, accusing Him of impropriety. Everywhere, people blame Rāma for accepting you back. This public censure pains Him unbearably. O Sītā, I know that you are faultless and so does Rāma. Therefore, do not misunderstand the king, for He has been forced to relinquish you to maintain the good name of the Ikṣvāku dynasty. O princess of Vidarbha, do not be broken hearted, for the abodes of the *brahmarṣis*

that are situated on the banks of the Gaṅgā are celestially beautiful. You should take shelter of the great sage Vālmīki, for he was a good friend of your father-in-law, Mahārāja Daśaratha. Always think of Rāma within your heart and remain unflinchingly devoted to Him. In this way, you will attain the highest happiness, O Jānakī."

Upon hearing of her cruel destiny, Sītā immediately fainted. Then, coming to her senses, she pitifully cried out, "Now I can see that this life was awarded to me simply for suffering. What great sin did I commit in the past? What poor girl's marriage did I obstruct to now cause Rāma to cast me off?

"I faithfully followed my husband into exile and remained content, despite innumerable hardships. O Lakṣmaṇa, how shall I be able to survive here alone? What will I tell the *ṛṣis* when they ask me why I was abandoned? What wrong have I done? I would gladly end my life by throwing myself into the Gaṅgā, but that would bring about the end of Rāma's dynasty."

Becoming somewhat more composed, Sītā told Lakṣmaṇa, "I know that You are merely carrying out Your duty. I do not blame You. Go back to Ayodhyā now and offer my respects to my mothers-in-law. Touch the feet of my husband and please deliver the following message: 'O Rāma, You know that my devotion has always been fixed upon You without deviation. You know of my chastity and my unfailing love. Still, from fear of dishonor and shame, You have spurned me. O Rāma, my Lord and only refuge, You should not have done so. My dear husband, I do not grieve for my own misfortune, for I know that I am faultless.

For a chaste woman, the husband is as good as God. Therefore, I must accept that whatever You may order is best for my welfare, even if it means giving up my life.'"

Lakṣmaṇa circumambulated Sītā, and crossed to the Gaṅgā's opposite shore. As Lakṣmaṇa mounted His chariot, He turned his head, just to have one last glimpse of Sītā. Likewise, Sītā gazed sorrowfully at Lakṣmaṇa as He receded into the distance. Then, alone and unprotected, Sītā fell on the ground, crying uncontrollably.

The grief-stricken Lakṣmaṇa said, "O Sumantra, what terrible pain Rāma will have to suffer now that He has abandoned His dear wife! Alas! He who wrathfully destroyed the Rākṣasas appears to be Himself ruled by cruel destiny! The sorrow Rāma will feel shall far exceed what He experienced while living in exile under the order of His father."

Sumantra replied, "O prince, do not become overly aggrieved because of Sītā or Rāma. Long ago, Your father was informed that one day Rāma would have to abandon His wife and suffer the pangs of separation for the remainder of His life. O Lakṣmaṇa, I promised Your father that I would never disclose all of this. However, since You have inquired about Rāma's misfortune, I shall tell You everything. I should certainly obey the king's order, but it appears that fate is indeed supreme, for I feel impelled to speak. However, please do not repeat any of this to Bharata or Śatrughna."

Lakṣmaṇa exclaimed, "O Sumantra, please disclose everything!"

Sumantra said, "O prince, once upon a time, Durvāsā Muni resided at the *āśrama* of Vasiṣṭha during the four months

of the rainy season to execute the required penances for that season. One day, when Mahārāja Daśaratha came to visit Vasiṣṭha, he saw Durvāsā Muni seated by the *ṛṣi's* side. Thus, he respectfully worshipped both sages. In turn, the two *ṛṣis* welcomed Mahārāja Daśaratha and invited him to sit down with them. In the course of their conversation, Mahārāja Daśaratha asked about his own longevity, along with that of his sons.

"Durvāsā Muni told him, 'My dear king, once, long ago, when the Daityas were hard pressed in battle against the demigods, they took shelter of Bhṛgu Muni's wife, for she had previously assured them of protection. Seeing this, Lord Viṣṇu became enraged, and by employing His Sudarśana *cakra*, He severed the head of the ascetic woman. In retaliation, Bhṛgu Muni angrily cursed Lord Viṣṇu to be born upon the earth as a human being and suffer the pangs of separation from His wife.

"'After venting his anger in this way, however, Bhṛgu Muni became sorry. Repentantly, he began to worship Lord Viṣṇu. The Lord became satisfied with Bhṛgu Muni, and He voluntarily agreed to accept the consequences of the *ṛṣi's* curse.

"'My dear Daśaratha, it is for this reason that Lord Viṣṇu has appeared as your son, Rāma. From Ayodhyā, He will rule over the earth for 11,000 years, and two sons will be born unto Him through the womb of His beloved wife, Jānakī.'"

Sumantra then said, "My dear Lakṣmaṇa, all this was foretold by the great sage Durvāsā to Your father. Now You should give up Your grief, knowing well that whatever

takes place is in accordance with the will of the Supreme Lord."

Hearing Sumantra's words, Lakṣmaṇa felt great relief, and expressed His sincere gratitude to the chief minister. Lakṣmaṇa and Sumantra passed the night on the banks of a river, and the next morning resumed their journey.

Some disciples of Vālmīki happened to see Sītā weeping, and they ran to their master, saying, "O master, come quickly! There is a woman who resembles the goddess of fortune herself, sitting alone in the forest crying."

By dint of his mystic power, Vālmīki could understand everything. He rushed to the place where the bereaved Sītā sat. The *ṛṣi* humbly approached her and said, "O devoted wife of Lord Rāma, O daughter of King Janaka, by the strength of my austerities, I know all that takes place within the three worlds. Thus, I understand your plight. Please do not be afraid. Near my *āśrama* there are ascetic women who will devotedly care for you as if you were their daughter. Please come with me now, and consider this to be your new home." Vālmīki then took Sītā and placed her under the care of the female ascetics.

Meanwhile, Lakṣmaṇa arrived at Ayodhyā. Wondering what He would say, He entered the royal palace. Lakṣmaṇa saw Rāma seated upon the throne, shedding tears and lost in deep contemplation. Seeing His elder brother's pitiful condition, Lakṣmaṇa's eyes also filled with tears.

Bowing down before Lord Rāma, Lakṣmaṇa addressed Him in a voice laden with great sorrow: "My dear brother, in accordance with Your order, I abandoned Sītā on the

banks of the Gaṅgā near the *āśrama* of the great sage Vālmīki. O Rāma, there is no use giving way to grief. Indeed, in this world, meeting and separation are concomitant factors. It is inevitable that one's wife, one's son and one's very life must one day be given up. Therefore intelligent persons always pass through life's journey with an attitude of detachment. My dear brother, Your unlimited prowess controls the three worlds. Why then do You not suppress this despondency? Cast off this weakness! Otherwise, more rumors will circulate. What will people think?"

Rāma became pacified by Lakṣmaṇa's words, and His grief gradually faded. Rāma said, "My dear Lakṣmaṇa, for the last four days I have completely neglected My royal duties. Please summon all the royal ministers, priests and people in general with whom You do business. The king who does not look daily at the state administration is certainly doomed to suffer in hell.

"You must know the story of King Nṛga. He once gave away millions of cows in charity to a *brāhmaṇa*, but one of them happened to belong to another *brāhmaṇa*. When they discovered this discrepancy, the *brāhmaṇas* cursed the king to become a lizard. It was ordained that King Nṛga would be delivered in the distant future when Lord Viṣṇu would appear as the son of Vasudeva in the line of Yadu. Even now that great king suffers because of the *brāhmaṇa's* curse. Thus, it can be understood just how much misery can be incurred due to a king's injustice. Therefore, let all people come to Me who seek My audience. My dear brother, if You wish, I can entertain You with other interesting histories regarding the lives of great kings."

Lakṣmaṇa replied, "My dear Rāma, the more I listen to these wonderful stories, the more I am eager to continue hearing."

In response, Rāma narrated the history of King Nimi: "This twelfth son of Ikṣvāku once asked Vasiṣṭha to officiate at his sacrifice. However, because Vasiṣṭha was already engaged in performing a sacrifice on behalf of Indra, he requested Mahārāja Nimi to wait. But instead of waiting, Mahārāja Nimi appointed Gautama as his sacrificial priest. When Vasiṣṭha learned of this, he came to the king and cursed him to die. In retaliation, Mahārāja Nimi cursed Vasiṣṭha to die, and thereafter they were both forced to relinquish their material bodies.

"Vasiṣṭha then approached Lord Brahmā, who advised him to enter the semen about to be discharged by Mitra and Varuṇa. Vasiṣṭha quickly went to the shore of the ocean where Mitra and Varuṇa were residing. Just at that time, the beautiful Apsarā Urvaśī came by. Becoming overwhelmed by lust, Varuṇa pleaded with Urvaśī to accept him. But Urvaśī replied that Mitra was first to beg union with her. At this, Varuṇa declared, 'O beautiful one, if you do not accept my embraces at once, I shall discharge my semen into this celestial pitcher!'

"Being pleased by this statement of ardent love, Urvaśī replied, 'My dear Varuṇa, although my body belongs to Mitra, my heart belongs to you!'

"Mitra became extremely irritated at Urvaśī's words, and cursed the Apsarā to pass some time on earth. Mitra was first to discharge his semen into the celestial pitcher. As a result, the great sage Agastya rose from the vessel and

said, 'O Mitra, I am your only begotten son.' Saying this, Agastya went away. Then, after Varuṇa discharged his semen into the pitcher, it mixed with the semen of Mitra. Thus, from this mixture, Vasiṣṭha took birth.

"Meanwhile, after the death of Mahārāja Nimi, the priests continued the sacrifice after preserving his body in oil. At the completion of the sacrifice, Bhṛgu Muni utilized his mystic powers to invoke the soul of King Nimi. The demigods were very pleased with this act, and when they offered him a benediction, Mahārāja Nimi requested, 'O celestials, may I always reside in the eyes of all creatures.'

"The demigods gave their consent, saying, 'O king, you shall visit every eye in the form of air. Because of this, all creatures will be seen to blink periodically.'

"The demigods departed, and thereafter, the priests began to churn the body of King Nimi. Thus, Mithi was born. Since he was born from a dead body, he was known as Videha, as well as Janaka."

After narrating this story, Rāma hastened to the royal assembly, eager to attend to the duties of state administration. There Rāma ordered Lakṣmaṇa, "Go to the palace gate and bring Me all those who have come with their petitions."

Lakṣmaṇa soon returned, saying, "O Lord, it appears that there is no one in the Kosala kingdom who is in need of anything."

Rāma, however, insisted, "Go again and look more carefully. I do not wish to be accused of the slightest neglect.

Nor do I want the least bit of irreligion to go undetected in My kingdom."

Going out again, Lakṣmaṇa then noticed a dog sitting near the palace gate, its head bleeding. While staring at Lakṣmaṇa, the dog whined mournfully. Lakṣmaṇa asked, "What is wrong? Why have you come here? Please do not fear, for you may tell Me everything."

The dog replied, "I wish to speak directly to Lord Rāma, whose lotus feet award one fearlessness, and who is the shelter of the distressed."

Lakṣmaṇa then said, "If you have something to say, then you are welcome to come speak to the king Himself."

However, the dog replied, "I am a very low-born creature. I am unworthy of entering temples, the houses of *brāhmaṇas* or royal palaces. The king is the embodiment of all religious principles, the representation of all the demigods and the benefactor of all living beings. Without Rāma's special permission, I cannot dare come before Him."

When Lakṣmaṇa reported the matter, Rāma immediately commanded, "Whoever it may be, usher him in without delay!"

The dog then humbly came before Rāma and said, "O Lord, the king is the representative of the Supreme Personality of Godhead. Thus, he is the savior of all creatures. While others sleep peacefully, the king remains alert, always working for the welfare of his subjects. However, since everything depends upon him, when the king is negligent, his subjects soon perish. The king is the upholder of religious principles, and thus curbs the forces of evil. Those who follow religious principles experience happiness in this life and the next. Thus, the king receives great merit for sustaining dharma. O Rāma, You are the model of a religious king. With my head placed at Your lotus feet I seek Your mercy. Do not become angry at what I have to say."

Rāma reassured the dog, saying, "Go on! Speak without fear!" Thus encouraged, the dog continued, "A mendicant *brāhmaṇa* named Sarvathā-siddha has injured my head, although there was no fault on my part."

Immediately, Rāma had His men summon Sarvathā-siddha. Soon thereafter, when the *brāhmaṇa* came before Him, Rāma inquired, "Why did you strike this dog? What was his fault? Anger is a deadly enemy. It is like a sharp sword that slashes away all of one's virtue. Anger nullifies one's long accumulated merit of austerity. Therefore, the wise rid themselves of anger by neglecting it in thought, speech and actions. O *brāhmaṇa*, one's true character cannot remain hidden, no matter how hard one tries to conceal it. Misdeeds will always betray those who have not conquered the forces of lust, anger and greed."

The *brāhmaṇa* replied, "I was wandering about, begging for alms, when I came upon this dog squatting in the middle of the road, blocking my path. I told him, 'Make way!' but he got up so slowly that I struck him over the head with my staff. I was famished and my anger was easily aroused. O king, I admit my guilt. You should punish me as You see fit, just to save me from falling down into the hellish condition of life."

Rāma turned to His ministers and inquired, "What should the punishment be? Justice must be done, for nothing

instills more confidence in people's minds than the administration of fair punishment to wrong-doers."

Bhṛgu, Vasiṣṭha, Kaśyapa and other knowers of religious principles replied, "A *brāhmaṇa* is never to be punished. This is the unanimous opinion of those conversant with religious principles. Still, O Rāma, You are the ultimate judge, for You are the Lord of the entire universe. You are Lord Viṣṇu Himself. Thus, whatever is spoken by You is eternal religion."

The dog interrupted, saying, "O king, You have asked, 'What can I do for you?' If You truly wish to please me, then kindly appoint this *brāhmaṇa* to be head of the Kālañjara Monastery."

Rāma fulfilled the dog's request, and thus the delighted *brāhmaṇa*, Sarvathā-siddha, became honored as a spiritual leader and was placed atop a magnificently decorated elephant. The ministers, however, became greatly upset, protesting, "O king, this cannot be considered a punishment! Rather than putting the *brāhmaṇa* to shame, You have awarded him an exalted position!"

Rāma replied, "You do not understand the intricacies of karma, but the dog does."

Prompted by Rāma, the dog explained, "In my last life I was the head of the Kālañjara Monastery. I duly worshipped the demigods and *brāhmaṇas*. I performed my sacred duties carefully, and properly maintained the servants and maidservants. Still, regardless of so much care, trying to leave nothing undone, I took my next birth as a dog due to some unknown fault. Now, just consider this *brāhmaṇa* who cannot even control his anger. He is certainly unfit to be a spiritual leader. For his audacity in accepting such a position, he will now degrade seven generations of his family. How can a man who is unable to control his temper be put in charge of *brāhmaṇas*, cows, and Deity worship? Anyone who steals from the *brāhmaṇas*, demigods, women or children is doomed, as is one who takes back a gift that was freely given. Indeed, even the very thought of stealing from the demigods and *brāhmaṇas* will send a man to the lowest of hells."

Saying this, the dog suddenly disappeared while Rāma and the others sat with wide-open eyes. Although previously born in a very high family, that living being had somehow been forced to accept the body of a dog. After leaving the royal court at Ayodhyā, the dog gave up his life by abstaining from food and water, with the hope of attaining a better birth.

One day, while Rāma was seated upon the royal throne, Sumantra informed Him that some *ṛṣis*, headed by Cyavana, had come to see Him. The sages were then escorted in, bearing gifts of fruit and water collected from holy places. After worshipping the *ṛṣis*, Rāma inquired as to the purpose of their visit, assuring them He was prepared to execute their command. Cyavana Muni replied, "My dear Lord Rāma, in the Satya-yuga there was a most pious Daitya named Madhu, the son of Loka. Being very pleased with Madhu, Lord Śiva awarded him an invincible lance. Madhu then requested that all his descendants might also possess this lance, but Rudra explained that this was not possible. However, Lord Śiva at last agreed that the lance could be transferred to Madhu's son. Thus, at the time of his death, the Daitya handed over the weapon to his son, Lavaṇāsura. O Rāma, this offspring

of Madhu is now residing at Madhuvana. Because he has become very formidable, he is greatly oppressing the *ṛṣis*. My dear Lord, You have already destroyed Rāvaṇa and his followers. We now beg You to please save us from the hands of Lavaṇāsura."

Rāma replied, "My dear *ṛṣis*, please give up all anxiety. I shall certainly kill this Rākṣasa."

Turning to His brothers, Rāma inquired, "Shall I kill this demon myself, or shall I allot the task to Bharata or Śatrughna?"

Bharata then expressed his eagerness to slay the demon. However, Śatrughna pleaded, "My dear Rāma, during Your exile, Bharata had to suffer so greatly. Therefore, please grant Me permission to destroy Lavaṇāsura."

Rāma replied, "O Śatrughna, let it be so! Indeed, I shall crown You at once as king of Madhuvana."

Hearing this, Śatrughna felt most ashamed and protested, "O Lord, it is not proper to install a younger brother as king in the presence of his elder brother. However, Your words cannot go in vain, and I must carry out Your order. I now realize it was wrong to protest Bharata's request. It is unrighteous for a younger brother to oppose his elder brother's wishes. I must have been prompted to do so by My evil stars!"

Rāma was pleased to hear Śatrughna speak this way. He then asked Lakṣmaṇa and Bharata to arrange for Their brother's coronation at once. Thereafter, when Śatrughna was crowned as king of Madhuvana, He shone like the radiant sun. The *ṛṣis*, headed by Cyavana, were fully assured by this sight.

Rāma then said, "My dear Śatrughna, it is Lavaṇāsura's habit to keep his lance inside his house when he goes out to collect food. It is only when he is challenged to fight that he takes up his invincible weapon. Therefore, You must confront the demon when he is outside. When You do this, block his entrance so he may not go into his house. Take 4,000 horse-soldiers, 2,000 chariot warriors, and 1,000 infantry with You. Let merchants also accompany You, along with their wares, and bring actors and dancers. Likewise, take one million gold coins to pay the soldiers' salaries. Proceed in a way that will disguise Your motive, for only by intercepting him unaware and unarmed will You be able to emerge victorious."

Śatrughna first dispatched His army, and then one month later, He set out. After passing two nights on the way, Śatrughna reached the *āśrama* of Vālmīki during the third day. Śatrughna explained to Vālmīki how He had been dispatched on a mission by the order of Lord Rāma, and the *ṛṣi* extended his hospitality to Him.

That night, as Śatrughna remained at Vālmīki's *āśrama,* Sītā gave birth to twin sons at midnight. Receiving the news from his disciples, Vālmīki performed the birth rituals with *kuśa* grass to ward off ghosts and Rākṣasas. Vālmīki then directed some elderly people to rub the body of the first-born child with the ends of *kuśa* grass, and the younger twin with the lower end of *kuśa* grass. Thus, the elder boy became known as Kuśa, and the younger boy as Lava ("lower end").

Śatrughna overheard the news, and was very happy to know that twin boys were born to Rāma and Sītā. In the

morning, Śatrughna set out, and after journeying for seven days, He arrived at the *āśrama* of Cyavana Muni on the banks of the Yamunā River.

That evening, as they were sitting at ease, Śatrughna inquired from Cyavana Muni about the prowess of Lavaṇāsura. The *ṛṣi* replied, "O prince, there was formerly a very powerful king in the dynasty of Ikṣvāku named Māndhātā. This king was so ambitious that he made preparations for conquering the entire three worlds. As a consequence, even the demigods became afraid. Indra then approached Māndhātā and suggested, 'O king, you should first subjugate the entire earth before thinking of conquering heaven.'

"With great surprise, Māndhātā inquired, 'O Indra, where is that person on earth who has not come under my subjugation?'

"In reply, the king of heaven named Lavaṇāsura, the son of Madhu, who resided at Madhuvana. Hearing this, Māndhātā angrily set out with his army. First the king sent forth his envoy. But when the envoy arrived at Madhuvana, Lavaṇāsura ate him up. In great rage King Māndhātā challenged Lavaṇāsura, who thus came out of his city wielding his terrible lance. In an instant, that invincible weapon destroyed King Māndhātā, then returned to the hands of its owner. Therefore, my dear Śatrughna, You must be sure to challenge this demon when he is away from home, searching for food."

The next morning, Lavaṇāsura went to the forest to hunt for animals. In his absence, Śatrughna crossed the River Yamunā and then besieged the city of Madhuvana. At noon, when Lavaṇāsura returned home, bearing heaps of dead animals, he saw Śatrughna standing at the city gates. Lavaṇāsura simply laughed with derision and said, "O fool! Regardless of Your audacity, all Your weapons shall be of no avail. Indeed, it is my great fortune that You have arrived at my mealtime!"

Śatrughna challenged, "I am the younger brother of Lord Rāma and Bharata, and My name is Śatrughna! I have come here to slay you as a just reward for your wicked deeds!"

Lavaṇāsura again laughed heartily, saying, "Even though Rāma killed Rāvaṇa, the brother of my aunt, Śūrpaṇakhā, I merely excused Him out of contempt, for I did not consider Him worthy of my challenge."

A fierce duel ensued between the two warriors. Then Lavaṇāsura suddenly struck Śatrughna over the head with a large tree, causing Him to fall unconscious on the ground. Thinking his adversary to be slain, Lavaṇāsura picked up his animal carcasses and entered his city. However, within a moment Śatrughna came to His senses. Standing up, He fixed a supremely powerful arrow upon His bowstring. Indeed, even the demigods were struck with fear upon seeing the terrible arrow, and they quickly sought the shelter of Lord Brahmā. The grandsire explained to them, "My dear celestials, with this arrow, Lord Viṣṇu formerly killed Madhu and Kaiṭabha. Rāma has given this arrow to Śatrughna, knowing well that it would be put to use at this time. You should all go witness with your own eyes the death of this great demon."

Śatrughna then released that wonderful arrow, and after soaring magnificently through the air, it pierced Lavaṇāsura's heart, making him fall to the ground dead. The victorious

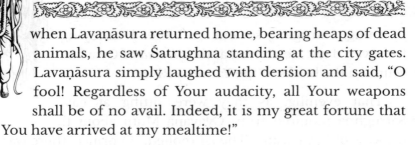

Śatrughna shone like the sun, and the demigods praised Him for His wonderful achievement.

Thereafter, Śatrughna settled at Madhuvana, residing there with His army and followers. He built a great city there called Madhupuri, which soon became highly prosperous. It was only after twelve years that Śatrughna at last decided to return to Ayodhyā.

When Śatrughna came to the *āśrama* of Vālmīki, He was very respectfully received by the *ṛṣi* and offered ample hospitality. While congratulating Śatrughna for killing the terrible demon Lavaṇāsura, Vālmīki smelled His head repeatedly with great affection.

After taking His meal, Śatrughna sat down to listen as Lava and Kuśa recited Vālmīki's composition of the *Rāmāyaṇa* to the accompaniment of music. The poetic expressions were so enrapturing, and the descriptions of Lord Rāma's transcendental pastimes so vivid, that tears soon came to Śatrughna's eyes. Even the soldiers became entranced while hearing the history, for they appeared to be reenacted before their eyes in the *āśrama* of Vālmīki. One listener exclaimed, "How wonderful this reenactment is! It appears as though we are dreaming! My dear Śatrughna, please ask Vālmīki who has composed this wonderful song."

Śatrughna replied, "My dear soldiers, we should not question the *ṛṣi* about this, because many wonderful occurrences take place in his *āśrama*. We should not be so astonished or express our curiosity unnecessarily."

That night, while resting, Śatrughna could think of nothing other than the sweet lyrics describing the pastimes of His worshipable brother, Lord Rāma. The next morning

Śatrughna departed, and soon arrived at Ayodhyā. Upon entering the royal palace, Śatrughna saw Rāma, like a second Indra, surrounded by His ministers. Bowing before His elder brother, Śatrughna said, "My dear Rāma, I have carried out Your command and killed the wicked Lavaṇāsura. Since that time, I have been residing at Madhupuri. By Your mercy, it has become extremely prosperous. My dear brother, I am most aggrieved, having lived in separation from You for these past twelve years. Therefore, I beg You to give Me permission to now reside in Ayodhyā, without going anywhere else in the future."

Rāma feelingly embraced Śatrughna and replied, "My dear brother, You should not speak like this. A heroic *kṣatriya* must not express such sorrow or feel any inconvenience while living in a distant kingdom. It is the duty of a king to rule over his subjects according to religious principles. You have to return to Madhupuri. I hope, of course, You may visit Ayodhyā from time to time to see Me. My dear Śatrughna, You are more dear to Me than life itself. Therefore, please stay here for seven days before setting out." With a sorrowful heart, Śatrughna assented, and after spending seven days in Ayodhyā, He left for his own kingdom.

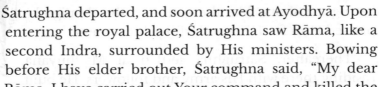

Once an elderly *brāhmaṇa* villager arrived at the gate of Rāma's palace, bearing the body of his child. Delirious with grief, the old *brāhmaṇa* cried out, "O my son! My dear child! What terrible crime did I commit in a previous life to deserve the death of my only child? He was just a child, not yet fourteen, and now his mother and I shall die from grief. What wrong did I commit? I have never spoken a lie or injured either man or animal. Never before in the kingdom of Rāma has a son died before his parents. Therefore, the death of my son must be due to some fault of Rāma Himself. It is well known that when the king becomes negligent in performing his duties that such anomalies occur. O Rāma, You must return my innocent son to me, or else my wife and I will give up our lives at Your doorstep. In this way You will become guilty of killing *brāhmaṇas*. O king, You claim to be a great ruler in the line of Ikṣvāku. How will You be able to go on living happily when the great sins You have perpetrated continue to haunt You?"

Rāma hurriedly summoned His advisors, Mārkeṇḍeya, Maudgalya, Kaśyapa, Katyāyana, Jābāli, Gautama and Nārada. After seating the great *ṛṣis* and offering them respects, Rāma informed them of the elderly *brāhmaṇa's* accusations.

To relieve the king's anxiety, Nārada said, "O king, I shall disclose to You the reason for this child's death. Then You may act as You see fit. In the Satya-yuga, everyone was spiritually qualified, and by performing austerity, they achieved liberation from material bondage. In that golden age, wisdom was the rule and there were no untimely deaths. Then, in the beginning of Treta-yuga, the four social divisions were created. The *kṣatriyas* were practically as qualified as the *brāhmaṇas*, and they were both allowed to perform austerities. In the Dvāpara-yuga, irreligiosity will increase, and thus many irregularities will be introduced. As a concession, the *vaiśyas* will also be allowed to perform austerities, but the *śūdras* will be strictly forbidden to do so. Thereafter, in the Kali-yuga, even *śūdras* will be allowed to perform austerities. Indeed, in that degraded age, there will be practically no qualified *brāhmaṇas*, *kṣatriyas* or *vaiśyas*.

"O Rāma, it is a serious offense for a *śūdra* to practice austerity in this Treta-yuga. It happens, however, that there is one *śūdra* in Your kingdom executing very severe penances. He is the cause of this child's death.

"O king, irreligiosity is a state's worst enemy. Therefore, the ruler who fails to punish wrongdoers deserves to suffer in hell. You must find out this culprit at once so that religious principles may be upheld, and the *brāhmaṇa's* son may be restored to life."

Pleased by this advice, Rāma ordered Lakṣmaṇa, "Go at once to the palace gate and tell the *brāhmaṇa* to preserve the dead body of his child in a vat of oil after supplying the necessary herbs."

Rāma then mentally summoned the Puṣpaka chariot. Leaving Ayodhyā in the care of Lakṣmaṇa and Bharata, He departed to search for the culprit. Rāma first flew over the western region, then north to the Himālayas. Finding no sign of irreligion, He next examined the eastern provinces, and finally began searching in the south. There, near a great mountain and beside a large lake, Rāma sighted an ascetic hanging head downward, engaged in executing severe penances.

"What great austerity! What fixed determination!" Rāma declared. "Tell Me, O formidable one, who are you and what is your caste? I am Rāma, the son of Daśaratha, and you have aroused My curiosity. For what purpose are you undergoing so much trouble? Are you seeking the heavenly planets, or have you some other goal? Are you a *brāhmaṇa*, a heroic *kṣatriya*, a *vaiśya*, or a *śūdra*? Please tell Me the truth."

From his awkward position the ascetic replied, "O illustrious king, My name is Śambuka. I was born the son of a *śūdra*. Regardless of this handicap, I am performing

austerities so that in my next life I can attain the planets of the demigods."

Śambuka had hardly finished speaking when Rāma unsheathed His terrible sword and slashed off the *śūdra's* head. From the sky came shouts of, "Well done! Excellent!" as flowers rained down on all sides. Being exceedingly pleased, the demigods appeared before Rāma and declared, "O Lord, You have done us a great favor! By performing this noble act You have insured that this *śūdra* will not attain to heaven, in violation of religious principles."

With folded hands, Rāma replied by requesting the thousand-eyed Indra, "O king of heaven, if you are truly pleased with Me, then kindly restore the *brāhmaṇa's* son to life. It was due to My own fault that the boy died. I promised the *brāhmaṇa* that I would restore his life. O best of the demigods, please allow My words to hold true."

Indra happily replied, "My dear Lord, certainly the child has already been revived and reunited with his parents. He regained his life as soon as the *śūdra's* head fell to the ground.[10]

---

10. It is understood that a person is born in a *śūdra* family due to past sinful activities. He must gradually become free from sinful reactions by faithfully serving the higher castes who are engaged in performing pious activities. To attempt to circumvent the proper expiation of sinful reactions, and to undertake pious activities for which he is not fit, constitutes an aberration of dharma. To punish the *śūdra* and to check others born in *śūdra* families from such presumptuousness, Lord Rāma, as the ideal king dedicated to maintain order in society, executed him. However, in the modern age such rules of dharma do not apply, for even those born in *brāhmaṇa* families are generally more degraded than *śūdras.* For this fallen age, the recommended religious activity for all is

Some years later, Rāma decided to visit the sage Agastya, who had just completed executing austerities by living within water for twelve years. Accompanied by the demigods on the Puṣpaka chariot, He arrived at the *ṛṣi's āśrama.* Lord Rāma then reverently bowed His head to the *ṛṣi,* who in turn received Rāma with all due hospitality. Agastya said, "My dear Lord, it is my great fortune that You have come here as my respected guest. Please honor me in return by accepting these golden ornaments manufactured long ago by Viśvakarmā."

Rāma replied, "My dear *ṛṣi*, only *brāhmaṇas* are permitted to accept charity, not *kṣatriyas*. The only gift I may receive from you is your valuable words of instruction."

Agastya said, "My dear Rāma, in the Satya-yuga there were no kings. Thus, one day, the people went to Lord Brahmā and requested him to assign them a ruler. In response, Lord Brahmā called for the principal demigods and commanded them to donate various portions of their potencies. Thereafter, Lord Brahmā sneezed, and from his nostrils was born a king named Kṣupa. Lord Brahmā endowed Kṣupa with a portion of Indra's energy so that he could rule over the earth, a portion of Varuṇa's energy for the maintenance of his body, a portion of Kuvera's energy for possession of wealth, and a portion of Yamarāja's energy for chastising wrongdoers. My dear Lord Rāma, in the same spirit, You should take these celestial ornaments from me."

Rāma replied, "My dear *ṛṣi*, I accept your words, and I will accept the ornaments. Now please describe how you came to possess them."

---

chanting the names of Kṛṣṇa and Rāma, which frees one from all sinful reactions and awards love of God.

Agastya replied, "Long ago, during the present Treta-yuga, I performed penances in this vast forest. I originally entered the forest out of curiosity. Thus I found a desolate, enchanting *āśrama.* After passing the night there, however, I found a dead body lying on the ground. To my surprise, I was struck by the beauty of the corpse, and stared at it for some time. Suddenly, a celestial chariot descended from the sky. Within it was an effulgent person, surrounded by Gandharvas and Apsarās who were singing and dancing. That splendorous person got down from the chariot and began to feed on the dead body. I was astonished to see this, and asked him, 'Alas! How is it that you can do such an abominable act?'

"That person replied, 'O *ṛṣi,* my name is Śveta. I am the son of the illustrious Sudeva, and my brother is Suratha. After the death of my father, the citizens made me their king. Then, after ruling for a great while, I considered my duration of life was coming to an end. Thus, I retired to the forest after installing my brother Suratha on the royal throne. Finally, after executing severe austerities for 3,000 years, I ascended to Brahmaloka. However, I was surprised to find that I was still afflicted by great pangs of hunger and thirst. I therefore inquired, 'My dear Lord Brahmā, the residents of your supreme abode are free from such disturbances. How then am I suffering from hunger and thirst?' The grandsire replied, 'O Śveta, although you performed penances for a long time, you never gave in charity. Thus, for this reason you now suffer from hunger and thirst even here, in Brahmaloka. Now, to appease you, I ordain that human flesh shall be your meal. O king, you shall suffer the effects of this curse until you meet the great sage Agastya.'"

Agastya then said, "My dear Lord Rāma, as arranged by destiny, I one day came to meet Śveta. In gratitude for being relieved from his distress, he begged me to accept these ornaments."

Rāma inquired, "My dear *ṛṣi,* why is it that this place, where Śveta formerly performed austerities, is devoid of all beasts and birds?"

Agastya replied, "My dear Rāma, in the Satya-yuga, there lived a great king named Manu, who was the founder of the social system, consisting of the four occupational duties. Later, Manu's son, Ikṣvāku, inherited the kingdom. In his turn, he begot 100 sons. The youngest son of Ikṣvāku was very dull and never obeyed his brothers. Thus, he received the name Daṇḍa. Daṇḍa founded the kingdom that extends between the Vindhya Mountains and the Saivala Mountains. His capital city was named Madhumantra, and Śukrācārya became his sacrificial priest.

"One day, after having ruled over the kingdom for a long time, Daṇḍa went to visit the *āśrama* of Śukra. Upon his arrival, he happened to see the *ṛṣi's* beautiful daughter, Arajā, loitering there alone. The very sight of her caused the king to immediately be overcome by lust. Daṇḍa forcibly embraced Arajā and proceeded to gratify himself with her against her will. The king then returned to his capital.

Soon thereafter, Śukra was informed by a disciple of what had happened. When he returned to his *āśrama,* his daughter was there, shedding tears. The *ṛṣi* angrily cursed the king, saying, 'Let Indra devastate Daṇḍa's entire kingdom by raining down dust for seven days so that everything becomes buried and all creatures die!' Śukra then ordered

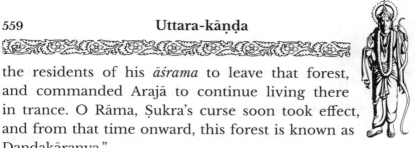

the residents of his *āśrama* to leave that forest, and commanded Arajā to continue living there in trance. O Rāma, Ṣukra's curse soon took effect, and from that time onward, this forest is known as Daṇḍakāraṇya."

Lord Rāma passed the night at Agastya's *āśrama,* and the next morning departed for Ayodhyā.

Soon after His return, Lord Rāma expressed His desire to perform the *Rājasūya-yajña*, an elaborate sacrifice that establishes who is the emperor of the world by subduing all the kings therein. Bharata said, "My dear elder brother, all the kings of the earth look upon You just like a father. Therefore, You should not do anything that will cause them to suffer. All of these kings are fully obedient to You, and thus You should not threaten them with destruction by performing this sacrifice."

Lord Rāma gladly accepted Bharata's advice. Lakṣmaṇa then proposed that He perform a horse sacrifice instead. Lakṣmaṇa cited how Indra formerly became freed from all sinful reactions after the slaying of Vṛtrāsura by performing a horse sacrifice. In turn, Rāma pointed out how Ila, the son of Kardama, regained his manhood by a similar sacrifice. Lord Rāma had Lakṣmaṇa call for the great *ṛṣis* Vasiṣṭha, Vāmadeva, Jābāli and Kaśyapa. After receiving their approval, He sent out invitations to Sugrīva, Vibhīṣaṇa and all other kings friendly to Him. The challenge horse was then released to wander at will. Thereafter, the great sacrifice commenced at Naimiṣāraṇya.

As kings and princes poured in from all over the world, Bharata and Śatrughna received them with great hospitality. Sugrīva and the other monkeys were assigned to look after

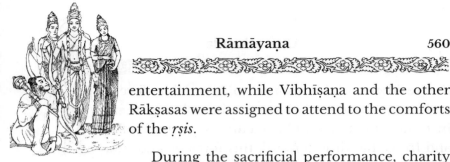

entertainment, while Vibhīṣaṇa and the other Rākṣasas were assigned to attend to the comforts of the *ṛṣis*.

During the sacrificial performance, charity and food were distributed in profusion. No one could be seen who appeared to be neglected. Indeed, wealth and clothing were heaped as high as hills all around the sacrificial arena. Thus, the festivities continued for one full year, as the challenge horse roamed the earth under the protection of Lakṣmaṇa.

Meanwhile, Vālmīki called for Lava and Kuśa and instructed them, "Please go out and continue reciting *Rāmāyaṇa* throughout the land. Go to the homes of *brāhmaṇas*, the āśramas of *ṛṣis*, and the palaces of great kings. Chant the *Rāmāyaṇa* while wandering through the city streets and countryside. However, please first go to Ayodhyā where Rāma is now engaged in performing a great horse sacrifice. If Rāma invites you to chant before the assembled *brāhmaṇas*, please do so. Chant twenty chapters at a time and do not accept any payment in return. Simply say, 'What good is gold for those who subsist upon fruits and roots?'

"If Rāma inquires, 'Whose sons are you?' then reply, 'We are Vālmīki's disciples.' Chant the verses of *Rāmāyaṇa* very sweetly, taking care that nothing displeases the king, for He is considered to be the father of all living beings."

Lava and Kuśa replied, "We shall do as you say." That night they slept peacefully with Vālmīki's words firmly fixed in their hearts.

Thereafter, it came to pass that Lava and Kuśa began to recite the epic *Rāmāyaṇa* in the sacrificial arena at Ayodhyā,

accompanied by stringed instruments. Indeed, the two brothers had voices that made their recitations appear more melodious than the singing of Gandharvas.

The audience was enthralled by their artistry. Likewise, Rāma listened intently, filled with great curiosity. Turning to one another, people remarked, "Except for their matted hair and deerskin dress, these boys exactly resemble Lord Rāma Himself!"

After listening to the first twenty chapters, Rāma ordered Lakṣmaṇa, "Give these noble minded boys 20,000 gold coins, costly garments and whatever else they desire."

However, when Lakṣmaṇa offered these rewards, Lava and Kuśa refused, saying, "What is the use of gold for ascetics who live on fruits and roots?"

Highly astonished, Rāma inquired, "How many parts are there in this epic poem, and which *ṛṣi* composed it?"

The twins replied, "O king, the great sage Vālmīki is our spiritual master and he is the author of this great literature that depicts the entire history of Your life. The poem consists of six parts, and a seventh describes Your concluding pastimes. If You desire, we shall recite the entire *Rāmāyaṇa* during the period of Your sacrifice."

Thereafter, Rāma listened with unbound pleasure as Lava and Kuśa recited the *Rāmāyaṇa* for many days. At last Rāma concluded, "These boys must be the twin sons of Sītā. There is no doubt of it."

Rāma's heart melted due to affection for His sons. After considering the matter very deeply, He called for messengers

of impeccable etiquette. He ordered them, "Go at once to the *āśrama* of the great sage, Vālmīki, and speak to him the following words: 'If Sītā is indeed blameless, if her character is faultlessly pure, then let her come here with your sanction so that she can prove her innocence before all the assembled citizens.'

"O messengers, please hurry back with their replies. Let Sītā come tomorrow at dawn and establish her purity in My presence."

When Sītā heard Rāma's proposal, she could not comply, for she considered such a public trial a great humiliation. Thus, coming to a firm decision in her mind, Sītā dressed herself in reddish cloth, and started for Ayodhyā with Vālmīki.

A large crowd had assembled from all over the Kosala kingdom, for everyone was very curious to see Sītā. Indeed, all of the demigods, headed by Lord Brahmā, as well as the foremost *ṛṣis*, Nāgas, Siddhas and other celestial beings came to witness the trial of Sītā's purity.

Finally Vālmīki arrived, followed by Sītā, her head bent low, her hands joined in supplication. Tears filled her large eyes, and Lord Rāma was firmly fixed in her heart. As the assembled citizens murmured in anticipation, Vālmīki approached Lord Rāma and said, "O son of Daśaratha, here is the impeccably righteous Sītā, whom You abandoned out of fear of public scandal. She has come here to prove her purity. Thus, she awaits Your command. O Rāma, I, who have never uttered a lie, make the following declaration, 'If Sītā is tainted by even the slightest guilt, then may the results of my accumulated austerities prove eternally fruitless.'

"Although You loved Sītā deeply and were convinced of her innocence, You still discarded her out of fear of public opinion. By dint of my spiritual vision, I can understand Sītā's complete purity. Thus I have come to proclaim this truth to You."

Rāma gazed upon Sītā for a moment and announced to the assembly, "So be it! I accept all the great *ṛṣi* has said. Previously, the demigods also testified as to Sītā's purity and I happily took her back to Ayodhyā. However, people began to criticize Me, and thus, with great reluctance I sent her away. Now I have decided that if Sītā can prove her innocence before this assembly, then I shall again accept her as the wife I dearly love."

Everyone fell silent and all eyes became fixed upon Sītā, who stood with her gaze lowered and her head bent slightly downward. After a short pause, Sītā said to the assembly, "O goddess of the earth, please hear my petition. If, since the time of my marriage, I ever thought of anyone but Rāma, or if I ever loved any man but Rāma, then refuse me shelter. However, if I have only dwelt in Rāma in thought, word and action, then please give me a place within you so I need not experience the shame of facing these slanderous people."

While Sītā spoke, the earth suddenly opened up, and from the crevice the goddess Bhūmi majestically rose up, seated upon a golden throne borne by divine serpents. The goddess welcomed Sītā, took her in her arms and seated her at her side on the throne. Then, while from the sky and from the earth, the demigods and *ṛṣis*, kings and common people looked on in astonishment, the celestial throne slowly descended into the bowels of the earth.

There was an uproar as all beings uttered exclamations of wonder, praising Sītā for this glorious confirmation of her purity. From the heavens, the demigods rained down showers of flowers, and there was singing, dancing and playing of musical instruments.

After Sītā disappeared from sight, tears welled up in Rāma's eyes and anger flared within His mind. Rāma lowered His head and declared, "Earth, I order you to return Sītā immediately. Open up and bring her here so we may

again be united. Sītā is your daughter, and I am your son-in-law. Give Me Sītā without delay or I shall crush your mountains, burn your forests and smash you into atoms!"

Lord Brahmā then spoke to appease the raving, tortured Rāma. "O Lord, please remember Your identity! You are the Supreme Personality of Godhead, Lord Viṣṇu, and Sītā is the goddess of fortune herself. Sītā has now entered the planet of the Nāgas and very shortly she will be reunited with You in Your transcendental abode, Vaikuṇṭha. O Supreme Hero, Lord of the universe and maintainer of all that lives, why must I remind You of Your divine position?

"O Rāma, give up Your grief and hear from Your sons the concluding portion of the great narration that describes Your transcendental pastimes. This epic poem, composed by Vālmīki, will spread Your glories throughout the three worlds for as long as the universe continues to exist." Saying this, Lord Brahmā disappeared.

Rāma went to Vālmīki's *āśrama* with Lava and Kuśa. After passing the night grieving over the loss of Sītā, Rāma summoned all the *ṛṣis* and requested His sons to recite the Uttara-kāṇḍa of the *Rāmāyaṇa*.

Thereafter, Rāma returned to Ayodhyā, but found life barren without His beloved Sītā. Rāma continued to rule over the kingdom strictly according to religious principles. Thus, the rains showered forth regularly, crops were abundant, and everywhere were seen signs of prosperity.

Then, after the passage of many years, Kauśalyā passed away, then Sumitrā and then Kaikeyī, so that they all

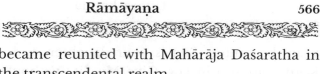

became reunited with Mahārāja Daśaratha in the transcendental realm.

Sometime thereafter, Yudhājit, the king of Kekaya, came to see Lord Rāma at Ayodhyā, requesting Him to conquer the Gandharva king, who resided north of the River Indus. Rāma immediately appointed Bharata's two sons, Takṣa and Puṣkala, as rulers of the Gandharva kingdom. Bharata then proceeded with a large army and established Takṣa in Takṣaśila and Puṣkala in Puṣkalāvaṭī. Finally, after five years passed, Bharata returned to Ayodhyā. Rāma then made Lakṣmaṇa's two sons, Aṅgada and Candraketu, the rulers of Karupatha, after bringing that territory under subjugation. Lakṣmaṇa had accompanied His two sons, and returned to Ayodhyā after an absence of one year.

Since the closing of Lord Rāma's earthly pastimes was close at hand, Time personified came to Ayodhyā one day in the guise of a wandering ascetic. After arriving at the palace gate, Time announced to Lakṣmaṇa, "I am a messenger from Lord Brahmā. Since I have come on a very important mission, I desire to see Lord Rāma at once."

When Time, in the form of a dazzling effulgent *ṛṣi*, entered the palace, Rāma respectfully seated him upon a golden throne and inquired, "O holy one, what is the nature of your visit? Is there some message you have come to deliver?"

The messenger replied, "O king, if You honor the wishes of Lord Brahmā, then our meeting must be held in private, for his words are not meant for others. Indeed, let it be known for certain that anyone who overhears our conversation will soon meet with death. O Rāma, You must

promise that if anyone comes and interrupts our meeting, then You will unhesitatingly give up all connections with him."

Rāma replied, "Let it be so!" To Lakṣmaṇa He ordered, "Dismiss the doorman. I want You to personally guard the entrance, for this meeting must be strictly private."

Thereafter, when the two were alone, Death in the form of a messenger said, "In a previous birth I was a son of Lord Brahmā. Now I am appearing as all-devouring, eternal Time (Kāla). O king, the universal grandsire speaks unto You the following words: 'O Lord Rāma, O Supreme Personality of Godhead, I offer my obeisance unto You. After the dissolution of the universe, You sleep in the waters of devastation in the form of Garbhodakaśāyī Viṣṇu. Then, when there is need of recreating the universe as it was before, I, Lord Brahmā, take birth from the effulgent lotus that grows from Your navel.

"'After my birth, I was entrusted with the creation of the three worlds. In turn, I requested You to assume the form of Kṣīrodakaśāyī Viṣṇu to become the maintainer of the universe. Ever since that time You have appeared in many transcendental forms whenever there is a need to relieve the burden of the world. Now, You have appeared to kill Rāvaṇa and rule over the earth for 11,000 years. O Lord, since this allotted time is now concluded, You need no longer remain within this material world. If You so desire, You may once again ascend to heaven to resume Your rule over the demigods. O all pervading Supreme Personality of Godhead, You are the source of my strength and my very existence.

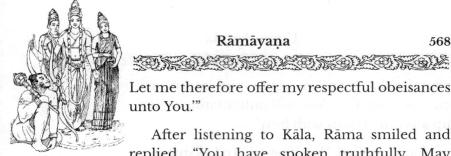

Let me therefore offer my respectful obeisances unto You.'"

After listening to Kāla, Rāma smiled and replied, "You have spoken truthfully. May there be all good fortune for you. You may now go and tell Lord Brahmā that because I have fulfilled the purpose of the demigods, I will very soon return to My own transcendental abode."

As Rāma and the messenger were conversing, it happened that Durvāsā Muni arrived at the royal palace. When Lakṣmaṇa went to receive him, the *ṛṣi* insisted, "I am here on most urgent business and must see Lord Rāma at once!"

Lakṣmaṇa replied, "Rāma has given me strict orders that He cannot be interrupted under any circumstance. O foremost of *ṛṣis*, please be patient and wait for a short while."

At this, Durvāsā lost his temper. With fiery eyes, he screamed, "Go and announce my presence at once! If you are so foolish to disobey me, then I shall curse Rāma, Bharata, yourself, the entire Ikṣvāku dynasty, and the entire Kosala kingdom! Hurry, for my patience wears thin!"

Lakṣmaṇa knew that to interrupt Rāma's conversation with Kāla would soon bring about His own death. However, thinking of Durvāsā's curse, He concluded, "It is better if I suffer alone, rather than cause everyone's ruination."

Lakṣmaṇa then entered the room. Being informed of Durvāsā's arrival, Rāma took leave of Kāla and hurriedly went out to meet the *ṛṣi*. As He stood before Durvāsā Muni with folded hands, Rāma inquired, "O foremost of ascetic

brāhmaṇas, what can I do to please you?"

Durvāsā replied, "O righteous king, I have just now completed a one-thousand year fast. What can You give me to eat?" Thereafter, Rāma provided Durvāsā with a sumptuous feast, and the *ṛṣi* was highly gratified.

After Durvāsā's departure, however, Rāma remembered the promise He had made to Kāla. Thus, a horrible grief overtook Him. Fearing the loss of His most intimate associate, Rāma stood as though deprived of reason, His head bowed in dejection.

Lakṣmaṇa then approached His aggrieved brother and cheerfully said, "O Rāma, do not lament for that which is inevitable under the control of supreme destiny. Duty must be carried out without attachment or aversion. Therefore, keep Your promise and banish Me without hesitation."

Rāma summoned His ministers, and after describing all that had happened, He asked for their advice. Finally, after a long silence, Vasiṣṭha said, "My dear Rāma, by dint of my ascetic prowess I could foresee all this happening to You. Now You must keep Your promise. Otherwise, Your life long adherence to righteousness will be blighted. With the decay of religious principles, the world gradually comes to perish. Therefore, adhere to truthfulness and banish Lakṣmaṇa."

Rāma appeared to think deeply over the matter. Then He announced to the assembly, "Adhering to righteousness, I hereby order the banishment of Lakṣmaṇa from Ayodhyā."

The ministers all applauded Rāma's decision, and thereafter Lakṣmaṇa went to the banks of the River Sarayū

and absorbed His mind in the practice of mystic yoga. Then, when the time became ripe, King Indra suddenly appeared there, riding a celestial chariot. Thus, in His self-same transcendental body, Lakṣmaṇa ascended to heaven amidst the singing of Gandharvas, the dancing of Apsarās and showers of fragrant flowers.

After Lakṣmaṇa's disappearance, Rāma decided to install Bharata upon the royal throne so that He could be free to follow the Lakṣmaṇa's path. However, Bharata refused to occupy the throne, for He preferred to accompany Rāma to the forest rather than enjoy the kingdom without Him. Rāma then divided the kingdom between His sons, giving Kuśa the northern part of Kosala and Lava the southern part. After the coronation, Rāma embraced His twin sons and then presented them vast amounts of gold, jewels, thousands of chariots, and countless horses and elephants.

When the citizens heard of Rāma's intention to retire to the forest, they became determined to follow Him. Their grief due to the impending separation was unbearable. Śatrughna was also intent upon following Rāma, and thus, when the Lord finally came out of the city, there was a great procession following Him. Indeed, because of their love and devotion, every living entity followed Rāma to the forest, so that not even an animal could be seen in Ayodhyā.

While Rāma silently walked along, everyone could see that He was exhibiting a mood of complete detachment and indifference, as if preparing to give up the world. All of Rāma's potencies appeared in personified form to accompany Him. Śrī walked on Rāma's right side and Bhūmi on His left. Śakti walked in front, and innumerable other energies followed

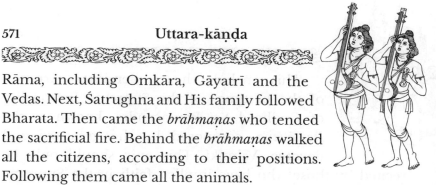

Rāma, including Oṁkāra, Gāyatrī and the Vedas. Next, Śatrughna and His family followed Bharata. Then came the *brāhmaṇas* who tended the sacrificial fire. Behind the *brāhmaṇas* walked all the citizens, according to their positions. Following them came all the animals.

When He arrived at the banks of the River Sarayū, Rāma paused. At that time Lord Brahmā and the demigods appeared overhead in their celestial chariots. The sky was thus lit up with a transcendental radiance, and gentle, sweet-smelling breezes began to blow. The Gandharvas and Apsarās sang and danced, and the demigods showered the most fragrant of celestial flowers.

As Lord Rāma entered the water, Lord Brahmā offered his prayers as follows: "O Lord, O Supreme Personality of Godhead, You are now concluding Your earthly pastimes and are preparing to return to Your transcendental abode beyond this material world. You are the eternal Lord Viṣṇu, and although You appear in various incarnations, Your body is unchanging and original. It is You alone who are the cause of all causes and the support of all existence. Everything is thus part and parcel of You, for You are the Supreme Absolute Truth, the source of all emanation. O Lord, You have so kindly appeared to remove the burden of the earth. Thus, let us offer our respectful obeisances unto You, again and again."

Followed by Bharata and Śatrughna, Lord Rāma thus returned to His eternal abode in the spiritual sky. Indeed, not only the sons of Daśaratha, but all of Their followers, attained the Vaikuṇṭha planet where Lord Rāma eternally resides.

This concludes the transcendental narration of the pastimes of the Supreme Personality of Godhead Śrī Rāmacandra, known as the *Rāmāyaṇa*, composed by the great *ṛṣi* and devotee, Vālmīki. This epic should only be recited by those who have implicit faith in the Supreme Lord, for it is nondifferent from Lord Viṣṇu Himself. Hearing even a single verse has the potency to eradicate all sins committed by a person that day. Therefore, those who seek liberation from the cycle of repeated birth and death always relish this great transcendental literature.

The recitation of the *Rāmāyaṇa* grants one all the fruits of *dharma, artha, kāma* and *mokṣa*. Beyond that, it helps one to advance toward life's ultimate goal, the development of love of Godhead. May the readers of this book thus become blessed and inspired in Kṛṣṇa consciousness. May the transcendental forms of Lord Rāmacandra and Sītā forever remain situated within their hearts.

Oṁ Tat Sat

Appendix

Śrīla Prabhupāda on the position of Lord Rāmacandra and purposes for His advent

Compiled from Śrīla Prabhupāda's translation and commentary of the Śrīmad-Bhāgavatam, Ninth Canto.

The Personality of Godhead Śrī Rāma assumed the form of a human being and appeared on the earth for the purpose of doing some pleasing work for the demigods or the administrative personalities to maintain the order of the universe. Sometimes great demons and atheists like Rāvaṇa and Hiraṇyakaśipu and many others become very famous due to advancing material civilization by the help of material science and other activities with a spirit of challenging the established order of the Lord. For example, the attempt to fly to other planets by material means is a challenge to the established order. The conditions of each and every planet are different, and different classes of human beings are accommodated there for particular purposes mentioned in the codes of the Lord. But, puffed up by tiny success in material advancement, sometimes the godless materialists challenge the existence of God. Rāvaṇa was one of them, and he wanted to deport ordinary men to the planet of Indra (heaven) by material means without consideration of the necessary qualifications. He wanted a staircase to be built up directly reaching the heavenly planet so that people might not be required to undergo the routine of pious work necessary to enter that planet. He also wanted to perform other acts against the established rule of the Lord. He even

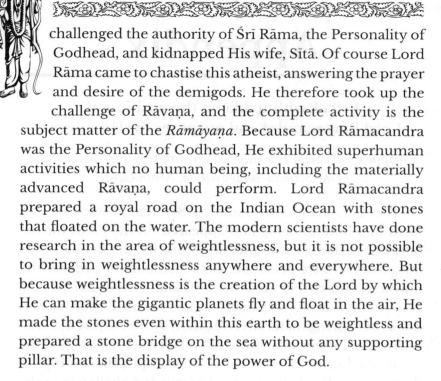

challenged the authority of Śrī Rāma, the Personality of Godhead, and kidnapped His wife, Sītā. Of course Lord Rāma came to chastise this atheist, answering the prayer and desire of the demigods. He therefore took up the challenge of Rāvaṇa, and the complete activity is the subject matter of the *Rāmāyaṇa*. Because Lord Rāmacandra was the Personality of Godhead, He exhibited superhuman activities which no human being, including the materially advanced Rāvaṇa, could perform. Lord Rāmacandra prepared a royal road on the Indian Ocean with stones that floated on the water. The modern scientists have done research in the area of weightlessness, but it is not possible to bring in weightlessness anywhere and everywhere. But because weightlessness is the creation of the Lord by which He can make the gigantic planets fly and float in the air, He made the stones even within this earth to be weightless and prepared a stone bridge on the sea without any supporting pillar. That is the display of the power of God.

Due to His causeless mercy upon all living entities, the Supreme Personality of Godhead, along with His plenary extensions, appeared in the family of Mahārāja Ikṣvāku as the Lord of Sītā, His internal potency. Under the order of His father, Mahārāja Daśaratha, He entered the forest and lived there for considerable years with His wife and younger brother. The powerful Rākṣasa Rāvaṇa, committed a great offense against Him and was thus ultimately vanquished.

Lord Rāma is the Supreme Personality of Godhead, and His brothers, namely Bharata, Lakṣmaṇa and Śatrughna, are His plenary expansions. All four brothers are *viṣṇu-tattva.* They were never ordinary human beings. There are many unscrupulous and ignorant commentators on *Rāmāyaṇa*

who present the younger brothers of Lord Rāmacandra as ordinary living entities. But *Śrīmad-Bhāgavatam,* the most authentic scripture on the science of Godhead, clearly states that His brothers were His plenary expansions. Lord Rāmacandra is the incarnation of Vāsudeva, Lakṣmaṇa is the incarnation of Saṅkarṣaṇa, Bharata is the incarnation of Pradyumna, and Śatrughna is the incarnation of Aniruddha, all expansions of the Personality of Godhead. Lakṣmījī Sītā is the internal potency of the Lord. She is neither an ordinary woman nor an incarnation of Durgā. Durgā is the external potency of the Lord, and she is associated with Lord Śiva.

The question may be asked why the Lord, who is omnipotent, comes here to diminish the burden created upon the world by the unscrupulous kingly order. Certainly the Lord does not need to come here personally for such purposes, but He actually descends to exhibit His transcendental activities in order to encourage His pure devotees, who want to enjoy life by chanting the glories of the Lord. In the *Bhagavad-gītā* (9.13–14) it is stated that the *mahātmās*, great devotees of the Lord, take pleasure in chanting of the activities of the Lord. All Vedic literatures are meant for turning one's attention towards the Lord and His transcendental activities. Thus the activities of the Lord, in His dealings with worldly people, create a subject matter for discussion by His pure devotees.

When the Lord appears in this universe in the form of a human being, He has two purposes, as stated in *Bhagavad-gītā* (4.8)—*paritrāṇāya sādhūnāṁ vināśāya ca duṣkṛtām*: to destroy the demons and protect the devotees. To protect the devotees, the Lord not only satisfies them by His personal presence but also teaches them so that they will not fall down from devotional service. By His personal example, Lord Rāmacandra taught the devotees that it is better not to enter married life, which is certainly followed by many tribulations. As confirmed in *Śrīmad-Bhāgavatam* (7.9.45):

> *Kṛpaṇas,* those who are not advanced in spiritual knowledge and who are therefore just the opposite of *brāhmaṇas,* generally take to family life, which is a concession for sex. Thus they enjoy sex again and again, although that sex is followed by many tribulations. This is a warning to devotees. To teach this lesson to devotees and to human society in general, Lord Śrī Rāmacandra, although the Supreme Personality of Godhead Himself, underwent a series of tribulations because He accepted a wife, mother Sītā. Lord Rāmacandra underwent these austerities, of course, only to instruct us; actually He never has any reason to lament for anything.

Another aspect of the Lord's instructions is that one who accepts a wife must be a faithful husband and give her full protection. Human society is divided into two classes of men—those who strictly follow the religious principles and those who are devotees. By His personal example, Lord Rāmacandra wanted to instruct both of them how to fully adopt the discipline of the religious system and how to be a beloved and dutiful husband. Otherwise He had no reason to undergo apparent tribulations. One who strictly follows religious principles must not neglect to provide all facilities for the complete protection of his wife. There may be some suffering because of this, but one must nevertheless

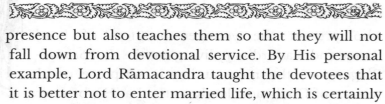

endure it. That is the duty of a faithful husband. By His personal example, Lord Rāmacandra demonstrated this duty. Lord Rāmacandra could have produced hundreds and thousands of Sītās from His pleasure energy, but just to show the duty of a faithful husband, He not only rescued Sītā from the hands of Rāvaṇa, but also killed Rāvaṇa and all the members of his family.

Another aspect of the teachings of Lord Rāmacandra is that although Lord Viṣṇu, the Supreme Personality of Godhead, and His devotees may apparently suffer from material tribulations, they have nothing to do with such tribulations. They are *mukta-puruṣas*, liberated persons, under all circumstances. A Vaiṣṇava is always firmly situated in transcendental bliss because of engagement in devotional service. Although he may appear to suffer material pains, his position is called transcendental bliss in separation. The emotions a lover and beloved feel when separated from one another are actually very blissful, although apparently painful. Therefore the separation of Lord Rāmacandra from Sītādevī, as well as the consequent tribulation they suffered, is but another display of transcendental bliss.

Glossary

Aditi—a wife of Kaśyapa Muni and the mother of the demigods.

Ādityas—demigods who are descendants Aditi.

Agastya Muni—a great sage who authored many Vedic hymns and writings on Āyurvedic medicine.

Agni—the demigod who controls fire.

Airāvata—the elephant carrier of Lord Indra.

Akṣauhiṇī—a military division consisting of 21,870 chariots, 21,870 elephants, 109,350 infantrymen and 65,610 horsemen.

Anusūyā—wife of Atri Muni.

Apsarā—heavenly courtesan. The most beautiful women in the heavenly planets, who are expert at dancing.

Artha—economic development.

Aśvini-kumāras—the physicians among the demigods.

Atri Muni—one of the seven great sages born directly from Brahmā;. He is the husband of Anusūyā and father of the Lord's incarnation Dattātreya. He contributed to the knowledge of astronomy.

Bharata—the son of Mahārāja Daśaratha and Kaikeyī, and half-brother of Lord Rāma. He ruled Ayodhyā during Lord Rāma's exile.

Bhṛgu—the most powerful of the sages born directly from Brahmā.

Bhūmi—Mother Earth; the deity of the earth planet.

Brahmaloka—the highest planet of the universe, that of the demigod Lord Brahmā.

Brahmarṣi—"sage among the *brāhmaṇas.*" The highest stage among *ṛṣis.*

Brahmāstra—a weapon invoked by mantra, more powerful than many atomic bombs.

Bṛhaspati—the spiritual master of King Indra and chief priest for the demigods.

Caitanya (Lord), (1486-1534)—Lord Kṛṣṇa Himself who appeared as His own devotee, in Navadvīpa, West Bengal, and inaugurated the congregational chanting of the holy names of Kṛṣṇa to teach pure love of God.

Cāraṇas—a type of demigod.

Challenge horse—a horse sent throughout the world to establish the supremacy of an emperor over subordinate kings. The horse would be accompanied by soldiers of the emperor, and upon its arrival in a kingdom, the local king would either have to offer tribute to the emperor's representatives, or fight to capture the horse.

Cyavana—a son of Bhṛgu Muni and the author of a text on astronomy.

Daityas— the sons born to Kaśyapa Muni by his wife Diti; a race of demons.

Dakṣa—one of the sons of Brahmā and a chief progenitor of universal population.

Dānavas—the sons born to Kaśyapa Muni by his wife Danu; a race of demons.

Daśagrīva—another name for Rāvaṇa.

Dilīpa—the son of Aṁśumān and father of Bhagiratha. He was an ancestor of Lord Rāmacandra.

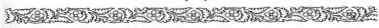

Diti—a wife of Kaśyapa Muni, and the mother of the demons known as the Daityas.

Durgā—Lord Śiva's wife in a fierce form. She is empowered by the Supreme Lord to preside over the material nature and bewilder the souls situated there into misconceiving themselves to be their material bodies, and enjoyers and controllers of the mundane creation.

Durvāsā Muni—a partial incarnation of Lord Śiva, and a powerful yogi famous being easily angered and pronouncing fearful curses.

Dvāpara-yuga—the third age of the cycle of a *mahā-yuga*. It lasts more than 864,000 years.

Gandharvas—the celestial demigod dancers, singers, and musicians of the heavenly planets.

Garbhodakaśāyī Viṣṇu—the second Viṣṇu expansion, who enters each universe and from whose navel grows a lotus upon which Lord Brahmā appears. Brahmā then creates the diverse material manifestations.

Garuḍa—the giant eagle who is Lord Viṣṇu's eternal carrier; he appears in this world as a son of Kaśyapa and Vinatā.

Gautama Muni—one of the seven sons born from Lord Brahma's mind. He is the author of *Nyāya-śāstra,* the science of logic.

Guha—a jungle king who hosted Lord Rāma.

Hare Kṛṣṇa mahā-mantra—Hare Kṛṣṇa, Hare Kṛṣṇa, Kṛṣṇa Kṛṣṇa, Hare Hare, Hare Rāma, Hare Rāma, Rāma Rāma, Hare Hare.

Heavenly planets—the higher planets of the universe, the residences of the demigods.

Horse sacrifice—One of eight types of sacrifice recommended in Vedic scriptures, it is to be performed by kings.

Ikṣvāku—king of the earth in ancient times, the first ruler of Ayodhyā, and an ancestor of Lord Rāma.

Indra—the chief demigod of heaven and presiding deity of rain. He is a son of Aditi.

Janaka Mahārāja—a great authority on spiritual knowledge, king of Mithilā, and the father of Sītā.

Jaṭāyu—the king of the vultures, and the brother of Sampāti. He fought with and was slain by Rāvaṇa when the latter kidnapped Sītā.

Kaikeyī—the third wife of Mahārāja Daśaratha and the mother of Bharata. It was on her order that Rāma was banished to the forest.

Kali-yuga—the "Age of Quarrel and Hypocrisy." The fourth and last age in the cycle of a *mahā-yuga*. This is the present age in which we are now living. It began 5,000 years ago and lasts for a total of 432,000 years. It is characterized by irreligion and stringent material miseries.

Kāmadhenu—wish-fulfilling cow.

Kapila—an incarnation of Kṛṣṇa who appeared in Satya-yuga and expounded devotional Sāṅkhya philosophy, the analysis of matter and spirit, as a means of cultivating devotional service to the Lord. (There is also an atheist named Kapila, but he is not an incarnation of the Lord.)

Karma—(1) material action; (2) reaction to material action; (3) fruitive activity performed in accordance with Vedic injunctions; (4) law governing material action and reaction.

Kārttikeya—a son of Lord Śiva and Pārvatī. He is the presiding deity of warfare. Also known as Subrahmaṇya or Skanda.

Kaśyapa—a great saint who was the father of many living beings, including most of the demigods, and also of the Supreme Lord's incarnation Vāmana; one of the seven mental sons of Lord Brahmā.

Kauśalyā—the first wife of Mahārāja Daśaratha, and the mother of Lord Rāma.

Kiṣkindhyā—the forest abode of the monkeys who helped Lord Rāma.

Kṛṣṇa—the original, two-armed form of the Supreme Lord, who is the origin of all Viṣṇu forms, including that of Lord Rāma.

Kṛṣṇa consciousness—the perfectional stage of always thinking of Kṛṣṇa.

Kṣīrodakaśāyī Viṣṇu—the expansion of the Supreme Lord who enters within each atom and into the heart of every living entity.

Kuśa—an auspicious grass used in Vedic rituals and sacrifices.

Kuvera—one of the important demigods, and the treasurer of the demigods.

Lakṣmaṇa—a younger brother of Lord Rāmacandra. He accompanied Rāma and Sītā in Their exile.

Lakṣmī—the goddess of fortune and the eternal consort of the Supreme Lord as Lord Nārāyaṇa, who resides in the unlimited spiritual realm of Vaikuṇṭha. Sītā is an expansion of Lakṣmī, as Rāma is of Nārāyaṇa.

Lokapāla—a generic term for a demigod presiding over one of the directions of the universe.

Mahā-mantra—(See Hare Kṛṣṇa *mahā-mantra*)

Mahā-yuga—the combined duration of the four yugas or ages of the universe, namely Satya-yuga, Treta-yuga, Dvāpara-yuga and Kali-yuga, consisting of 4,320,000 earthly years. Also sometimes simply called a yuga.

Mantharā—the hunchbacked maidservant on whose instigation Kaikeyī had Rāma exiled to the forest.

Maruts—demigod associates of King Indra; the gods of air.

Mātali—the charioteer of Indra.

Meru—the golden mountain that is the pivot of the universe.

Mithilā—the kingdom ruled by King Janaka, father of Sītā; now covers part of Bihar and part of southern Nepal.

Mitra—the demigod who controls death.

Nāgas—a race of serpents with mystic powers who can assume human forms.

Nārada Muni—a pure devotee of the Lord and one of the mental sons of Lord Brahmā. He travels throughout the universes in his eternal body, preaching the science of *bhakti*.

Pārvatī—a name for the wife of Lord Śiva.

Pitās—forefathers; especially those departed ancestors who have been promoted to one of the higher planets.

Pulastya—one of the seven great sages who were born directly from Lord Brahmā.

Rājarṣi—a sage among kings.

Rākṣasas—man-eating demons.

Rākṣasī—female Rākṣasa.

Rāma or Rāmacandra—the eighteenth incarnation of the Supreme Personality of Godhead; the killer of Rāvaṇa.

Rāvaṇa—the ten headed demon king who kidnapped Sītā and was eventually killed by Rāma.

Ṛṣi—a sage or ascetic.

Sādhyas—a class of demigods.

Sanat-kumāra—a great mystic yogi and devotee.

Sapta-ṛṣis—seven prominent sages

Śatrughna—the twin brother of Lakṣmaṇa and son of Mahārāja Daśaratha and Sumitrā.

Siddhas—a class of demigods.

Sītā—the beloved consort of Lord Rāmacandra.

Śiva—the superintendent of the mode of ignorance who takes charge of destroying the universe at the time of annihilation. He is considered the greatest devotee of Lord Kṛṣṇa.

Śrī—honorific prefix to a name.

Śrīla Prabhupāda (1896-1977)—His Divine Grace A. C. Bhaktivedanta Swami Prabhupāda. The Founder-*Ācārya* and first spiritual master of the International Society for Krishna Consciousness (ISKCON), and author of more than seventy books on Kṛṣṇa consciousness.

Sudarśana cakra—the disc weapon of the Supreme Lord, Viṣṇu.

Śūdra—a member of the fourth social order; the class of laborers and artisans in the Vedic social system. *Śūdras* render service to the three higher classes, namely the *brāhmaṇas,* the *kṣatriyas,* and the *vaiśyas.*

Sumantra—the chief minister of Mahārāja Daśaratha.

Sundara—beautiful.

Sūrya—the sun-god.

Svayaṁvara—a ceremony in which a princess selects her own husband, after a contest of military skill by prospective suitors.

Tapasya—austerity; voluntary acceptance of difficulty to achieve either material or spiritual advancement.

Tilaka—sacred clay markings placed on the forehead and other parts of the body to distinguish one as a specific follower of Viṣṇu, Rāma, or a demigod.

Tretā-yuga—the second in the cycle of the four ages of the universe or *mahā-yuga.* It lasts 1,296,000 years. In this age Lord Rāmacandra appeared.

Umā—a name for the wife of Lord Śiva.

Uttara—in the term Uttara-kāṇḍa, *Uttara* means "concluding."

Vaikuṇṭha—the eternal planets of the spiritual world, the abode of Lord Nārāyaṇa, which lies beyond the coverings of the material universe. Literally, "the place with no anxiety."

Vāli—a monkey who was a son of Indra and elder brother of Sugrīva.

Vaiśya—a member of the mercantile or agricultural commumity, the third class in the Vedic social system.

Vālmīki—author of the *Rāmāyaṇa.*

Vāmadeva—a great sage who was the secretary of Daśaratha Mahārāja, the father of Lord Rāma.

Vāmana—the Supreme Lord's fifth incarnation, as a dwarf brāhmaṇa.

Varuṇa—the demigod in charge of the oceans.

Vasiṣṭha—a great sage who was the family priest of Mahārāja Daśaratha, the father of Lord Rāmacandra.

Vibhīṣaṇa—a grandson of Pulastya Muni and the pious brother of Rāvaṇa.

Videha—another name for the kingdom of Mithilā.

Vidyādharas—a race of celestial beings who are attendants of Lord Śiva.

Viṣṇu—the Supreme Personality of Godhead in His four-armed expansion in Vaikuṇṭha; a plenary expansion of the original Supreme Personality of Godhead, Śrī Kṛṣṇa. Viṣṇu supervises the maintenance of the material universe, within which He is immanent. He is worshipped by all the demigods and sages, and is described throughout the Vedas as the Absolute Truth.

Viṣṇu-tattva—in the category of Viṣṇu.

Viśvakarmā—the engineer and architect of the demigods.

Viśvāmitra—a prominent sage.

Vṛndāvana—Kṛṣṇa's eternal abode, where He fully manifests His quality of sweetness; the village on this earth in which He enacted His childhood pastimes 5,000 years ago; the topmost transcendental abode of the Supreme Lord.

Vṛtrāsura—a great demon killed by Indra, but who was actually a devotee.

Yakṣa—ghostly followers of Kuvera.

Yamadūtas—messengers of Yamarāja.

Yamarāja—the demigod of death, who passes judgment on non-devotees at the time of death. He is the son of the sun-god.

Yojana—a Vedic measurement equal to eight miles.

Guide to Diacritical Marks

Within this book a standard transliteration system accepted by scholars to indicate standard pronunciation of Sanskrit is used.

Long vowels are indicated by a line above the letter representing it.

The short vowel a is pronounced like the *u* in ***but,*** long ā as in ***far***. Short **i** is pronounced as in *w**i**n,* long ī as in *piq**ue**;* short **u** as in ***bull,*** long **ū** as in ***rule.***

The vowel **ṛ** is pronounced like the *ri* in ***rim;*** **e** and **ai** as in *th**ey**;* **o** and **au** as in *g**o**.*

The *anusvāra* (**ṁ**), a pure nasal sound, is pronounced as in the French word ***bon;*** the *visarga* (**ḥ**), a strong aspirate, like a final **h** sound. At the end of a couplet **aḥ** is pronounced *aha,* **iḥ** pronounced *ihi,* and so on.

The guttural consonants **k**, **kh**, **g**, **gh**, and **ṅ** are pronounced from the throat in much the same manner as in English—**k** as in ***k**ite,* **kh** as in *pac**k-h**orse,* **g** as in ***g**ive,* **gh** as in *bi**gh**earted,* and **ṅ** as in *si**ng**.*

The palatal consonants **c**, **ch**, **j**, **jh**, and ñ are pronounced: **c** as in ***ch**air,* **ch** as in *Fren**ch h**orn,* **j** as in ***j**oy,* **jh** as in *bri**dgeh**ead,* and ñ as in *ca**ny**on.*

The retroflex consonants **ṭ**, **ṭh**, **ḍ**, **ḍh**, and **ṇ** are pronounced with the tip of the tongue turned up and drawn back against the dome of the palate—**ṭ** as in ***t**ub,* **ṭh** as in *righ**t-h**and,* **ḍ** as in ***d**emigod,* **ḍh** as in *gla**d h**eart,* and **ṇ** as in ***n**eem.*

The dental consonants **t**, **th**, **d**, **dh** and **n** are pronounced in the same manner as the celebrals, but with the tip of the tongue against the inside of the upper teeth.

The labial consonants **p**, **ph**, **b**, **bh**, and **m** are pronounced with the lips—**p** as in ***p**ine,* **ph** as in *u**ph**ill,* **b** as in ***b**oon,* **bh** as in *gra**b h**old,* and **m** as in ***m**an.*

The semivowels **y, r, l,** and **v** are pronounced as in ***y**et, **r**ain, **l**ove,* and ***v**ow,* respectively.

The sibilants **s, ṣ,** and **ś** are pronounced: **s** as in ***s**un;* **ṣ** as in ***sh**ine,* but with the tip of the tongue turned up and drawn back against the dome of the palate; and **ś** as in ***sh**ine* but the tip of the tongue against the inside of the upper teeth.

Acknowledgments

The first, hand-written, manuscript for this book was drafted by Pūrṇaprajña Dāsa, based on a translation of the original Rāmāyaṇa by Vālmīki. It was typed in and renovated by Tīrtha Dāsa. Further editing was done by Kṛṣṇa Kīrti Dāsa and Jagat Puruṣa Dāsa. Final editing, proofreading and overhauling was done by Bhakti Vikāsa Swami, who oversaw the project to bring out this edition of Rāmāyaṇa. Citrakara Dāsa painted the pictures. Kṛṣṇa Kīrti Dāsa did the layout, and Vijaya Govinda Dāsa did the cover design and supervised the printing.

For the revised edition, Bharata Dāsa did the layout and oversaw the printing, Jagadīsa Dāsa provided new drawings and designed the cover. Jaya Dāmodara Dāsa and Gaṅgādevī Dāsī were proofreaders.

Other Books by Bhakti Vikāsa Swami

A Beginner's Guide to Kṛṣṇa Consciousness

Read this book and improve your life!

All you need to know to get started in Kṛṣṇa consciousness. Easy-to-understand guidance on daily practices that bring us closer to Kṛṣṇa. Packed with practical information. Suitable both for devotees living in an ashram or at home.

Guaranteed to make you a better, more spiritual person

120 x 180 mm • 132 pages • line art • softbound

Available also in Bengali, Croatian, Gujarati, Hindi, Indonesian, Kannada, Malayalam, Marathi, Nepali, Oriya, Polish, Russian, Slovene, Tamil, Telugu, and Urdu

A Message to the Youth of India

Youth of India, Awake!

Your country is destined to lead the world by spiritual strength. Understand the power of your own culture, which is attracting millions from all over the world.

Religion, philosophy, social and historical analysis. Compelling insights, not only for the youth but for all interested in the future of India and the world.

Arise, come forward, be enlightened

120 x 180 mm • 128 pages • softbound

Available also in Bengali, Gujarati, Hindi, Marathi, Tamil, and Telugu

Brahmacarya in Kṛṣṇa Consciousness

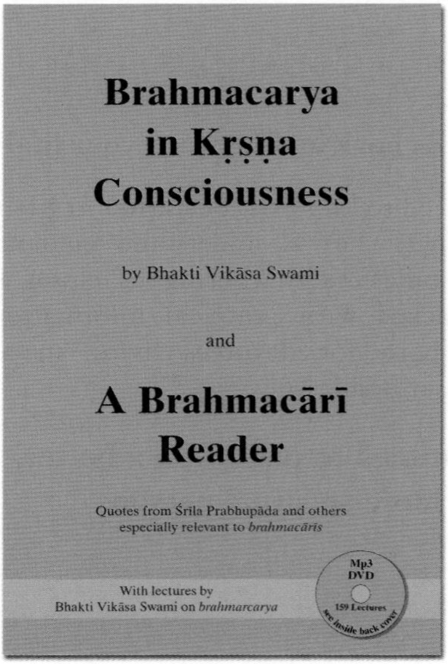

A "user's guide" to *brahmacārī* life. The first part consists of elaborate discussions and practical guidance regarding many aspects of *brahmacarya*. The second portion is a compilation of quotations on *brahmacarya* from Śrīla Prabhupāda's books, letters, and recordings.

Invaluable not only for *brahmacārīs* but for all devotees seriously interested in improving their spiritual life.

140 x 216 mm • 272 pages • softbound • DVD with 159 lectures on *brahmacarya*

Available also in Bengali, Croatian, German, Gujarati, Hindi, Indonesian, Italian, Mandarin, Tamil, Telugu, Portuguese, and Russian

Glimpses of Traditional Indian Life

Journey to the real India. Discover the wisdom and devotion at the heart of Indian life. Meet people who were raised in a godly atmosphere and learn how it shaped their character and enriched their life. Explore the adverse effects of India's technological development, the downfall of her hereditary culture, and other causes of India's present degradation.

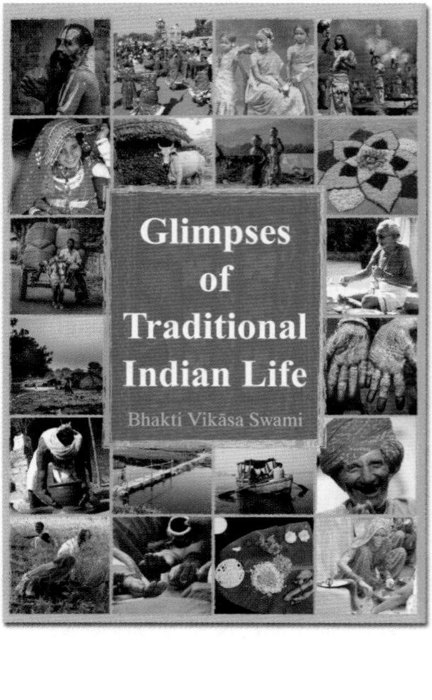

140 x 216 mm • 256 pages • 16 color plates • softbound

Available also in Croatian, Hindi, and Russian

Jaya Śrīla Prabhupāda!

There is no limit to Śrīla Prabhupāda's transcendental attributes, nor do we wish to ever stop describing them. His qualities, combined with his achievements, undoubtedly establish Śrīla Prabhupāda as an extraordinarily great transcendental personality.

Śrīla Prabhupāda is still with us, watching over the continuing expansion of the Kṛṣṇa consciousness movement. If we simply follow his instructions carefully, we can expect many amazing, unimaginable things to happen.

140 x 216 mm • 240 pages • pictures and line art • softbound

Available also in Gujarati, Hindi, Russian, and Tamil

My Memories of Śrīla Prabhupāda

An ISKCON sannyasi recalls his few but precious memories of the most significant personality to have graced the earth in recent times.

Also includes:

- On Serving Śrīla Prabhupāda in Separation
- Vyasa-pūjā Offerings

140 x 216 mm • 230 pages • full-color with 39 pictures • hardbound

Available also in Croatian, Czech, Hindi, Gujarati, and Russian

On Pilgrimage in Holy India

Travel with an ISKCON sannyasi, including to some of India's less-known but most charming holy places.

210 x 280 mm • 196 pages
• full-color with 191 pictures
• hardbound

Available also in Russian

On Speaking Strongly in Śrīla Prabhupāda's Service

Why followers of Śrīla Prabhupāda should speak strongly, as he did. A comprehensive analysis of how to present Kṛṣṇa consciousness straightforwardly, intelligently, and effectively. Features many anecdotes and more than five hundred powerful quotes.

140 x 216 mm • 272 pages
• hardbound • multimedia CD

For more information, please visit:
www.speakingstrongly.com

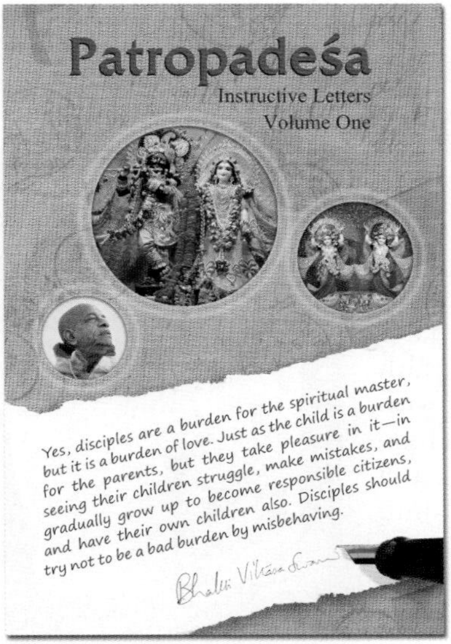

Patropadeśa

An anthology of selected correspondence with disciples and other devotees.

Packed with realistic advice on how to practice Kṛṣṇa consciousness in a complex world.

With many valuable philosophical insights and perspectives of guru-disciple interactions in the age of the internet.

140 x 216 mm • 424 pages • softbound

Available in English

Mothers and Masters

Mothers and Masters presents traditionalist arguments for the direction of the Kṛṣṇa consciousness movement, proposing that we should take up Śrīla Prabhupāda's mandate to establish *varṇāśrama-dharma* rather than capitulate to the norms and ideologies of secular culture. Particularly discussed are gender roles, parental responsibilities, feminist follies, and some of Śrīla Prabhupāda's more controversial teachings, such as those concerning early marriage, divorce, and polygamy.

140 x 216 mm • 320 pages
• softbound • Lecture DVD

Available also in Hindi and Spanish

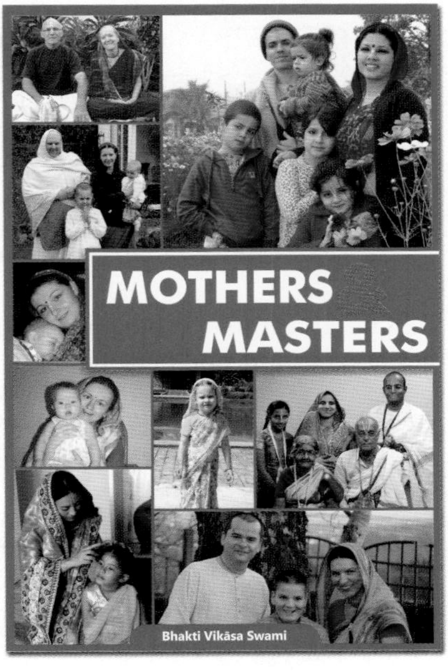

Śrī Bhaktisiddhānta Vaibhava

Śrīla Bhaktisiddhānta Sarasvatī Ṭhākura altered the course of religious history by reviving and forcefully propagating pure Kṛṣṇa consciousness. His boldness in combating cheating religion earned him the appellation "lion guru"—yet his heart was soft with divine love for Kṛṣṇa.

The result of over twenty years of research, *Śrī Bhaktisiddhānta Vaibhava* presents a wealth of newly translated material. Replete with anecdotes told by disciples who lived with him, this devotional, philosophical, cultural, and historical study gives intimate insights into the activities, teachings, and character of an empowered emissary of the Supreme Lord.

160 x 240 mm • 1576 pages • 164 black-and-white photos • 9 color photos • hardbound • decorative protective box

Śrī Bhaktisiddhānta Vaibhava is presented in three volumes

Volume 1 features a biographical overview, plus detailed analysis of the message, mission, and personality of Śrīla Bhaktisiddhānta Sarasvati.

Volume 2 details the preaching challenge that Śrīla Bhaktisiddhānta Sarasvati faced, and also includes biographical sketches of several of his disciples and associates.

Volume 3 features an overview of Śrīla Bhaktisiddhānta Sarasvati's contributions, with selections from his lectures, writings, and colloquies, also his astrological chart, and appendixes that include important details concerning Śrīla Bhaktisiddhānta Sarasvati and the Gauḍīya Maṭha.

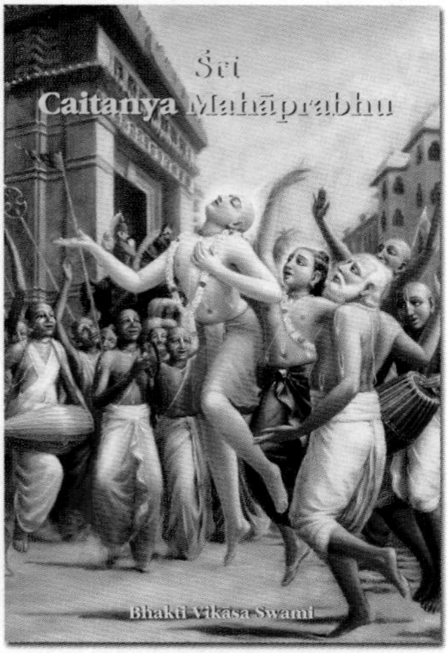

Śrī Caitanya Mahāprabhu

Hundreds of thousands of people throughout the world now follow the spotless path of Kṛṣṇa consciousness as given by Lord Caitanya. Chanting the holy names of Kṛṣṇa and dancing in ecstasy, they desire only love of Kṛṣṇa and consider material enjoyment to be insignificant. This book gives an overview of the life and teachings of Śrī Caitanya Mahāprabhu, the most munificent avatar ever to grace this planet.

120 x 180 mm • 176 pages • 16 color plates • softbound

Available also in Gujarati, Hindi, Russian, Tamil, and Telugu

Śrī Vaṁśīdāsa Bābājī

Śrīla Vaṁsīdāsa Bābājī was a great Vaiṣṇava who although physically present in this world, had little communication with it. His hair and beard were uncut, matted, and dishevelled. He almost never bathed, and his eyes looked wild. He wore only a loin cloth, and nothing more.

This book introduces us to a personality of such extraordinary, inscrutable character that we simply offer him obeisance and beg for his mercy.

140 x 216 mm • 152 pages • 8 color plates • softbound

Available also in Croatian, Hindi, and Russian